Tomart's Price Guide to

by Ken Clee
and Suzan Hufferd

with additional research and compilation
by T.E. Tumbusch

Photography by T.E. Tumbusch

TOMART PUBLICATIONS
Division of Tomart Corporation
Dayton, Ohio

To Susan, Ken's Fiancée

Acknowledgements

The authors would like to extend thanks to the following individuals for their help in making this book a reality:

To Joyce Losonsky and Meredith Williams, who provided early encouragement to tackle this project, and later provided some of the toys. To Nate Downs, Lance Golba, Martha Gragg, Bill and Pat Poe, Bonnie Poiset, Bill Sikora, Jerry Soltis, Peggy Stockard and all of the great friends we made at the various restaurant Home Offices, for sending us items for the book. To the Poes, E.J. Ritter, Alyce Roberts, Martha Gragg and T.E.Tumbusch who helped with pricing. Additional information and items were provided by Don and Audree Anderson, Ilene Blankman, Fred Waterman, Oleta Smith, Ted Blanton, Nancy Raines, Dave Conrad, Jim Silva, Al Hinkle, Doug Reece, Robin Hufferd, and Gilly's Antique Mall. The following Kid's Meal producers and promoters also have our thanks: Pat Rowell (Carl's Jr.), Karen Randell (Denny's), Mary Golden (Roy Rogers),Mariann Nuss (Hardee's), Margi Rzeszut (Taco Bell), Sue Willis (Wendy's), Sharon Broda (Wendy's), and Debbie Cline (White Castle). Special acknowledgment for their support to the family and friends of Suzan Hufferd, especially Judy Whittaker for her help with reviewing and editing, and Mike Fleming. We are greatly indebted to Deirdre Root of the Middletown Public Library, who was able to find the answers no one else could provide at the last minute.

The staff of Tomart Publications has been invaluable to the production of this book. To Rebecca Trissel for manuscript editing. The photo scanning and correction is the work of Elisabeth Cline and Nathan Zwilling. Finally, special thanks to desktop publishing coordinator T.N.Tumbusch.

Much of the material in this book had to be borrowed or photographed at various locations around the country, causing delay in publication. To alleviate this problem on future editions Tomart Publications will buy collections of fast food kids meal premiums, which include a substantial amount of material issued prior to 1988.

If interested in selling please contact:
Tom Tumbusch
Tomart Publications
3300 Encrete Lane
Dayton Ohio 45439
(513) 294-2250

First printing, 1994

Published by Tomart Publications, Dayton, Ohio 45439-1944

Library of Congress Catalog Card Number: 93-60871

ISBN: 0-914293-24-9 Manufactured in the United States of America

1 2 3 4 5 6 7 8 9 0 8 7 6 5 4 3 2 1 9 0

INTRODUCTION

This book is an attempt to chronicle kid's meal premiums from fast food and food outlets (other than McDonald's) with regular or occasional kid's promotions. More nearly 30 restaurants which do this type of promotion are listed to some extent, but there are many more. Of the selected restaurant chains, eight are national, the rest are regional.

A kid's meal promotion theme normally lasts four to six weeks, with a new premium each week. There is usually a standard bag or box for each promotion. Each week millions of premiums are distributed.

The premiums can range from colorful plastic toys to a simple sticker sheet or a few crayons with pictures to color. Kid's meal premiums keep getting better because it's often the prize which determines where the family will eat. Just as the quality of toy has improved steadily, the number of places to obtain them has increased. Even discount stores — such as Target and Wal-Mart — and food services facilities at museums, zoos, and amusement parks have recognized kid's meal promotions as an important part of their business.

Cartoon characters, movie heroes, favorite toy brands, super heroes, and many other interesting subjects have been featured as premiums. These items are also favored by collectors in other fields.

Finding all the best premiums requires the inside knowledge provided in this book. The kid's meal promotion industry is serviced by companies which develop unique programs for a single restaurant chain, as well as others which develop a catalog of stock programs for use by regional and local restaurants.

Of the non-McDonald's chains, Burger King, Pizza Hut, and Wendy's are the leading examples of those using eight to twelve exclusive promotions a year. Each item from premium to point-of-purchase is custom-designed for every promotion.

Most regionals have a mascot or cast of kid's meal characters. This allows them to use a mixture of specialty and stock items. Regionals generally run six to eight promotions per year. Non-competing regionals sometimes join together to use all or some of the same premiums in different parts of the country.

As the quality and quantity of premiums have improved, an inexpensive new hobby has been attracting thousands of new collectors each year. Yet it's still a young hobby. There is a good supply of past premiums available for new collectors, and more new premiums are being issued every week. With the expansion of kid's meal premium use comes the promise of continued growth of the hobby for many years to come.

Tom Tumbusch
Publisher

HISTORY OF FAST FOOD KID'S MEAL PREMIUMS

KID'S MEALS – A Historical Perspective

By 1960, fast food restaurants largely replaced the carhop drive-ins popular in the post-war '40s and '50s. The decade of the '60s saw the number of fast food franchise opportunities explode and the number of restaurants in each chain multiply. By 1970, growth had matured to the point fast food restaurants began to crowd around every shopping mall and major freeway exit in the country.

The new decade ushered in competitive promotions largely focused on premiums to attract hungry patrons of all ages. In 1973, the golden era of cartoon and promotional glasses was catching fire nation-wide. Meanwhile, a small, regional hamburger chain in the Midwest was perfecting an on-going promotion for kids. They called it the "Funmeal."

There had been special promotions for kids by virtually every fast food restaurant over the years. Often it was a contest or drawing for tickets to a sporting event, amusement park, zoo, or similar recreation. Sometimes there were discount coupons or comic or coloring book giveaways...maybe even a small toy or magic trick tied to a current promotion event. These were all different, however, from the weekly Fun Meal concept being developed by Burger Chef management in Cincinnati, Ohio. The company had previously positioned its outlets as "Family Restaurants" and was one of the first to realize the place where the kids want to go is usually the place where the whole family eats. The concept they developed had become so important by the beginning of the '90s, even many airlines, museums, amusement parks, children's hospitals, discount store snack bars, and upscale restaurants offer some variation of the Burger Chef marketing plan to kids.

Box and premium for Delta Airlines' Fantastic Flyer Fun Feast

Early Funmeal boxes from Burger Chef

The oldest dated Burger Chef Fun Meal premium found bears a 1971 copyright date. By 1973, the major feature of the promotion was the meal container. Unlike the familiar boxes which would become standard several years later, the original design was more of a carrying tray for the child size burger, drink, and fries. The back panel of the tray extended about 7" higher than necessary. The back and the bottom panels contained games or punch-out toys for the child's amusement. On occasions, additional blow-molded plastic pieces accompanied the standard cardboard container to help convert the meal box into a car, sailboat, or birdhouse.

Burger Chef was also the first to acquire a major license for its Fun Meal promotion. It bought the rights to Lucasfilm's *Star Wars* for 1978, probably because the Kenner Toy Company, also headquartered in Cincinnati, was having great success selling *Star Wars* toys. There were seven different Fun Meal trays produced, mostly cardboard punch-out models of the spaceships and droids from the film.

***Star Wars* Funmeal box**

Dick Brams, the Regional Promotions Manager for McDonald's, had competing Burger Chef restaurants in his territory. He had been watching the Burger Chef promotion for several years, but the phenomenal success of the *Star Wars* promotion was the last bit of ammunition he needed to get McDonald's off the dime on a kid's meal promotion. They tested two different concepts in 1978 and 1979 before choosing the "Happy Meal" program over the "Fun-to-Go" concept. *Star Trek: The Motion Picture* was the first big national tie-in and forever imbedded the McDonald's Happy Meal into our national culture.

The decade of the '80s found other fast food chains responding with their own kid's meals. Burger King was the first in 1981. Wendy's got things going strong by 1983 and the rest quickly fell into line! Pizza Hut was one of the longest hold-outs. They continued the occasional promotion until 1990 when they too introduced a weekly kid's pack promotion.

The additional prize in the box is largely the result of the McDonald's testing in the late '70s, but there are many examples of additional items or prizes before this period. After the *Star Trek* Happy Meal virtually all had a premium, even if it was only a lollipop or cookie...probably the most unsuccessful premium types ever inserted in a kid's meal. The kids have been conditioned. They want toys.

The competition to attract kids has resulted in more licensed character promotions. The toys have gotten so good, a child often spends more play hours with premium toys than purchased toys. This quality, the limited time availability and regional promotions, plus the millions distributed has given rise to a new hobby enjoyed by children and adults alike...collecting

The kid's meal concept has spread overseas. These Pizza Hut *Star Trek* cups were only available in the United Kingdom.

their favorite characters or restaurant premiums. A brave few accept the impossible challenge to "Collect 'Em All". The major force driving this fast-growing hobby is the relative ease and low cost of obtaining premiums from the national chains and a good sample of regionals in the collector's area of the country. A sizeable starter collection can be acquired from just about any flea market, antique or toy show. Friendships have already been formed by phone and mail by collectors trading items from different regions.

The Kid's Meal idea has also been exported. Another phenomenon of the '90s has been the use of American style premiums in the proliferating fast food outlets throughout Europe, Japan, and other countries. Aggressive U.S. collectors have shown a limited degree of interest thus far, but can global Kid's Meal collecting be far behind?

Because of the availability and durability of PVC figures and plastic toys, the values on most items have remained relatively low. As collector interest increases, availability will decrease and values could rise dramatically. Unfortunately, such a bright future was not to be for the kid's meal originators.

The opportunity Burger Chef recognized also made them a prime candidate for a corporate buy-out. The name remained on a few independently owned outlets which were allowed to keep it when corporate-owned restaurants were sold to Hardee's, but most have since closed.

Each chain and many regions have developed promotional themes or have acquired licenses which have been copied by others and have become part of the Kid's Meal arsenal of proven promotions. What chain hasn't used some form of Crayola or Golden Books promotion? Super Heroes, popular toy brands, Halloween collection containers, sand buckets, beach balls, trolls, frisbees, back-to-school supplies, 3-D and glow-in-the-dark items have been used by virtually every fast food chain. And while most are exclusive for the run of the promotion, a single company can license different promotions simultaneously. Christmas 1992 found Burger King using Disney *Aladdin* toys, Pizza Hut doing two promotions based on the release of Disney's *Beauty and the Beast* video, Target offering Disney *Rescuers* Kid's Meals; while competing Wal-Mart packed Disney's Mickey Mouse Friends ornaments with their discounted hot dog, chips, and kid's meal drink.

Most fast food chains have developed a cast of characters to accompany the kid's meal promotions. It is difficult not to notice these and the philosophy behind them. They are all variations of Ronald McDonald and his highly successful product-oriented entourage. Burger King's Kids Club was more politically cast — including to the handicapped. They tend to appear on educational and environmental premiums. Sonic has a unique approach in making characters and toys based on the employee service they seek to provide. Wendy's Good Stuff Gang projected a quality image for its food products, but became inactive after a few years. A particular favorite was the Jack-in-the-Box "Jack Pack" which made good toys and promoted food items in the process. White Castle, however, has probably fared better than most with its Castle Meal Friends, which perfectly personalize the hamburger chain identity and translate to great toys you can find nowhere else.

The constant battle to keep the kid's meal cost competitive at around $2.00 has vastly reduced the number of boxes used to package the meal. To a large degree, these have been replaced by bags.

The mix of premiums from promotion to promotion reflects a larger variance in premium costs. The creativity of kid's meal promotion packagers have responded beautifully to the challenge by intriguingly using less dollars on one promotion in order to afford unbelievably wonderful toys for the next. The best ones always seem to be done when school is not in session. Burger King and others have also used multiple premiums in the same week during these periods...to encourage more frequent repeat visits.

The Kid's Meal concept of 1971 is still a growing institution in the 1990s. Toys are better overall...and the family eating place without a regular Kid's Meal promotion risks sales losses much greater than the price of a child's meal or two. Mediocre toys or the lack of Kid's Meal promotions can cost sales losses of 2 to 4 times or more when the family eats elsewhere.

WHAT ARE KID'S MEAL COLLECTIBLES?

Any item designed to "entice" kids to bring their parents into the restaurant is considered a kid's meal collectible. This book attempts to be consistent and list only premiums tied to meals, but there are some exceptions noted. In a few cases there was no way to verify how the items were distributed, so some items included may not fit the basic premise.

Restaurants are not always consistent with their approach to promoting meals, and not all promotions have premiums, boxes, or accompanying point of purchase promotional items. With the exception of Wendy's promotions since 1990 and selected Subway and Pizza Hut promotions, there are few "under-3" premiums to collect. Unlike McDonald's Happy Meals, there are very few test-market or "regional" promotions...just regional restaurants. Most restaurants did not use translites on a consistent basis, with the notable exceptions of Carl's Jr., Hardee's, Roy Rogers and Burger King. The others only use translites for very special promotions. Burger King displays associated with Disney promotions have easily rivaled the best McDonald's displays. Aside from these, displays from the other restaurants have been anything from a poster to a cardboard mobile to a permanent display box (such as those used by Burger King, White Castle, and Wendy's) displaying the current premiums. Most organizations used boxes for their kid's meals in the '80s, but these have been replaced, for the most part, by bags in the '90s. Some are still tied to the promotion, but Wendy's, Burger King, and others have gone to standard bags used for an extended period.

Where an item is known, be it a premium, display, or translite, it has been assigned a code and a value. Some chains occasionally use stock premiums where the toys and/or boxes do not identify the restaurant running the promotion. There are companies such as Admark, Western Publishing, Selling Solutions, CDM, and others which specialize in off-the-shelf promotions with or without name identification. Even larger chains use such toys from time to time. The fast-growing Sonic Drive-In chain has used many stock promotions, while Hardee's and others have used them only occasionally. Some Wendy's restaurants use stock items while others are involved in a national promotion, apparently

Catalog for Admark, one of several companies specializing in stock promotions.

opting out of the national for whatever reason. For the most part, such promotions have been excluded unless there is some special collector interest.

Some premiums were issued by two or more restaurant chains. This occurs when chains in different markets "share" a promotion to get a better price. For example, the Fender Bender 500 promotion was held by both Hardee's and Carl's Jr. at about the same time. Apart from the packaging, the toys are identical. White Castle and Carl's Jr. both used the Stunt Grip Geckos promotion, but with color variations. The same is true of the Camp California promotion shared by Carl's Jr. and Hardee's more than a year apart. Snap-together dinosaurs and other animals have been used at various times by McDonald's in Canada, Chick-fil-A, Carl's Jr., Big Boy, and others.

There are some chains with few national promotions, such as Dairy Queen. Depending on which location you visit, multiple premiums may be available at the same time. When not involved in a national promotion, individual stores can choose from a variety of promotions, which may or may not identify the restaurant. This often results in different stores within the same chain running the same promotion months apart.

Long John Silver's, Taco Bell, and others fall somewhere in between. The same promotion usually occurs at all of the outlets, but there are exceptions. Many collectors visit multiple locations of these chains to reduce the risk of missing special premiums.

Every kid's meal premium verified by the publication deadline has been included, including boxes, translites, and other related materials. It is the most complete illustrated listing ever published. Yet it is by no means all-inclusive, and there are premiums to be found, photographed, and listed in future editions. **If you'd like to help by supplying information on premiums not listed, or spot a date which is wrong, please send a photocopy or other supporting data to the authors. Their addresses are found in the "Where to Buy Sell" section on page 7.**

HOW TO USE THIS BOOK

Tomart's Price Guide to Kid's Meal Collectibles was designed to be an authoritative and easy-to-use reference guide. It utilizes an identification and classification system designed to create a standard identification number for each individual premium or associated item. No one has yet identified the thousands of different kid's meal premiums produced, but this system contains the framework in which they may be organized.

Promotions are arranged alphabetically by restaurant. Each item has a code made up of the first two or three letters of the restaurant name and a 3-4 digit identification number. For example, a Wendy's premium might have the code "WE1001." Use of these numbers in dealer and distributor ads and collector's correspondence is encouraged. Permission for such use to conduct buying, selling and the trade of premiums in trading lists, letters or ads is hereby granted. Rights for all other uses are reserved, and must be cleared with the publisher, including, but not limited to, checklists, reporting values in newsletters, independent updates, or advisory services.

The identity code numbers also serve to match the correct listing to a nearby photo. Usually, there is a listing for every photo, but unfortunately not all items can be depicted. This book utilizes a code system which is inconsistent with other Tomart Photo Price Guides.

THE VALUES IN THIS PRICE GUIDE

Price values in this book indicate a range based on condition. The low-end value indicates an out-of-package toy in good condition with all pieces, decals, accessories, or other items found in the original package. Items without all the original pieces, decals, or accessories are therefore worth less than the lowest value listed.

The high range indicates an item which is mint in an original, mint package. This means the unopened item is in perfect condition, with no scratches, tears, fading, food stains, or other damage.

Be wary of the phrase "mint in package." This is frequently interpreted by dealers to mean the item *inside* the package is mint, but the package itself could be re-glued, bent, faded, marred, stained, taped, or covered with adhesive tags which are difficult to remove without damage. Re-packaged premiums are another thing to watch out for.

The values in this guide are based on the experience of the authors, the publisher, and the national panel of dealers and collectors credited in the acknowledgements. The real value any particular item will bring depends on what a buyer is willing to pay...no more, no less. Prices constantly change up and down.

Many factors influence any given transaction. Not the least of these are perceived value, emotional appeal, or competitive drive for ownership. Everything people buy is motivated by a need or a want. There are few who actually need kid's meal collectibles, but a lot of people buy them out of interest or desire. Dealers usually want the highest returns possible and collectors want the most for their money. Out of this process prices are established.

Supply and demand have always been important factors in determining value, and are a bit more predictable for those knowledgeable in a given area. The supply is still ample for most kid's meal premiums, so these market forces have yet to meet a true test. Kid's meal production had its origins in the '70s, making it one of the most recent collectible fields. All premiums and associated items are collectible, including many produced in the last few years. As such, they aren't old enough to consider the known quantities a valid basis for establishing values.

The market for an entire collection at retail value is slim and difficult to find. There have been numerous examples in recent years where collections of nostalgia collectibles were sold at auctions or purchased by dealers at a fraction of their estimated value. Except for a very limited number of high-demand items, the process of turning a good-sized collection back into cash can be a long and expensive one. Even when a retail buyer can be found, there are sales costs and perhaps a middle man who is working for a percentage.

This book reports market prices based on items sold or traded by dealers and collectors nationwide.

Collectors who buy at garage sales, flea markets, or thrift shops generally purchase for less. Often they have first choice of items offered for sale — sometimes at exceptional bargain prices — but they also incur substantial time and travel expenses. When shopping at secondary market sources beware of missing parts and pieces. The only way to be assured of getting the entire premium is to find mint packaged items.

Mail order is often preferred by collectors who don't have the time to spend hunting and pay extra for the service. Mail-order buyers, however, must reach an advertiser before a particular item is sold, and often go to extra expense for long-distance phone calls or to ensure faster shipping of publications which contain dealer advertisements. Not being able to see the item prior to purchase creates the risk of dissatisfaction with its condition, which can be further complicated by shipping damage.

Collecting should be pursued for the interest and satisfaction involved. There are much better investments at most financial institutions. *Fortune*, *Business Week*, and other business publications have done extensive articles on the pitfalls of speculating in what they term "exotic" investments.

Every attempt has been made to have this price guide reflect the market in its broadest sense. The research effort covers extensive travel each year to attend leading toy, antique, and advertising shows. The up-to-date values in this edition are a compilation of information received through April, 1994. All prices shown in this book are U.S. dollar values with the dollar signs removed to permit inclusion of more information.

There are three additional factors affecting value which can be measured more precisely: rarity, completeness, and demand.

Rarity, Completeness, and Demand

Some items are available for a long time, such as stock premiums or bags. Others are available only briefly, such as the Pizza Hut *Rocketeer* promotion (which sold out in less than two weeks), or are available only in limited areas. How widely an item is distributed usually depends on the size of the chain which offers it. Some premiums are sold only by region or have color variations (the latter most commonly from Burger King).

Rarity doesn't always equate to value. In collecting, the strongest demand is often generated by people wishing to obtain items of special interest. Thus rarity is only a part of value. The collectibility of an item is also determined in part by how "likable" a toy is, or how desirable an item is to collectors from other fields. Toys which display well, are fun to play with, or are tied to a hit movie or cartoon generate an additional demand. Character popularity, cross-overs to other collecting fields (such as Disneyana, Warner Brothers, and advertising), and the type of item (action figure, PVC figure, watch, comic book, Golden Book, etc.) may be stronger factors, as other collectors often specialize in areas which cross the kid's meal line.

Price also has some regional influences. In California and New York, prices are often higher. Regional selling prices are the lowest in the areas where items are most commonly found so collectors outside the area, served by the restaurant, may pay a little more..

Another factor which enhances value is the completeness of the original box or package. Some premiums also included instructions, extra accessories, or other items which must be intact if the item is to realize top value.

Rarity, condition, and the amount of material available in the market place all have a direct effect on value. The overriding factor, however, is the number of individuals who wish to acquire a given item and have the money to satisfy their desire.

TIPS ON FINDING KID'S MEAL COLLECTIBLES

Collecting kid's meal premiums has mushroomed since the early '80s, and there is no want to find dealers at toy and character collectible shows which have a large selection of items for sale. Finding special items may be a bit more difficult, but there are many tools available.

Publications

World of Fast Food Collectibles Newsletter is a monthly newsletter designed to keep collectors up-to-date on which promotions are going on at various restaurants. To obtain subscription information, contact Dream Enterprises, P.O. Box 64, Powder Springs, GA 30073.

The Fast Food Collector's Express is a monthly publication consisting of classified ads placed by subscribers. It is available from Paradise Publications, Box 221, Mayview, MO 64071.

Shows

Toy, advertising, and collectibles shows throughout the U.S. offer ready access to mail order and other dealers offering kid's meal-related items. Some of the more prominent ones include the monthly Long Beach and Rose Bowl shows in Los Angeles; Antique Toy World shows held May, July, and October at the Kane County Fairgrounds located in St. Charles, IL approximately 40 miles west of Chicago; The Toledo Toy and Character Collectible shows, Lucas County Recreation Center, Maumee, OH; the New York City Pier shows; the complex of shops, malls, and supershows at Adamstown, PA; and the Mid-West Collectors Toy Association's Toy and Doll Show, April and October each year, Wampler's Area, Dayton, OH.

A lot of kid's meal items are available to room-hoppers on Friday and Saturday night at the annual McDonald's Convention, even though the Sunday show is for McDonald's items only.

Most sections of the country have regional restaurants which are not accessible to collectors in other parts of the country. Those who want to "collect 'em all" often trade toys from restaurants in their area with collectors in other parts of the country. Forming a network of collectors is an easy way to increase a national collection without paying a premium. Please include the authors and the publisher in your network.

And don't forget local antique shows, flea markets, thrift shops, antique shops and malls, and garage sales.

Acquiring Promotional Items

Kid's Meal premiums, boxes, and bags are easy to obtain...just order a kid's meal (some stores will sell the premiums without a kid's meal purchase, but remember the primary goal of these promotions is to generate food sales). Promotional items are more difficult because there is only one set per store. As the number of collectors grows, distribution is becoming more of a problem to store owners and managers. In some cases there is a policy of not giving out promotional materials because aggressive collectors have caused unpleasant situations. Understanding will yield more materials than making demands or arguing with the owner or manager in charge.

Many fast food restaurants are operated by independent owners. When a store has sold all its premiums, they usually get rid of the promotional items. Employees often have first choice, so getting a job at a particular restaurant is sometimes the best way to acquire them. Many store owners or managers are collectors themselves, so these materials don't get very far.

Members of the general public acquire these items according to the policies of individual restaurants. In some cases, the first person who asks gets the prize. Names are often written on the backs of displays for the person to pick up the day after the promotion is concluded.

First, you need to determine the policy of the restaurant in question and respond accordingly — always remembering to be polite and understanding, even if you are unsuccessful.

WHERE TO BUY AND SELL

Many readers select this book because they want to get connected to the kid's meal network or have items they wish to sell. Apart from the ideas presented above, special mention of the dealers and collectors who have been particularly helpful to Tomart Publications in publishing this book is due.

Those listed are by no means the total number of dealers or collectors from whom items were purchased. These are, however, the ones who were most cooperative, handled orders without delay or foul-up, and sent items in a condition consistent with the way they were advertised.

This list also contains the names of those dealers and collectors who spent the time to review a fledgling version of the manuscript for this book, made suggestions, and provided estimates of values. It seems likely they would do the same for anyone wishing to buy, sell, or trade.

Ken Clee
P.O. Box 11412
Philadelphia, PA 19111

Suzan Hufferd
6625 Sunbury Dr.
Indianapolis, IN 46241

Bill & Pat Poe
220 Dominica Circle E.
Niceville, FL 32578

E.J. Ritter
6803 Idaho Ave.
Hammond, IN 46323

Pat Multz
3035 Sprague Ave.
Anoka, MN 55303

Martha Gragg
5910 NW 56th
Oklahoma City, OK 73122

Reaching the Publisher

The staff of Tomart Publications may be reached on the Compu-Serve network at 71034,1607. We can also receive messages from the Internet at 71034,1607@CompuServe.Com.

All Inquiries Welcome, but Nothing for Sale

ARBY'S

Arby's is a national chain which formalized its regular kid's meal promotion program in 1986 after testing various spot promotions since 1984. With few exceptions, Arby's tends to make agreements with a given group of characters for a long period of time, and then create a series of themed promotions around the license for a period of 12 to 30 months. Each promotion also lasts longer than a month.

AR0101 AR0102 AR0103 AR0104 AR0105 AR0107

AR0108 AR0109 AR0111 AR0112 AR0114 AR0113

AR0115 AR0116 AR0117 AR0118 AR0119 AR0120

AR01331 AR01332

AR01333 AR01334

ADVENTURES OF MR. MEN & LITTLE MISS, 1981

Solid rubber 1½"-2¼" figures of Roger Hargreaves' Mr. Men and Little Miss cartoon characters were used for several kid's meal promotions. Only those with an Arby's logo imprinted on the bottom of one foot were kid's meal premiums.

AR0101	Little Miss Giggles	2 - 6
AR0102	Little Miss Helpful	2 - 6
AR0103	Little Miss Late	2 - 6
AR0104	Little Miss Lucky	2 - 6
AR0105	Little Miss Naughty	2 - 6
AR0106	Little Miss Scatterbrain	5 - 8
AR0107	Little Miss Shy	2 - 6
AR0108	Little Miss Splendid	2 - 6
AR0109	Little Miss Sunshine	2 - 6
AR0110	Little Miss Trouble	5 - 8
AR0111	Mr. Bounce	2 - 6
AR0112	Mr. Bump	2 - 6
AR0113	Mr. Daydream	2 - 6
AR0114	Mr. Funny	2 - 6
AR0115	Mr. Greedy	2 - 6
AR0116	Mr. Mischief	2 - 6
AR0117	Mr. Nosey	2 - 6
AR0118	Mr. Rush	2 - 6
AR0119	Mr. Strong	2 - 6
AR0120	Mr. Tickle	2 - 6
Boxes		
AR0131	Haunted House	5 - 10
AR0132	Treasure Ship	5 - 10
AR0133	Traveling Circus	5 - 10
AR0134	Amusement Park	5 - 10

AR0142 AR0145

MR. MEN & LITTLE MISS™ ADVENTURE BOOK AND POSTER

MEET MR...

ARBY'S® COLLECTOR SERIES

AR0147 AR0151

AR0152 AR0153

AR0154 AR0155

ADVENTURES OF MR. MEN & LITTLE MISS JIGSAW PUZZLE BOOKS, 1986

Each 4" x 4" cardboard booklet contained an interlocking jigsaw puzzle. The cover showed various characters, the name of the promotion.

AR0141	Puzzle #1	3 - 8
AR0142	Puzzle #2	3 - 8
AR0143	Puzzle #3	3 - 8
AR0144	Puzzle #4	3 - 8
AR0145	Puzzle #5	3 - 8
AR0146	Puzzle #6	3 - 8
AR0147	Adventure Book and Poster	3 - 8
Boxes		
AR0151	Explore Nature	6 - 12
AR0152	Bicycle Fun	6 - 12
AR0153	Baseball Fever	6 - 12
AR0154	Out West	6 - 12
AR0155	On the Lake	6 - 12

AR0350 AR0381 AR0382

BABAR'S BUCKET OF FUN, 1992

Several "Bucket of Fun" offerings were issued with Adventure Meals. For one back-to-school period, school related scenes featuring the Barbar characters were silk-screened around a white bucket with film strip type borders above and below the screen. For the Halloween season, the Babar characters were featured in a trick-or-treating scene. The plastic buckets had a 6¾" diameter and were 5¾" deep.

AR0350	Bucket of Fun, school	3 - 6
AR0351	Bucket of Fun, ghosts	3 - 6

BABAR CHRISTMAS CUPS, 1992

These hot mugs came with a package of Swiss Miss drink mix in each premium cup: Rich Chocolate Hot Cocoa mix w/mini-marshmallows or Milk Chocolate Hot Cocoa mix with marshmallows.

AR0381	Toboggan scene w/green handle	4 - 6
AR0382	Snowmobile scene w/red handle	4 - 6

AR0432 AR0433 AR0434

BABAR'S KIDS WORLD STICKER BOOKS, 1993

This promotion featured "In Babar's Kids World, you do make a difference" booklets and stickers. Each 6" x 4" 4-page color booklet came with a folded 2-page sticker sheet. The Arby's and Babar logos appeared on the back cover.

AR0432	World of Fun Sticker Book	2 - 5
AR0433	Planet Earth Sticker Book	2 - 5
AR0434	All About Animals Sticker Book	2 - 5

BABAR'S MAGIC SHOW CUPS MEAL, 1992

Magic pictures appear when cold liquid is put in cup.

AR0551	Arthur	3 - 6
AR0552	Babar	3 - 6
AR0553	Rataxes	3 - 6

AR0561 AR0563 AR0562 AR0564

BABAR'S WORLD TOUR FINGER PUPPETS, 1990, 1993

Laurent de Brunhoff's Babar characters were featured as 2⅞" - 3½" painted hollow rubber figures with a hole in the base to fit on the tip of a finger. This series was repeated in 1993, changing only the copyright date. Values are the same for both years.

AR0561	King Babar w/camera	1 - 3
AR0562	Queen Celeste w/shoulder strap tote	1 - 3
AR0563	Pom w/binoculars	1 - 3
AR0564	Arthur & Zephir	1 - 3
Boxes		
AR0566	#1 - Green Train	2 - 5
AR0567	#2 - Blue Plane	2 - 5
AR0568	#3 - Yellow Submarine	2 - 5
AR0569	#4 - Red Car	2 - 5

AR0566 AR0567

AR0568 AR0569

AR0574

AR0572

AR0573 AR0571

BABAR'S WORLD TOUR JIGSAW PUZZLE BOOK, 1990

A series of 4 puzzle books were issued as part of the ongoing Babar tour promotion. Each is a 4" x 4" booklet along with a scene relating to the story contained within.

AR0571	Cousin Arthur's New Camera	2 - 4
AR0572	Babar's Gondola Ride	2 - 4
AR0573	Babar and the Haunted Castle	2 - 4
AR0574	Babar's Trip to Greece	2 - 4
Boxes		
AR0576	#9 - Red Balloon	2 - 4
AR0577	#10 - Purple Whale	2 - 4
AR0578	#11 - Blue Bus	2 - 4
AR0579	#12 - Babar Reading	2 - 4

AR0576 AR0577

AR0578 AR0579

AR0581 AR0582

AR0583 AR0584

AR0586 AR0587

AR0588 AR0589

BABAR'S WORLD TOUR LICENSE PLATES, 1990

Plastic 5⅜" x 2¾" license plates came with "Babar's World Tour" across the top and the Arby's name at the bottom in red. A colored sticker featured the name of a city/country.

AR0581	Paris	1 - 4
AR0582	Brazil	1 - 4
AR0583	U.S.A.	1 - 4
AR0584	South Pole	1 - 4
Boxes		
AR0586	#5 - White boat	2 - 4
AR0587	#6 - Tan Camel	2 - 4
AR0588	#7 - Green Truck	2 - 4
AR0589	#8 - Yellow Junk	2 - 4

AR0592 AR0591 AR0593

BABAR'S WORLD TOUR PULL-BACK RACERS, 1992

Non-removable Babar characters drove plastic convertibles which roll forward after being pulled backward. Each 2" car had 3 wheels.

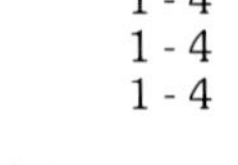

AR0591	Green car w/Queen Celeste	1 - 4
AR0592	Red car w/King Babar	1 - 4
AR0593	Yellow car w/Cousin Arthur	1 - 4

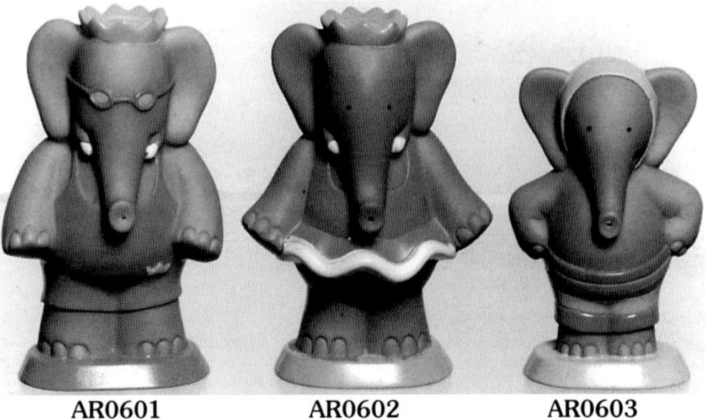

AR0601 AR0602 AR0603

BABAR'S WORLD TOUR SQUIRTERS, 1992

Babar characters as 3"-3¾" hollow rubber figures which squirted water from the end of the trunk.

AR0601	Babar in green swimsuit	1 - 4
AR0602	Celeste in purple swimsuit	1 - 4
AR0603	Alexander in striped swimsuit	1 - 4

AR0611 AR0612 AR0613

BABAR'S WORLD TOUR STAMPERS, 1991

Stampers for personalizing stationery and books featured Babar characters. Each 2¾" premium had a PVC character which was attached to a plastic base, on the bottom of which was the rubber stamp. All had plastic base covers of the same color.

AR0611	Rataxes – "Message from," white base	2 - 4
AR0612	Zephir – "This Book Belongs To," blue base	2 - 4
AR0613	Babar – "Now Read This," gray base	2 - 4

AR0621 AR0622 AR0623

BABAR'S WORLD TOUR STORYBOOK, 1991

Accordion-fold 4" x 4" storybooks featured an illustrated story on one side of the pages and a different activity to be completed on the other.

AR0621	Read and Get Ready – Set – Go, calendar	2 - 4
AR0622	Read and Have Fun, game	2 - 4
AR0623	Read & Grow & Grow ..., growth chart	2 - 4

BABAR'S WORLD TOUR SUMMER SIPPERS, 1991

White plastic 4½" drink bottles with screw-on lids and plastic straws featured Babar in summertime scenes. A color-coordinated lid had "Babar" embossed on opposing sides of the rim. Blue plastic tubing served as the "straw."

AR0631	On Surfboard, purple top	1 - 3

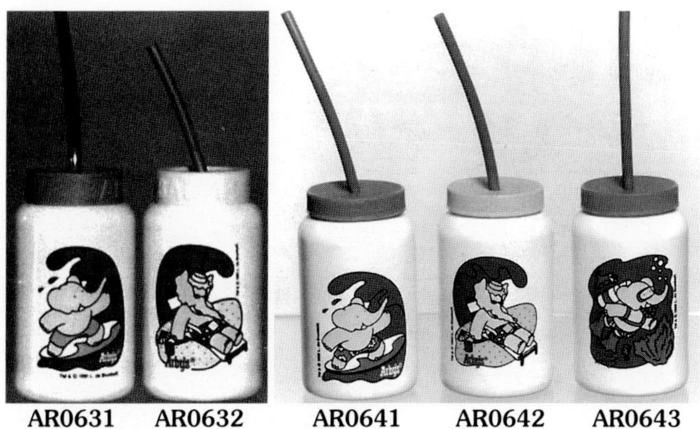

AR0631 AR0632 AR0641 AR0642 AR0643

AR0632 On the Beach, yellow top 1 - 3
AR0633 Scuba Diving, orange top 1 - 3

BABAR'S WORLD TOUR SUMMER SIPPERS, 1992

These were basically the same as those used in the 1991 promotion except the copyright date was changed and the screw-on lid was not embossed with the Character's name.

AR0641 On Surfboard, purple top 1 - 3
AR0642 On the Beach, yellow top 1 - 3
AR0643 Scuba Diving, orange top 1 - 3

AR0661 AR0662 AR0663

BABAR'S WORLD TOUR VEHICLES, 1990

Babar characters operated various modes of transportation for this promotion. Each 2"-3¾" plastic vehicle rolled on wheels and had a non-removable figure as its driver.

AR0661 Red 3-wheel motorcycle w/Arthur 1 - 4
AR0662 Green helicopter w/Babar 1 - 4
AR0663 Blue amphibian w/Zephir 1 - 4
Boxes
AR0666 #13 - Prop Plane 2 - 4
AR0667 #14 - Yacht 2 - 4

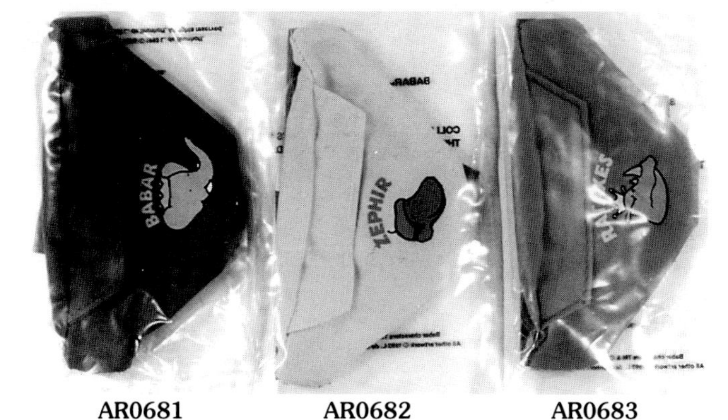

AR0681 AR0682 AR0683

BABAR'S WRISTPACKS, 1992

Pictures of Babar characters were featured on vinyl 4½" x 2½" pouches with velcro wrist straps. Each wristpack featured a different character with its name above it.

AR0681 Babar, green/purple strap 2 - 4
AR0682 Zephir, yellow/blue strap 2 - 4
AR0683 Rataxes, purple/green strap 2 - 4

BABAR MULTI-USE SACKS, 1991-92

The following sacks were used on several World Tour Promotions in 1991-92. These came in glossy and kraft versions.

AR1021 AR1022 AR1023 AR1024

AR1051 AR1052 AR1053

AR1055 AR3810

Sacks
AR1021 Babar's World Tour - Kenya, 1991 1 - 2
AR1022 Babar's World Tour - Casablanca, 1991 1 - 2
AR1023 Babar's World Tour - Brazil, 1991 1 - 2
AR1024 The World of Babar, 1992 1 - 2

CLASSIC FAIRY TALES, 1993

Favorite fairy tales on audio cassette tapes came in a cardboard sleeve with full-color illustration of the tales.

AR1051 Jack and the Beanstalk 2 - 4
AR1052 The 3 Little Pigs 2 - 4
AR1053 Hansel and Gretel 2 - 4
Sack
AR1055 Classic Fairy Tales 1 - 2

LAND OF DINOSAURS, 1984

The only item found from this promotion is a box copyrighted 1984. No other details available.

AR3810 Box 5 - 10

LOONEY TUNES CAR-TUNES, 1989

Looney Tunes characters formed as 1-piece 3½" molded vehicles. None have rolling wheels.

AR4151 Sylvester Cat-illac 3 - 6
AR4152 Bugs Bunny Buggy 3 - 6
AR4153 Daffy Duck Dragster 3 - 6
AR4154 Yosemite Sam Rackin' Frackin' Wagon 3 - 6
AR4155 Road Runner Racer 3 - 6
AR4156 Tasmanian Devil Slush Musher 3 - 6

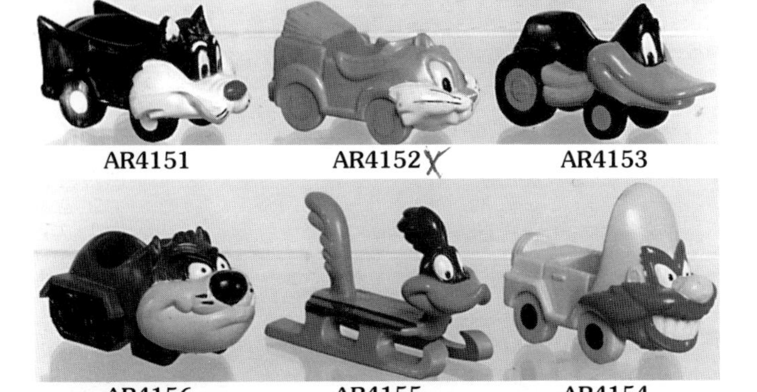

AR4151 AR4152 AR4153

AR4156 AR4155 AR4154

AR4161 AR4162

AR4164 AR4165

Boxes

AR4161	#5-Daffy Duck Ding Dong Academy	4 - 8
AR4162	#6-Tasmanian Devil Flyin' Devils Airlines	4 - 8
AR4164	#8-Mountain Lodge	4 - 8
AR4165	#9-Petunia Pig Ice Palace	4 - 8

AR4190 AR4201

LOONEY TUNES COLLECTIBLE WORLD FUN BUCKETS, 1989

White plastic buckets with a Looney Tunes scene. Each lid featured a different Looney Tunes character in the center.

AR4190	Hoppy the Kangaroo	3 - 6
AR4191	Daffy Duck	3 - 6
AR4192	Tasmanian Devil	3 - 6

LOONEY TUNES COLLECTIBLE WORLD FUN STUFF PACK, 1989

The first 12 Looney Tunes Adventure Meal boxes form a cartoon town. These punch-out props are road signs and little accessories to add play value to the town. Each "Fun Stuff Pack" contained an accordion-folded cardboard piece with punch-outs on 5 of the 6 pages.

AR4201	Pack #1	2 - 5
AR4202	Pack #2	2 - 5
AR4203	Pack #3	2 - 5
AR4204	Pack #4	2 - 5

Boxes

AR4211	#1 - Arby's Restaurant	4 - 6

AR4211 AR4212

AR4213 AR4214

AR4251 AR4252 AR4253

AR4254 AR4255 AR4256 AR4257

AR4261 AR4262 AR4263

AR4212	#2 - Bugs Bunny Pit Stop and Gaseteria	4 - 6
AR4213	#3 - Drive-In Movie Theatre	4 - 6
AR4214	#4 - Firehouse	4 - 6

LOONEY TUNES FIGURES, 1987

Seven Looney Tunes characters were issued as 2" PVC figures molded on thin, flat, oval bases.

AR4251	Porky Pig	3 - 6
AR4252	Bugs Bunny	3 - 6
AR4253	Yosemite Sam	3 - 6
AR4254	Sylvester	3 - 6
AR4255	Tweety Bird	3 - 6
AR4256	Pepe Le Pew	10 - 15
AR4257	Tasmanian Devil	3 - 6

Boxes

AR4261	Ice Cream Parlor	4 - 6
AR4262	Dog-Gone Wild!	4 - 6
AR4263	Who's Kitten Who?	4 - 6

LOONEY TUNES FREE-STANDING CHARACTERS, 1988

Thick legs and feet helped these 2½"-3" PVC figures stand.

AR4301	Tasmanian Devil	3 - 6
AR4302	Bugs Bunny	3 - 6

AR4301 AR4302 AR4303 AR4304 AR4305 AR4306

AR4303	Elmer Fudd	3 - 6
AR4304	Road Runner	3 - 6
AR4305	Wile E. Coyote	3 - 6
AR4306	Daffy Duck	3 - 6

AR4319 AR4320 AR4321

LOONEY TUNES FUN BUCKETS, 1987

White buckets featuring color scenes of Looney Tunes characters.

AR4319	Beach Buddies	3 - 6
AR4320	Daffy Doodles	3 - 6
AR4321	School Daze	3 - 6

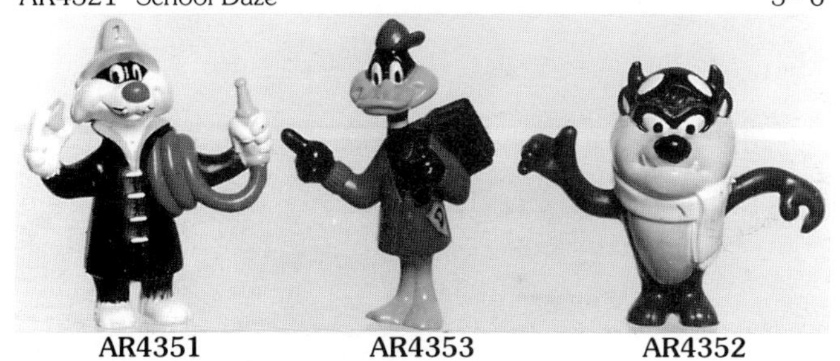

AR4351 AR4353 AR4352

LOONEY TUNES FUN FIGURES, 1989

Three Looney Tunes characters were issued as 2½"-2¾" PVC figures cast in the role of different occupations.

AR4351	Sylvester as a Fireman	3 - 6
AR4352	Tasmanian Devil as a Pilot	3 - 6
AR4353	Daffy Duck as a Schoolboy	3 - 6

AR4355

AR4356

AR4357 AR4358

LOONEY TUNES FUN 'N GAMES, 1988

A series of boxes with punch-out premiums issued in 1988. Possibly used with "Free Standing Characters" or "Pencil Toppers."

Boxes

AR4355	Bugs Bunny's Busy Boxes	4 - 8
AR4356	Pick-Your-Partner Party Cards	4 - 8
AR4357	Porky Pig's Picture Puzzle	4 - 8
AR4358	Taz Pick-Your-Partner Party Cards	4 - 8

LOONEY TUNES HATS

Vacuum formed meal containers.

AR4360	Bugs Bunny	10 - 15
AR4361	Tweety	10 - 15
AR4362	Daffy	10 - 15
AR4363	Sylvester	10 - 15

AR4401 AR4402 AR4403 AR4411

LOONEY TUNES HOLIDAY FIGURES CHRISTMAS ORNAMENTS, 1989

Three different Looney Tunes characters became PVC figures which could double as yuletide decorations. A box marked #7, similar to Looney Tunes Car-Tunes boxes, was used for this promotion.

AR4401	Bugs as Santa Claus	3 - 6
AR4402	Tweety Bird as an Elf	3 - 6
AR4403	Porky Pig as a Toy Soldier	4 - 7

Box

AR4411	#7-Holiday Box	3 - 6

AR4451 AR4452 AR4453 AR4454 AR4455 AR4456

LOONEY TUNES PENCIL TOPPERS, 1988

The heads of Looney Tunes characters were issued as pencil toppers. Each is approximately 1½."

AR4451	Yosemite Sam	3 - 7
AR4452	Tasmanian Devil	3 - 7
AR4453	Porky Pig	3 - 7
AR4454	Daffy Duck	3 - 7
AR4455	Tweety Bird	3 - 7
AR4456	Sylvester	3 - 7

AR4481 AR4482 AR4483 AR4484

LOONEY TUNES RINGS, 1987

Plastic rings featuring Looney Tunes characters in x-o-graph pictures on the top. Each 1¼" diameter round disc showed one side of a Looney Tunes Money coin when held at one angle; when the angle changed, so did the picture as the reverse side of that coin appeared.

AR4481	Porky Pig/Ten Oinks, gold ring	5 - 10
AR4482	Yosemite Sam/¢Nonsense¢, silver ring	5 - 10
AR4483	Daffy Duck/Quacker Dollar, silver ring	5 - 10
AR4484	Bugs Bunny/14 Carrots, gold ring	5 - 10

POLAR SWIRL PENGUINS, 1987

Penguins became "humanized" as 3" PVC figures. Each character sported a red bow tie, shorts, and footwear of some sort.

AR6101	Sunglasses, blue shorts, green loafers	5 - 10
AR6102	Sunglasses, yellow shorts, blue loafers	5 - 10
AR6103	Walkman, red shorts, tennis shoes	5 - 10
AR6104	Mask & snorkel, black swim trunks, green swim fins	5 - 10
AR6105	Surfboard, blue shorts, red thong sandals	5 - 10

AR6101 AR6102 AR6103 AR6104 AR6105

AR8771 AR8772

AR8773 AR8774

SCOOBY DOO HALLOWEEN BUCKETS, 1993

These 6½" diameter buckets were used to package kid's meals during the months of October and November. Each has a solid color lid.

AR8771	Frankenstein, Wolfman, Dracula	2 - 4
AR8772	Mummy	2 - 4
AR8773	Creature	2 - 4
AR8774	Ghosts	2 - 4

DECODER CARD
SCOOBY-DOO
MYSTERY PUZZLE
THE HUNT ON HAUNTED HILL
Arby's

AR8801 AR8802 AR8803 Decoder Card

SCOOBY DOO MYSTERY PUZZLES, 1993

These are sets of 6 cards: five which form a puzzle, plus a decoder card with a red cellophane window used to find clues in the picture.

AR8810 AR9105 AR9106

AR8801	The Hunt on Haunted Hill	1 - 2
AR8802	The Mystery of Monster Manor	1 - 2
AR8803	The Secret of Spooky Swamp	1 - 2
Sack		
AR8810	Yogi & Friends and Scooby Doo	1 - 2

YOGI & FRIENDS MINI-FRISBEES, 1993

Four flying disks, molded in blue, yellow, lime green, fuchsia or purple.

AR9101	Ranger Smith	1 - 2
AR9102	Yogi Bear	1 - 2
AR9103	Snagglepuss	1 - 2

AR9101 AR9102

AR9103 AR9104

AR9104	Cindy Bear	1 - 2
Sack		
AR9105	Summer version	1 - 2
AR9106	Winter version	1 - 2
Point of Purchase		
AR9110	Employee Badge	5 - 10

AR9106

AR9201 AR9202

AR9203 AR9204

YOGI & FRIENDS MUGS, 1994

The final promotion of the 1993-94 winter season featured four mugs with full color decals. Mugs could be used for hot or cold drinks.

AR9201	Boo-Boo	2 - 4
AR9202	Cindy Bear	2 - 4
AR9203	Ranger Smith	2 - 4
AR9204	Yogi Bear	2 - 4

AR9322 AR9324 AR9323

YOGI BEAR SPORTS BOTTLE, 1993

White 4½" Pescor plastic "sports bottles" with color scenes of Yogi Bear and his friends. Each flare-top mug came with matching snap-on lids and rippled plastic straws.

AR9321	Picnic Scene w/blue lid & straw	1 - 3
AR9322	Roller Blading Scene w/yellow lid & straw	1 - 3
AR9323	Beach Scene w/red lid & straw	1 - 3
AR9324	Baseball Scene w/green lid & straw	1 - 3

AR9400 AR9525 AR9410

AR9425 AR9426 AR9427

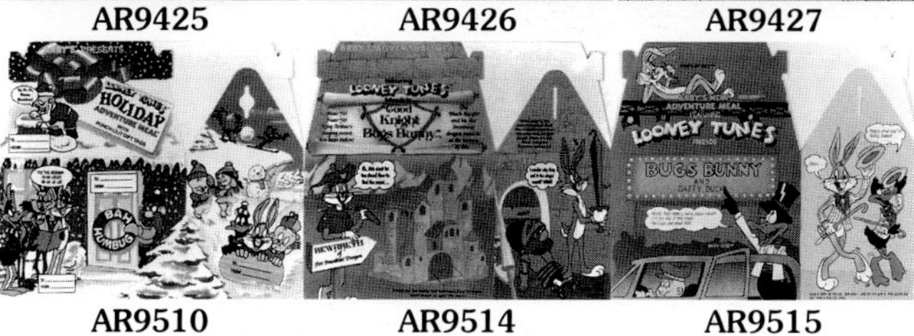

AR9510 AR9514 AR9515

MISCELLANEOUS ARBY'S ITEMS

The following are known to exist, but no further information is currently available.

AR9400	Babar Sledding Poster, 1991	2 - 6
AR9410	Poster & Coloring Page ("Beach Blanket Bingo")	3 - 7
AR9425	Looney Toons Disk (Armchair Athletes)	3 - 6
AR9426	Looney Toons Disk (Looney Gallery)	3 - 6
AR9427	Looney Toons Disk (Miami Ice)	3 - 6
Boxes		
AR9510	Looney Tunes Holiday w/Punch-out Gift Tags, 1988	5 - 8
AR9514	Good Knight Bugs Bunny, 1987	4 - 6
AR9515	Bugs Bunny & Daffy Duck (vaudeville)	4 - 6
Point of Purchase		
AR9525	Looney Tunes Employee Badge	5 - 10

BIG BOY

Big Boy is franchised by geographical territory. The first company was Frisch's Big Boy in Cincinnati, Ohio, which established the original territories. Shoney's held the Big Boy Franchise for many southern states before giving it up to expand outside established territories. Elias Brothers of Michigan and Bob's from the western states are other major Big Boy franchisors. Frisch's sold their interest, along with the Roy Rogers chain which they also owned, to Marriott Corporation. Marriott in turn sold off the majority of their outside food operations to various companies.

The Big Boy Comic series is probably the longest-running kid's promotion going, but is not connected to a special meal. Elias Brothers has been the source of most listed Big Boy premiums, most of which have been picked up in some form by other franchises.

BI0201

BI0301

BI3000

BIG BOY PVC, 1984

This early premium was a PVC figure of the Big Boy carrying a double decker hamburger on a tray.

BI0201	PVC Big Boy	3 - 7

BUCKET & SHOVEL, 1992

A white plastic bucket with a scene of the Big Boy as an underwater diver came with a red handle and blue plastic shovel.

BI0301	Bucket & Shovel	2 - 4

DINOSAUR POUCH, 1992

Clear plastic pouches with a dinosaur scene on the front. Each 9" x 3¾" case had a ziplock-type closure.

BI2100	Dinosaur Pouch	2 - 3

HALLOWEEN BUCKET, (no date)

A PVC bucket with a scene of ghosts flying out of pumpkins. The Big Boy figure was hand stamped around the scene.

BI3000	Bucket	2 - 4

BI3103 BI3102 BI3101

HELICOPTERS, 1991

Stock plastic 6" toy helicopters came in three colors each: orange, pink and yellow. When wound up, the propeller would spin and the helicopter would roll on the wheels.

BI3101	Fire Department	1 - 3
BI3102	Ambulance	1 - 3
BI3103	Police	1 - 3

MONSTER IN MY POCKET, 1992-93

Special Monster In My Pocket packages were manufactured for this promotion. Seven different monsters were used, each molded in one of four different colors (purple, pink, green or orange).

Each package included a perforated sheet of four trading cards: Invisible Man (46), Mummy (41), Big Ed (13), and D. Wolf Mon (3). The numbers on the cards refer to the character's number on the Monster In My Pocket checklist, but have misled some collectors to believe there is a larger set of cards.

BI4881	Dragon (#73)	2 - 3
BI4882	Bigfoot (#74)	2 - 3
BI4883	Set (#75)	2 - 3
BI4884	Amphisbaena (#76)	2 - 3
BI4885	Centaur (#77)	2 - 3

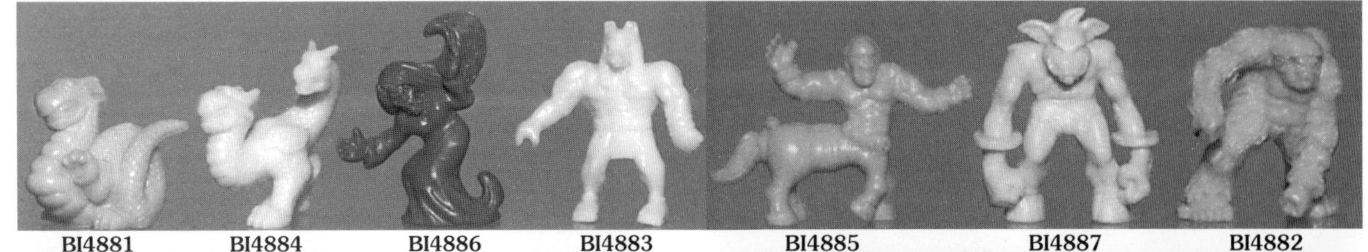

BI4881 BI4884 BI4886 BI4883 BI4885 BI4887 BI4882

Packaging and trading cards from *Monster In My Pocket*

BI6101 BI6102

Right: BI6100 and BI6101 on BI6112 and BI6110.

BI4886	Banshee (#79)	2 - 3
BI4887	Minotaur (#80)	2 - 3

PLAY YARD, 1992

Hard rubber 2" PVC "fruit" figures came with a plastic accessory piece of playground equipment. The type of fruit governed the color of figure.

BI6100	Grape, purple	1 - 2
BI6101	Blueberry, blue	1 - 2
BI6102	Strawberry, red	1 - 2
BI6110	Swing, red seat w/yellow frame	1 - 2
BI6111	Teeter-totter	2 - 3
BI6112	Slide, purple, red, yellow, green	2 - 3
BI6113	Sandbox	2 - 3

BI6742 BI6743 BI6741

RACERS, 1992

The were identical to the Big Boy race car used in the 1990 Sports Figures promotion, but were issued in 3 colors: yellow, orange and purple. They were sold for 99¢ each in some outlets.

BI6741	Yellow car	2 - 4
BI6742	Orange car	2 - 4
BI6743	Purple car	2 - 4

SPORTS FIGURES, 1990

Big Boy PVC figures in various sports poses were issued for premiums with kid meal orders. Each figure was marked on the bottom with "©1990 Elias Brothers Restaurants, Inc.

BI7802 BI7804 BI7801 BI7803

BI7801	Skater	2 - 5
BI7802	Baseball Player	2 - 5
BI7803	Surfer	2 - 5
BI7804	Race Car Driver	2 - 5

BI7921, BI7922, BI7923, & BI7924 BI7925

TIME CAPSULE, 1993

Big Boy traveled back in time for this promotion. The premium consisted of an accordion-fold 6" x 18" piece of index stock which contained punch-out pieces to be used to create a scene from a specific time period. Each came in a plastic capsule or glassine envelope with a printed time capsule

BI7921	Prehistoric Put-Togethers	1 - 3
BI7922	Fun with the Pharaohs	1 - 3
BI7923	Age of Discovery	1 - 3
BI7924	Go West	1 - 3
BI7925	Shuttle Cadet	1 - 3

BI9920 BI9922 BI9923

MISCELLANEOUS BIG BOY ITEMS

The following are known to exist, but no further information is currently available.

BI9850	Big Boy Yo-Yos - 1992 pink, green, or yellow	2 - 4
BI9851	Big Boy Colorforms Book - 2/92	3 - 5
BI9852	Big Boy Christmas Ornament, 1990	3 - 5
Sacks		
BI9910	Learning About Animals	1 - 2
BI9911	You Too Can Draw	1 - 2
Boxes		
BI9920	Home Safely!	3 - 5
BI9921	You Name the Sports	3 - 5
BI9922	Outer Space	3 - 5
BI9923	On Safari	3 - 5

BL2601

BL2602-6

BLAKE'S LOTA' BURGER

This regional chain serves the states of New Mexico and Arizona. It was founded by Blake Chanslor in 1954, and is based in Albuquerque, New Mexico. All stores are company-owned. In general, the chain uses off-the-shelf stock promotions.

GRIMMY, 1989

The loveable canine from the Mike Peters comic strip *Mother Goose and Grimm* inspired the PVCs for this Admark stock promotion.

BL2601 Grimmy w/food & dish
BL2602 Grimmy w/arms spread wide
BL2603 Grimmy w/leash
BL2604 Grimmy w/guitar "Dog Aid"
BL2605 Grimmy sitting down
BL2606 Grimmy w/sign on side "Fleas on Board"

BURGER CHEF

Even though the Cincinnati, Ohio based hamburger chain was sold to several different buyers in 1982, Burger Chef holds the distinction of developing the original concept of the kid's meal. Many chains had occasional kid's promotions as early as the 1960s, but Burger Chef was the first to put a permanent kid's "FUNMEAL Feast" on their menu. The word "feast" was dropped after a couple of years.

Burger Chef and Jeff were the two characters seen in cartoon strips on the back of the box and in TV commercials aired on Saturday morning. McDonald's observed the Burger chef FUNMEAL for nearly two years before they began testing Happy Meals versus Fun To Go Meals.

The FUNMEAL container was normally a cardboard tray with depressions for the burger and cup base. Fries were sandwiched in between. The back of the tray was a large display panel where games, punch-outs, and other activities were featured. The prize was the container and all the wonderful things a kid could do with it. The activities would almost always involve destroying the box and it is amazing any of them survived. Seven or eight new trays were designed each year. Each was numbered from 1972 to 1974. In 1975, kids could get a card table-size map on which buildings from new FUNMEAL hamburger boxes could be arranged to complete a town. Twenty to thirty different building boxes were created over the next year or two. Larger scale carnival punch-outs followed.

Burger Chef obtained the rights to Star Wars in 1978 to become the first fast food chain to use a major license. The company reverted to the tray format for the Star Wars promotion and seven different punch-out model and game trays were produced.

Vacuum-formed plastic was used with cardboard for several unique meal containers. Two cars, a ship, and bird feeders are known.

McDonald's tested a special prize in their Happy Meals in 1979. Their Star Trek Meal was one of the first to use kid's meal/movie tie-in toys, and the big national chain quickly overwhelmed the Burger Chef prize marketing strategy. Burger Chef was sold in 1982 with most of the locations going to Hardee's.

BUC001 BUC002 BUC001 (flat)

BIRDFEEDER BOXES, 1982

BUC001 Barn Swallow 15 - 20
BUC002 Goldfinch 15 - 20

FUNMEAL BOXES, (various dates)

The box which held the food items was the premium. On each box were several punch-outs which could be used to create a scene; fun money to save or swap; jokes; puzzle games: mazes, connect-the-dots, etc.; comics; masks; misc. write-ups.

BUC021 The Great Burgerini Magic Show, #1, 1973 15 - 20
BUC022 Burgerilla Lends a Hand, #2, 1973 15 - 20
BUC023 Blueburger's Pirate Crew, #3, 1973 15 - 20

BUC022 BUC026 BUC028 BUC021

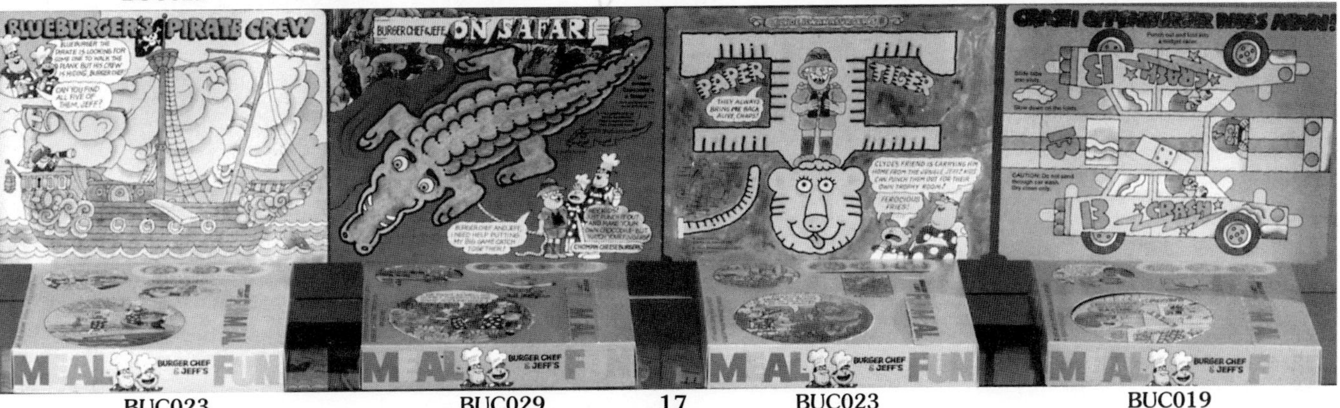

BUC023 BUC029 BUC023 BUC019

Complete assembled Fun Village

BUC026	Fangburger's Funhouse, #6, 1973	15 - 20
BUC028	In Days of Olde, #8, 1974	15 - 20
BUC029	On Safari, #9, 1974	15 - 20
BUC039	Crash Offenburger Rides Again!, #16, 1974	15 - 20
BUC042	Crankenburger Gets His Feet Wet!, #19, 1974	15 - 20
BUC043	Clyde Bwanaburger's Paper Tiger, #20, 1974	15 - 20

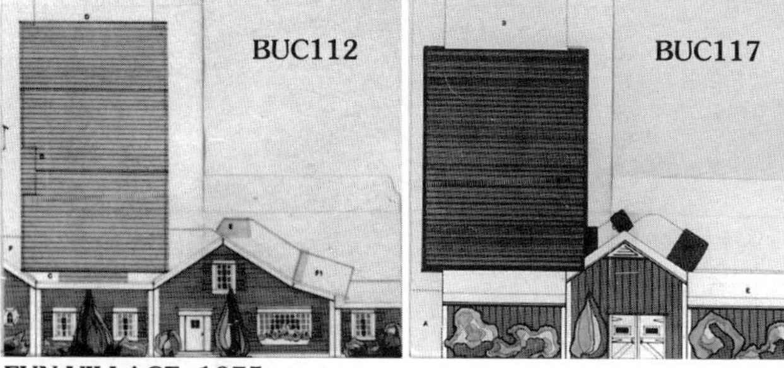

FUN VILLAGE, 1975

Punch-out buildings and accessories from "Fun Burger" hamburger containers. A city map for these items, which included additional punch-out accessories, was available from Burger Chef restaurants.

BUC101	Pirate Ship-1	10 - 15
BUC102	Castle-2	10 - 15
BUC103	Two Story-3	10 - 15
BUC104	Ranch-4	10 - 15
BUC105	Barn-5	10 - 15
BUC106	Cottage-6	10 - 15
BUC107	Haunted House-7	10 - 15
BUC108	Cottage-8	10 - 15
BUC109	Two Story-9	10 - 15
BUC110	Colonial-10	10 - 15
BUC111	Cape Cod-11	10 - 15
BUC112	Colonial-12	10 - 15
BUC113	Burger Chef-13	10 - 15
BUC114	Cape Cod-14	10 - 15
BUC115	Toy Shop-15	10 - 15
BUC116	Hardware Shop-16	10 - 15
BUC117	Bike Shop-17	10 - 15
BUC118	Beauty Shop-18	10 - 15
BUC119	Antique Shop-19	10 - 15
BUC120	Shoe Shop-20	10 - 15
BUC121	Bakery Shop-21	10 - 15
BUC122	Grocery Shop-22	10 - 15
BUC123	Gas Station-23	10 - 15
BUC124	Ranch-24	10 - 15
BUC125	Fun Village Map w/instruction sheet, punch-out people, vehicles, trees, and sign	30 - 50

STAR WARS FUNMEAL BOXES, 1978

BUC701	Flight	20 - 30
BUC702	Darth Vader Card Game	20 - 30
BUC703	Land Speeder	20 - 30

BUC701 BUC702 BUC703

BUC710

BUC704

BUC705

BUC706

BUC707

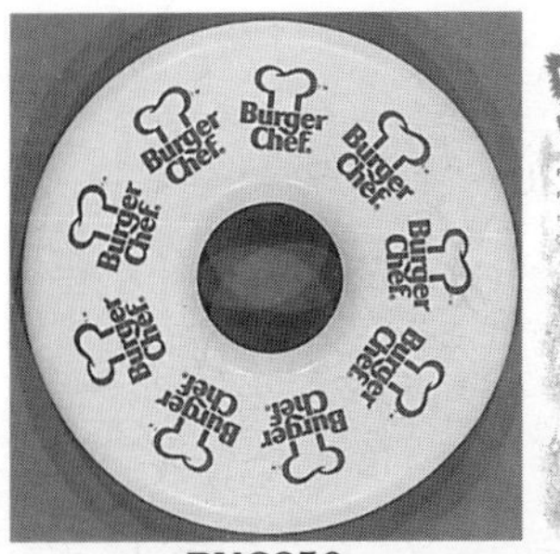

BUC850

BUC853

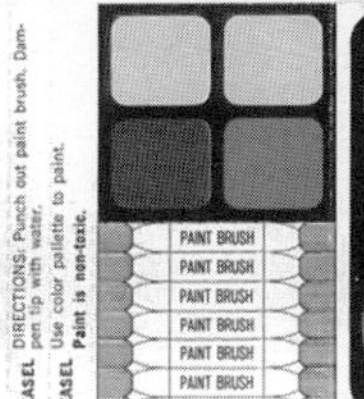

BUC855

BUC704	R2-D2 Droid Puppet	20 - 30
BUC705	Tie Fighter	20 - 30
BUC706	C-3PO Droid Puppet	20 - 30
BUC707	X-Wing Fighter	20 - 30
BUC710	Counter Card	10 - 15

BUC901 BUC902

BUC903 BUC904

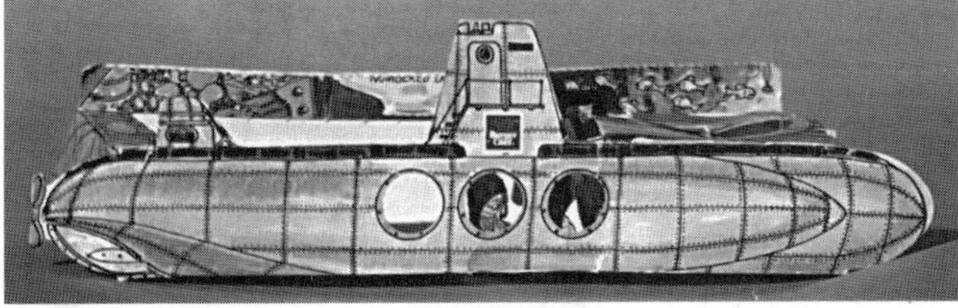

BUC905

MISCELLANEOUS PREMIUMS AND BOXES

The following items are known to exist, but no further information is currently available.

BUC850	"Donut" flying disc, white w/red Burger Chef logos	5 - 10
BUC851	Solid red 8½" Flying Disk	5 - 10
BUC852	Paints & Cartoon, 1972 - contained 2 frame cartoon to paint, 7 punch-out cardboard paint brushes, two palettes of paint chips	10 - 20
BUC853	Martian Monster Mask	15 - 30
Boxes		
BUC901	Kid Racer, blue race car	15 - 20
BUC902	Replica Camaro Pace Car, yellow race car	15 - 20
BUC903	Circus Wagon w/hippo puppet	15 - 20
BUC904	Surfchaser Boat	15 - 20
BUC905	Bubbles the Sub	15 - 20

BURGER KING

Burger King had plastic and other premiums built around a cartoon or live action Burger King character for many years before establishing a regular kid's meal promotion to compete directly with the McDonald's Happy Meal. Available evidence indicates regular kid's meal promotions began in the fall of 1981. Standard boxed promotions were used throughout the 1980's, but the kid's meal concept underwent a dramatic change in 1990 with the establishment of the Burger King Kids Club. A group of seven characters were created to be representative of young customers: Boomer, I.Q., Jaws, Kid Vid, Lingo, Snaps, and Wheels. Their identity and names appear on a standard sack which has changed little in the first four years this concept has been used. Boxes were eliminated. Packaged Kids Club premiums have the added benefit of a paper insert which usually shows all premiums in the series. Unfortunately, the Burger King headquarters has moved since kid's meals were started...records and samples for the first five years were pitched.

BU0052 BU0053 BU0055 BU0056

ACTION FIGURES, 1991

Articulated 3½"-4½" PVC figures of four of the Kids Club characters were offered as premiums during this promotion. A folded paper insert inside had a color picture of the character on the front. On the back was a Trans World Airlines ad. A color cartoon was printed on the inside. At least three variations exist in this set.

BU0051	I.Q. w/ light orange hair	1 - 3
BU0052	I.Q. w/dark orange hair	2 - 5
BU0053	Boomer w/ brown gloves, blue skates	1 - 3
BU0054	Boomer w/orange gloves & skates	2 - 5
BU0055	Kid Vid	1 - 3
BU0056	Jaws w/black hair	1 - 3
BU0057	Jaws w/gray hair	2 - 5
Point of Purchase		
BU0060	Translite	10 - 20

BU0161 BU0162 BU0163 BU0164 BU0165

ALADDIN, 1992

This Disney movie tie-in offered five 3"-4" PVC/plastic toys. Except for the 2-piece Jasmine and Rajah PVC, all were mechanical.

BU0161	Aladdin & Magic Carpet, 2 pieces	1 - 4
BU0162	Abu, 1 piece	1 - 4
BU0163	Genie & the Lamp, 1 piece	1 - 4
BU0164	Jasmine & Rajah, 2 pieces	1 - 4
BU0165	Jafar & Iago, 1 piece	1 - 4
Point of Purchase		
BU0169	Door decal	25 - 50
BU0170	Translite	20 - 40
BU0172	Mobile	15 - 30

ALF, 1987

Alf, the creature from Melmac, was the focus of this kid's meal promotion.

BU0181	Joke & Riddle Disc	3 - 7
BU0182	Door Knob Card	3 - 7

BU0181 BU0182

BU0183 BU0184

BU0186 BU0187

BU0188 BU0189

BU0183 Sand Mold, clear plastic 3 - 7
BU0184 Refrigerator Magnet, No Problem! 3 - 7
Boxes
BU0186 Another Sunday at the Shumway House... 3 - 5
BU0187 Eddie's Kat-Sup Diner 3 - 5
BU0188 Gordon's First Day on Orbit Guard Duty 3 - 5
BU0189 Go Melmac Orbiters 3 - 5
Point of Purchase
BU0190 Translite 15 - 25

BU0241 BU0242 BU0243 BU0244

ANIMAL ALPHABET, 1984

This promotion offered premiums coordinated with each box design. The four alphabet sticker sheets were reflective of the type of animal box. Five Burger King logo stickers were included on each sheet. On the back portion of each box was an area to write the "name" given to the animal container.

BU0246 BU0247

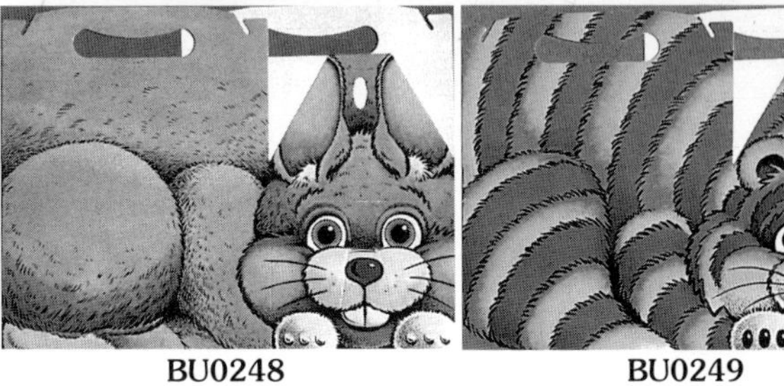

BU0248 BU0249

BU0241 Blue & white "fur" lettering 5 - 8
BU0242 Turquoise, white, yellow "sky" lettering 5 - 8
BU0243 Red & blue "bunny tail" lettering 5 - 8
BU0244 Blue w/green or red "stripes" lettering 5 - 8
Boxes
BU0246 Panda Bear 3 - 5
BU0247 Bird 3 - 5
BU0248 Bunny Rabbit 3 - 5
BU0249 Tiger 3 - 5

BU0266 BU0267 BU0268

ANIMAL BOXES ACTIVITY BOOKLETS, 1986

Animals are always welcome to kids. These activity books include games, cut-outs, and pictures to color.

BU0261 Book 1 3 - 5
BU0262 Book 2 3 - 5
BU0263 Book 3 3 - 5
BU0264 Book 4 3 - 5
Boxes
BU0266 Hippo 4 - 10
BU0267 Bear 4 - 10
BU0268 Lion 4 - 20
BU0269 unknown 4 - 20
Point of Purchase
BU0270 Translite 20 - 40

BU0411 BU0412 BU0413 BU0414

ARCHIES, 1991

Rolling 3" plastic cars with a character from the Archies comic strip. These are another variation of the pull-back and release idea.

BU0411 Archie, red car 2 - 4
BU0412 Jughead, green car 2 - 4
BU0413 Veronica, purple car 2 - 4
BU0414 Betty, blue car 2 - 4
Point of Purchase
BU0420 Translite 10 - 15

BU0495 Punch-outs from BU0495

AUTOMEALS

The inside flap on the box names the promotion "Automeals", but has no other identifying information. A cardboard punch-out with 4 accessory pieces came with the school bus box.

Box

BU0495 School Bus 10 - 15

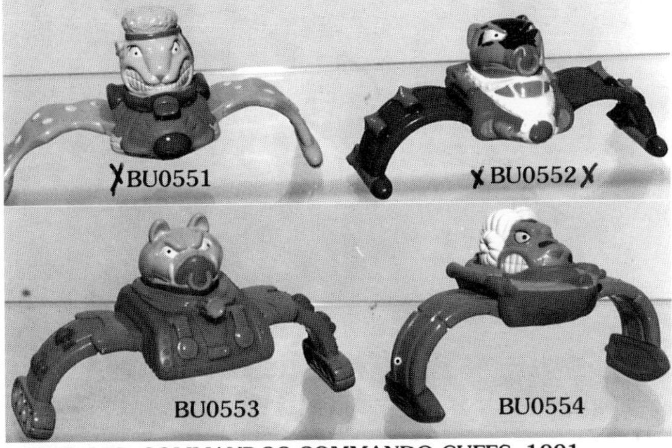

BU0551 BU0552 BU0553 BU0554

BARNYARD COMMANDOS COMMANDO CUFFS, 1991

Barnyard Commandos from TV cartoons were the subject of four PVC bracelets which converted to vehicles. Weird stuff.

BU0551	Sergeant Wooly Pullover/Submarine	1 - 3
BU0552	Sergeant Shoat N Sweet/Plane	1 - 3
BU0553	Private Side O' Bacon/Tank	1 - 3
BU0554	Major Legger Mutton/Boat	1 - 3
Point of Purchase		
BU0560	Translite	10 - 15

BU0591 BU0592 BU0593 BU0594

BEAUTY AND THE BEAST, 1991

Two action figures and two wind-ups based on Disney's *Beauty and the Beast* were the subject of this promotion. A special display was used.

BU0591	Belle	3 - 5
BU0592	Chip, the cup	5 - 10
BU0593	Cogsworth, the clock	4 - 8
BU0594	The Beast	3 - 5
Point of Purchase		
BU0599	Store Display	100 - 150
BU0600	Translite	15 - 25

BEETLEJUICE, 1990

Figures from the spooky, spoofy movie *Beetlejuice* were featured on six 2-sided 4" hollow rubber figures.

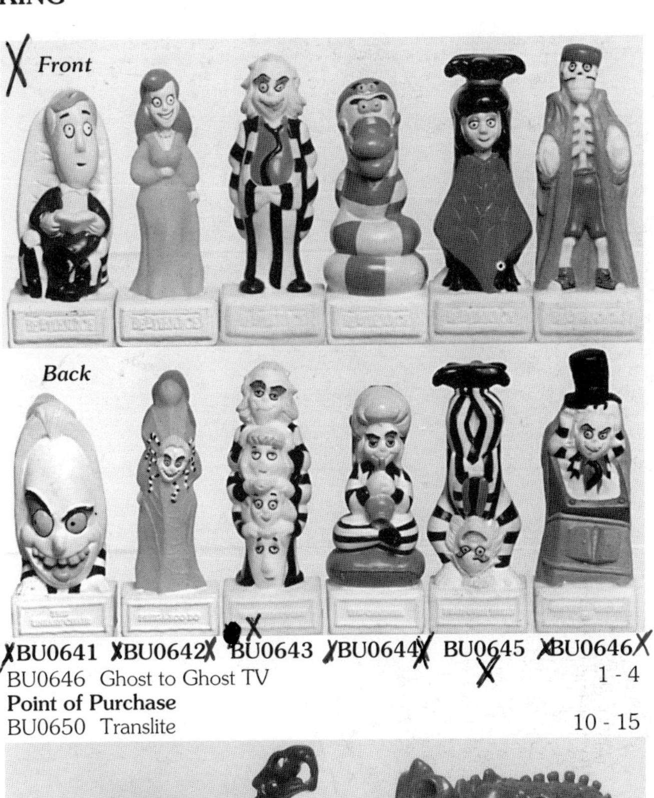

Front / Back

BU0641 BU0642 BU0643 BU0644 BU0645 BU0646

BU0641	The Uneasy Chair	1 - 4
BU0642	Peek-A-Boo Do	1 - 4
BU0643	The Ghost Post	1 - 4
BU0644	The Charmer	1 - 4
BU0645	Head Over Heels	1 - 4
BU0646	Ghost to Ghost TV	1 - 4
Point of Purchase		
BU0650	Translite	10 - 15

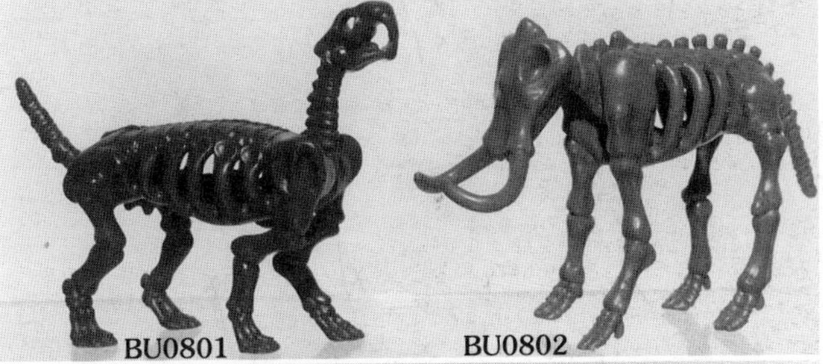

BU0801 BU0802

BU0803 BU0804

BU0806

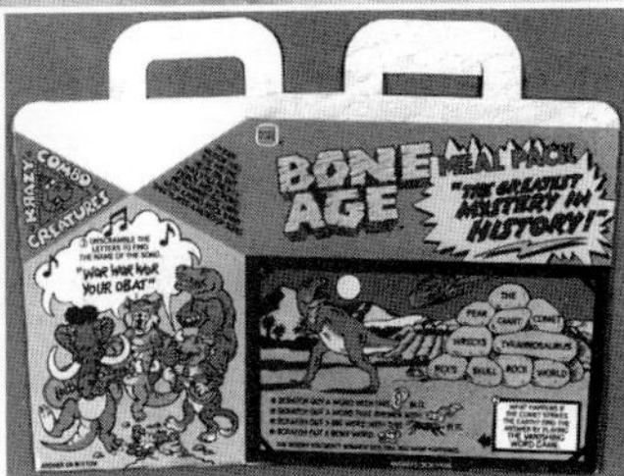

BU0807

BONE AGE, 1989

Prehistoric skeleton kits by Kenner were featured as premiums with Bone Age Meal Packs. The 4 pieces of each plastic model snapped together to create one mammal or dinosaur and could be interchanged with pieces from another kit to create your own prehistoric creature.

BU0801	Smilodon – Fangra, brown parts	2 - 6
BU0802	Mastodon – Mastus, gray parts	2 - 6
BU0803	Dimetrodon – Deitron, rust parts	2 - 6
BU0804	Tyrannosaurus Rex – T-Rex, white parts	2 - 6
Boxes		
BU0806	Zap Back to the Bone Age	3 - 7
BU0807	The Greatest Mystery in History	3 - 7

BU0808

BU0809

Congratulations!
You've discovered all the amazing Bone Age™ Creatures at Burger King®!

Enjoy a FREE Medium Soft Drink good on your next visit.
Good only at: 20840 Gratiot, East Detroit, MI

No bones about it, you've been a great detective.

Coupon expires May 31, 1989.

BU0811

BU0808	The Past is a Blast	3 - 7
BU0809	Prehistoric Creatures are Wonderful Teachers	3 - 7
Point of Purchase		
BU0810	Translite	20 - 30
BU0811	Sherlock Bones detective coupon	1 - 2
BU0812	Hanging Mobile Display	60 - 100

BU0851 BU0852 BU0853

BU0854 BU0855 BU0856

BONKERS, 1993

Five break-apart cars, each with cardboard backgrounds were given in a promotion tying-in with the introduction of this new Disney cartoon series. A special issue of *Disney Adventures* magazine with the Burger King logo was also given away as an under-3 premium.

BU0851	Toots - Yellow | ~~Blue~~ RED	2 - 4
BU0852	Fall Apart Rabbit RUST | YELLOW	2 - 4
BU0853	Bonkers GREEN | BLUE	2 - 4
BU0854	Jitters	2 - 4
BU0855	Detective Lucky Piquel DARK BLUE	2 - 4
BU0856	Disney Adventures Magazine	3 - 5
Point of Purchase		
BU0858	Door Decal	

BU0871

BU0872

BU0873

BURGER BOOK, 1985

Special game/activity books were produced by Western Publishing for use in this promotion. Each 6" x 12" heavy cardboard Burger Book had a punch-out handle at the top and a color cartoon of Travelin' Ted (a bear in a safari outfit) on the front cover.

BU0871	Travelin' Ted's Mix and Match Animals	4 - 5
BU0872	Travelin' Ted's Jungle Trail Game	4 - 5
BU0873	Prehistoric Times	4 - 5
BU0874	The Wild West	4 - 5
BU0875	The Future	4 - 5

BU1011 BU1012

Cardboard accessories not shown

BU1013 BU1014

CAPITOL CRITTERS, 1992

The daily routine of rats living in Washington, D.C. was the theme of this short-lived TV evening cartoon series. Four main characters came with punch-out paperboard backgrounds and accessories.

BU1011	Max/Jefferson Memorial	1 - 3
BU1012	President Cat/Capitol Building	1 - 3
BU1013	Jammet/White House	1 - 3
BU1014	Muggle/Lincoln Memorial	1 - 3
Point of Purchase		
BU1019	Door decal	20 - 25
BU1020	Translite	10 - 15

BU1052 BU1051 BU1053 BU1054

CAPTAIN PLANET, 1991

Characters from the ecology conscious TV cartoon appeared as drivers in "turn-over" cars. Pushing down on the driver on one side of these 3" plastic vehicles forced the driver on the reverse (turned over) side of the car to pop up into the top position.

BU1051	Wheeler/Duke Nukem in a snowmobile	1 - 3
BU1052	Linka & Ma-Ti/Dr. Blight in the ecomobile	1 - 3

BU1085

BU1091

BU1053	Gi & Kwame/Verminous Skumm in a helicopter	1 - 3
BU1054	Captain Planet/Hoggish Greedly in a boat	1 - 3

Point of Purchase

BU1060	Translite	10 - 15

CAPTAIN POWER, 1988

Four vacuum-formed meal containers came with a Captain Power eraser. Space ships came with wheels.

BU1081	Powerjet XT-7	5 - 10
BU1082	Bio-Dread Patroller	5 - 10
BU1083	Power Base	5 - 10
BU1084	Phantom Striker	5 - 10
BU1085	Captain Power eraser	1 - 4

Point of Purchase

BU1090	Translite	18 - 30
BU1091	Dangle Display	20 - 40

BU1122

BU1121 BU1124

CHIPMUNK ADVENTURE, 1987 BU1123

Alvin and the Chipmunks were promoted as premiums in one kid's meal offering. A 2" pencil topper featured Alvin and was imprinted "1987 Bagdasarian Productions." The 1½" fleck-filled rubber ball had a picture of Alvin with "Chipmunk Adventure" printed below it. Nine peel-off stickers were issued with a 8" x 4" folded-in-half courtyard scene. Three plush figures of the Chipmunks were also offered for purchase.

BU1121	Alvin Pencil Topper	3 - 6
BU1122	Bicycle License Plate	3 - 6
BU1123	Stick 'ems	3 - 6
BU1124	Sparkle Rubber Ball	3 - 6
BU1125	Plush Toy, Alvin	4 - 8
BU1126	Plush Toy, Simon	4 - 8
BU1127	Plush Toy, Theodore	4 - 8

Boxes

BU1131	Chipettes-Antarctica/Chipmunks-Jungle	4 - 8
BU1132	While in Mexico/Chipettes Must Rescue	4 - 8
BU1133	Solve Crossword Puzzle/Chipettes-Greece	4 - 8
BU1134	Chipettes Swim/Chase through the Airport	4 - 8

Point of Purchase

BU1135	Translite	20 - 30

BU1127 BU1125 BU1126

BU1131 BU1132

BU1133 BU1134

BU1181 BU1182 BU1183 BU1184

CHRISTMAS CRAYOLA™ BEARS, 1986

Plush 7" bears wearing a T-shirt with "Crayola™" printed in an oval were issued for this Christmas promotion.

BU1181	Blue	4 - 7
BU1182	Yellow	4 - 7
BU1183	Purple	4 - 7
BU1184	Red	4 - 7

Point of Purchase

BU1190	Translite	15 - 20

BU1211 BU1212 BU1213 BU1214

CHRISTMAS PURRTENDERS SOCK-EMS, 1987

For this Christmas season, plush cat dolls could "purrtend" to become another animal by simply pulling the attached transforming hood over the head. Then, by unrolling the velcro-fastened "pouch" from the cat's belly, a sock was revealed. Each of these 7" toys came with a folded tag which showed the name of the promotion. These over-the-counter sales required no special meal boxes.

BU1211	Dog-Romp-Purr	4 - 6
BU1212	Bunny-Hop-Purr	4 - 6
BU1213	Duck-Flop-Purr	4 - 6
BU1214	Mouse-Scamp-Purr	4 - 6
Point of Purchase		
BU1220	Translite	15 - 25

BU1261 BU1262 BU1263 BU1264

CHRISTMAS SING-A-LONG CASSETTES, 1989

Two yuletide songs from videos were recorded on each of the four audio cassettes released especially for Burger King. An 11" x 17" color cartoon poster illustrating the song theme was included with each tape. The wrapper featured an illustration and title of the promotion on the front and an ad for various Hanna Barbera videos on the back. Names of the Christmas songs and the Burger King logo were printed along both edges.

BU1261	We Three Kings/O Holy Night	4 - 6
BU1262	Deck the Halls/Night Before Christmas	4 - 6
BU1263	Joy to the World/Silent Night	4 - 6
BU1264	Up on the House Top/Jingle Bells	4 - 6
Point of Purchase		
BU1270	Translite	20 - 30

BU1371 BU1372

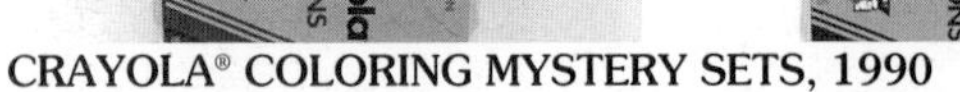

BU1373 BU1374

CRAYOLA® COLORING MYSTERY SETS, 1990

Each week a different activity was featured in the 8½" x 7" Crayola coloring book which came with a different pack of 6 crayons. Each included a new color Crayola was introducing.

BU1371	#1, Kid Vid's Video Vision, color & activity book	1 - 4
BU1372	#2, Snaps' Photo Power, sticker & color book	1 - 4

BU1375

BU1376

BU1373	#3, Jaws' Colorful Clue, color, cut & make book	1 - 4
BU1374	#4, Boomer's Color Chase, stencil & color book	1 - 4
BU1375	#5, I.Q.'s Computer Code, sticker & color book	1 - 4
BU1376	#6, Kid's Club Concert, giant color-in poster	1 - 4
Point of Purchase		
BU1380	Translite	10 - 15

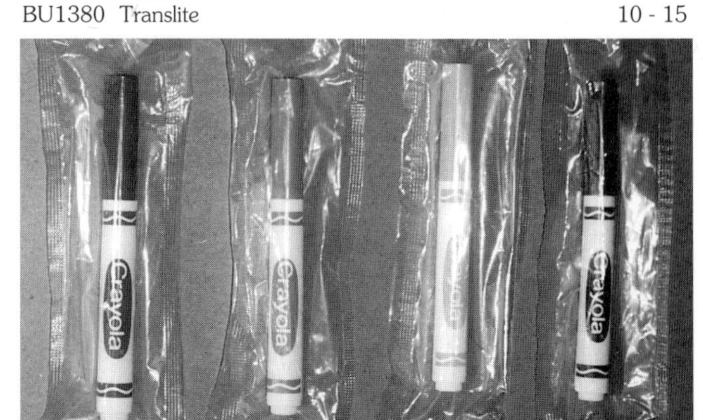

BU1402 BU1404 BU1403 BU1401

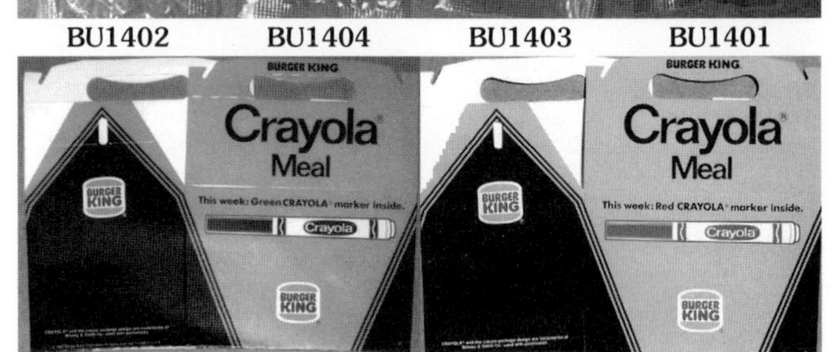

BU1405 BU1406

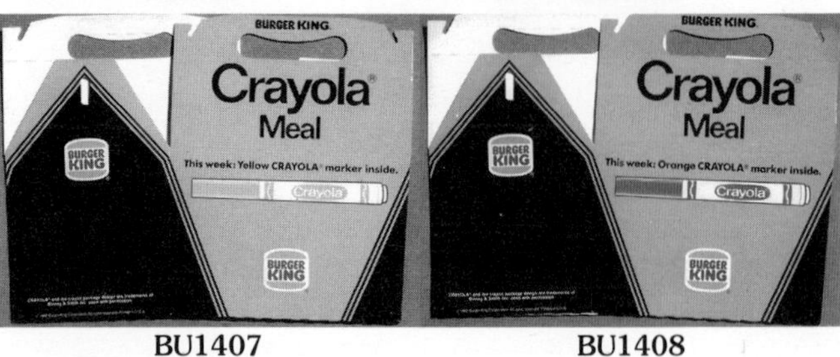

BU1407 BU1408

CRAYOLA® MEAL, 1982

A different color Crayola marker and activity box was used each week in this early promotion.

BU1401	Green Crayola Marker	2 - 4
BU1402	Red Crayola Marker	2 - 4
BU1403	Yellow Crayola Marker	2 - 4
BU1404	Orange Crayola Marker	2 - 4
Boxes		
BU1405	Circle Circus, green	10 - 15
BU1406	Alpha Graph Game, red	10 - 15
BU1407	Burger King or Bust Game, yellow	10 - 15
BU1408	Plot and Color Game, orange	10 - 15

CRITTER CARTON – PUNCH-OUT PAPER MASKS, 1985

Full-color masks were a separate cardboard-type piece given with the kid's meal in a coordinated box.

BU1531 BU1533

BU1534 BU1537

BU1521	Bird Mask	1 - 8
BU1522	Chicken Mask	1 - 8
BU1523	Tiger Mask	1 - 8
BU1524	Rabbit Mask	1 - 8
BU1525	Dog Mask	1 - 8
BU1526	Panda Mask	1 - 8
BU1527	Duck Mask	1 - 8
BU1528	Turtle Mask	1 - 8
Boxes		
BU1531	Bird	5 - 10
BU1532	Chicken	5 - 10
BU1533	Tiger	5 - 10
BU1534	Rabbit	5 - 10
BU1535	Dog	5 - 10
BU1536	Panda	5 - 10
BU1537	Duck	5 - 10
BU1538	Turtle	5 - 10
Point of Purchase		
BU1540	Translite	20 - 40

BU1541

BU1546

CRUISIN' RULES, 1987

Bicycle safety became the focus of one promotion.

BU1541	Fun Booklet - Bicycle Safety	5 - 7
Box		
BU1546	Cruisin' Rules	5 - 10

DINO CRAWLERS, 1994

A series of five mini wind-up vehicles with dinosaur-like heads. Each came with a punch-out "dino-obstacle" ramp to crawl over.

BU1601	Blue	1 - 3
BU1602	Red	1 - 3
BU1613	Aqua	1 - 3
BU1614	Purple	1 - 3
BU1615	Yellow	1 - 3

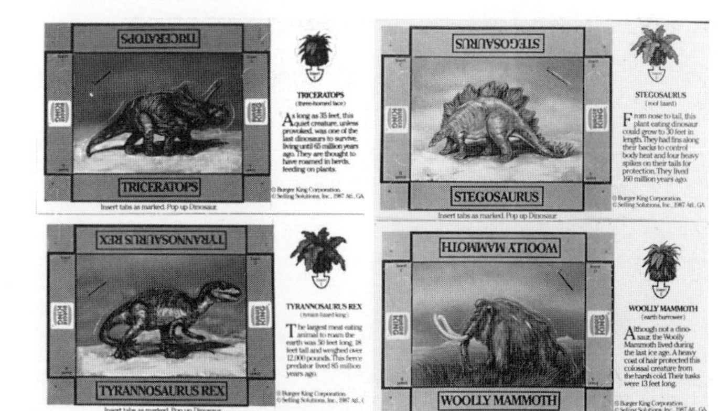

BU1741, BU1742, BU1743, & BU1744

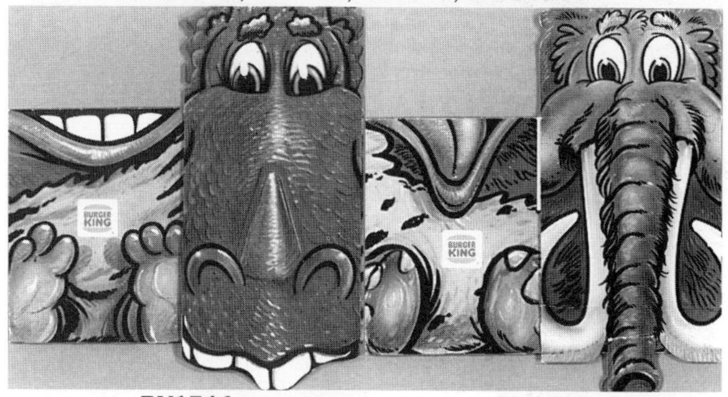

BU1746 BU1747

BU1748 BU1749

DINO-MEAL, 1987

Punch-out cardboard sheets measuring 7½" x 4½" were used to create a pop-up dinosaur on a 3⅞" x 2⅝" platform. The sides folded to form a ½" base which featured the name of the dinosaur on the front and back and the Burger King logo at either end. Information regarding the dinosaur and the copyright information were printed on the discarded portion of the cardboard sheet. The boxes designed for this promotion became cute "baby" dinosaurs. The nose and upper mouth section formed the lid to the box.

BU1741	Triceratops	4 - 6
BU1742	Woolly Mammoth	4 - 6
BU1743	Tyrannosaurus Rex	4 - 6
BU1744	Stegosaurus	4 - 6
Boxes		
BU1746	Triceratops	4 - 6
BU1747	Woolly Mammoth	4 - 6
BU1748	Tyrannosaurus Rex	4 - 6
BU1749	Stegosaurus	4 - 6
Point of Purchase		
BU1750	Translite	20 - 30

BU1601

BU1602

BU1603

BU1604

BU1605

BU2151 BU2152 BU2153 BU2154

BU2156 BU2157

BU2158 BU2159

FAIRY TALES CASSETTES, 1989

Audio tape recordings of 4 fairy tales accompanied an 11" x 17" color poster depicting the story.

BU2151	Goldilocks and the Three Bears	4 - 6
BU2152	Jack and the Beanstalk	4 - 6
BU2153	Hansel and Gretel	4 - 6
BU2154	The 3 Little Pigs	4 - 6
Boxes		
BU2156	Goldilocks and the Three Bears	3 - 6
BU2157	Jack and the Beanstalk	3 - 6
BU2158	Hansel and Gretel	3 - 6
BU2159	The 3 Little Pigs	3 - 6
Point of Purchase		
BU2160	Translite	10 - 20

BU2601 BU2602 BU2603 BU2604 BU2605

FOOD MINIATURES, c.1983

Figures of popular Burger King food items were used as premiums for an early promotion. The 1½ hard rubber pieces were marked "Russ. China."

BU2601	Hamburger	3 - 5
BU2602	Large Fries	3 - 5
BU2603	Small Fries	3 - 5
BU2604	Pepsi	3 - 5
BU2605	Hot Dog	3 - 5
Point of Purchase		
BU2610	Translite	10 - 20

FUN SCHOOL MEAL, 1981

For the return to school, Burger King offered school-related premiums. Two of the premiums had snap-together pieces. The red plastic

BU2705

BU2706 BU2707

clip-on had the head of the Burger King printed on the top piece. A red plastic figure of the Burger King appeared in the center of the Pencil Holder. The magic ruler had a colorful picture of the Burger King.

BU2701	Burger King Clip-On	10 - 15
BU2702	King Pencil Holder	10 - 15
BU2703	Magic Ruler	10 - 15
Boxes		
BU2705	Burger King Clip-On	1 - 5
BU2706	King Pencil Holder	1 - 5
BU2707	Magic Ruler	1 - 5

BU2801 BU2802 BU2803 BU2804

GLOW-IN-THE-DARK TROLLS!, 1993

Two popular concepts were combined for this Halloween time promotion. The Kids Club members became "Troll" figures with brightly colored hair and glow-in-the-dark bodies. There was a punch-out cardboard hat for each troll.

BU2801	I/Q. Troll	2 - 4
BU2802	Jaws Troll	2 - 4
BU2803	Snaps Troll	2 - 4
BU2804	Kid Vid Troll	2 - 4
Point of Purchase		
BU2810	Door decal	15 - 25
BU2811	Translite	10 - 20

GO-GO GADGET GIZMOS, 1991

Inspector Gadget of TV cartoon fame was featured in this Kids Club promotion. The accessory pieces could be interchanged and used on any of the 4 Gadget figures offered. Each 3½" plastic figure had moveable arms, moveable feet which also could be extended, and a head which turned.

BU2811	Copter Gadget w/red rotor gizmo	1 - 3
BU2812	Scuba Gadget	1 - 3
BU2813	Surfer Gadget w/green surfboard & sail	1 - 3
BU2814	Inflated Gadget	1 - 3

BU2811 BU2812 BU2813 BU2814

BU2851 BU2852 BU2853

BU2856 BU2857 BU2858

Point of Purchase

BU2820 Translite 10 - 15

GOOD GOBBLIN' MEAL PACKS, 1989

Pull-apart 3-piece plastic figures were issued during this Halloween promotion. 3" tall.

BU2851 Zelda Zoombroom 2 - 5
BU2852 Frankie Steen 2 - 5
BU2853 Gourdy Goblin 2 - 5
Boxes
BU2856 Haunted House 1 - 3
BU2857 Creepy Castle 1 - 3
BU2858 Monster Manor 1 - 3
Point of Purchase
BU2860 Translite 18 - 36

BU2921 BU2922 BU2923 BU2924

GOOF TROOP BOWLING TOYS, 1992

Disney's "Goof Troop" characters each held onto the ball in this promotion. Each character had his name etched in the clutched bowling ball and was mounted on a three-wheel friction mechanism. Each cardboard insert had 2 punch-outs to be used as the pins for the bowling game.

BU2921 Goofy 1 5
BU2922 Max 1 - 4
BU2923 Pete 1 - 4
BU2924 PJ 1 - 4
Point of Purchase
BU2929 Door decal 5 - 15
BU2930 Translite 10 - 20

BU2990

HALLOWEEN PAIL, 1988

A glow-in-the-dark pail was given away in this Halloween promotion.

BU2990 Pail 1 - 4

HAUNTED MANSION, 1987 BU3045

The graphics on the box used for this offering featured a dilapidated mansion haunted by every known creature associated with this "scary" time of the year.

BU3041 Glow-in-the-Dark Plastic Cup 3 - 4
Box
BU3045 Haunted Mansion 10 - 20

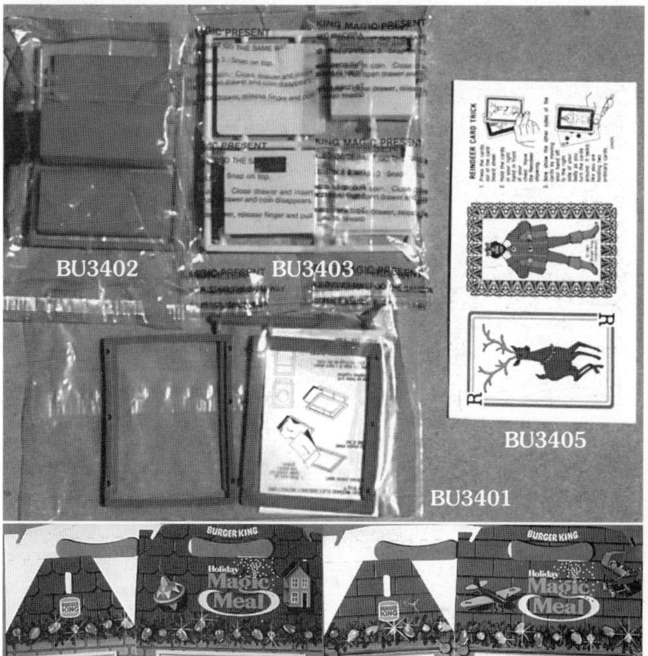

BU3402 BU3403 BU3405 BU3401

BU3406 BU3407

BU3408 BU3409

HOLIDAY MAGIC MEAL, 1981

Magic tricks were the focus during this yuletide season. Instructions were printed on an insert or on its clear sealed bag.

BU3401 Mystery Message Slate, blue 8 - 15
BU3402 Royal Box Trick, red 8 - 15
BU3403 King Magic Present, yellow 8 - 15
BU3405 Reindeer Card Trick, multi-color cards 10 - 20
Boxes
BU3406 Mystery Message Slate 5 - 10
BU3407 Royal Box Trick 5 - 10
BU3408 King Magic Present 5 - 10
BU3409 Reindeer Card Trick 5 - 10

BU3421 BU3422 BU3423 BU3424

HOLIDAY SERIES

The Thanksgiving and Christmas seasons became the focal points for premiums issued during this kid's meal promotion. Each of the 4 white plastic cups had a two-finger-hole type handle and an appropriate seasonal picture around the cup. A snap-on lid was shaped like a straw hat.

BU3421	Turkey w/orange hat	6 - 8
BU3422	Reindeer w/red hat	6 - 8
BU3423	Toy maker painting toy w/green hat	6 - 8
BU3424	Snowman w/light blue hat	6 - 8

BU3651 BU3652 BU3653 BU3654 X

IT'S MAGIC, 1992

Four plastic magic tricks were offered in this Kids Club promotion. Each had a cardboard insert featuring Kids Club characters.

BU3651	Kid Vid Remote Control, green	1 - 3
BU3652	Jaws Disappearing Food Trick, red	1 - 3
BU3653	I.Q.'s Magic Trunk, yellow	1 - 3
BU3654	Snaps Magic Frame, purple	1 - 3
Point of Purchase		
BU3659	Translite	20 - 25
BU3660	Door decal	10 - 15

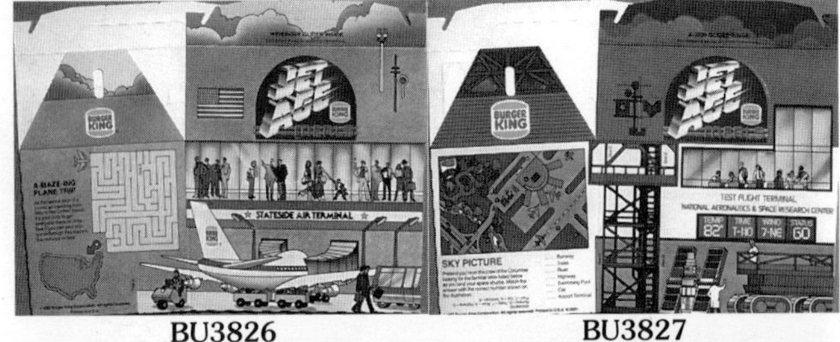

BU3826 BU3827

BU3825

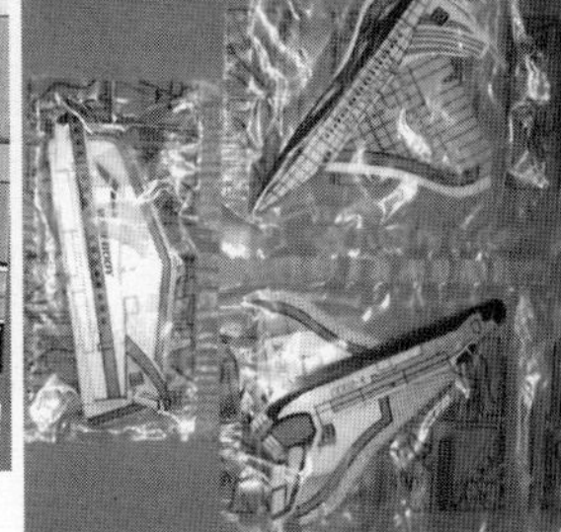

BU3822, BU3821, BU3823

JET AGE MEALS, 1982

Boxes became accessory play pieces for the premium. Various facts regarding airplanes and air travel were printed on the sides of each box. The punch-in piece of the handle contained the name of the aircraft premium inside. Note: the box called each aircraft a "glider"; while the assembly instructions were for the "jet."

BU3821	Magellan Glider/Jet	8 - 10
BU3822	Widebody Glider/Jet	8 - 10
BU3823	X-2000 Glider/Jet	8 - 10
Boxes		
BU3825	Global International Airport	5 - 10
BU3826	Stateside Air Terminal	5 - 10
BU3827	NASRC Test Flight Terminal	5 - 10

XBU4051 XBU4052 BU4053

BU4054 BU4055 X BU4056

KID TRANSPORTERS, 1990

The Kids Club characters were issued as hard rubber PVC figures which could be seated in appropriately designed rolling plastic vehicles.

BU4051	Snaps and her Camera Car	1 - 4
BU4052	Jaws and his Burger Racer	1 - 4
BU4053	Wheels and his Turbo Wheelchair	1 - 4
BU4054	Boomer and her Super Shoe	1 - 4
BU4055	Kid Vid and his SEGA Video Gamester	1 - 4
BU4056	I.Q. and his World Book Mobile	2 - 5
Point of Purchase		
BU4060	Translite	5 - 15

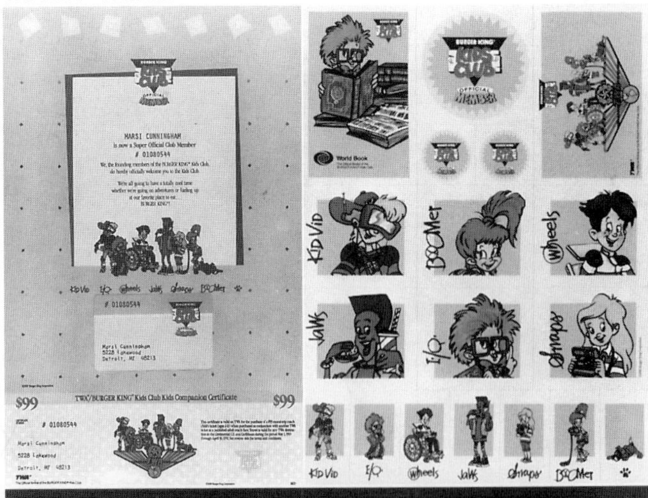

BU4101

KIDS CLUB KIT AND MULTI-USE SACKS

The Club Kit was a mail-in premium produced in conjunction with TWA. The complete kit includes a certificate, membership card, $99 TWA Certificate, sticker sheet, and a character poster.

BU4101	Kids Club Kit	5 - 15
Sacks		
BU4110	Kids Club	1 - 2
BU4111	Window Sack	1 - 2
BU4112	Bilingual Sack (Canada)	1 - 2

BU4110 BU4111 BU4112

BU4151 BU4153

BU4152 BU4154

KIDS CLUB SPINNING TOPS, 1992

A set of four tops with launchers featuring Kids Club characters.

BU4151	Jaws	1 - 3
BU4152	Boomer	1 - 3
BU4153	Wheels	1 - 3
BU4154	Kid Vid	1 - 3
Point of Purchase		
BU4160	Translite	10 - 20

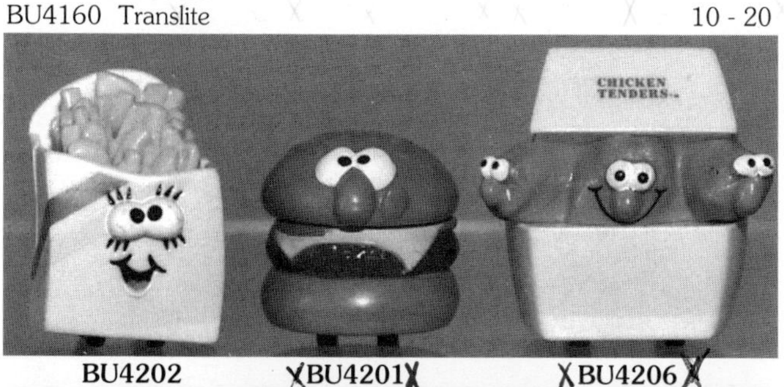

BU4202 BU4201 BU4206

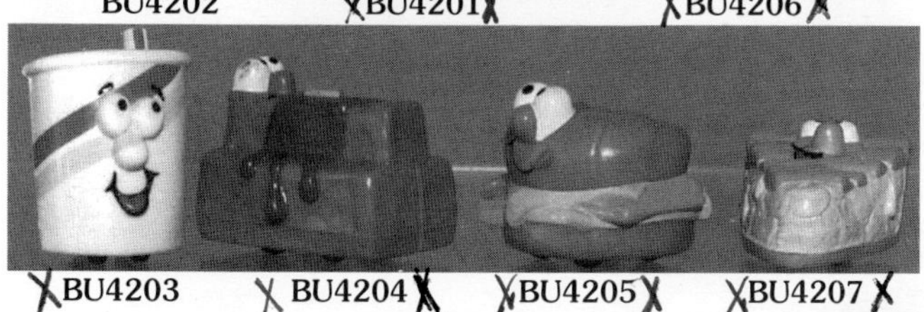

BU4203 BU4204 BU4205 BU4207

LICKETY SPLITS ROLLING RACERS, 1990

Food containers with given facial features and wheels. The first three 1-piece plastic food items were made by Hallmark and are so copyrighted. The final four were marked "©1989 Graphics Int'l, Inc.

BU4201	Flame Broiled Buggy, hamburger	1 - 4
BU4202	Spry Fries, french fries	1 - 4
BU4203	Carbo Cooler, drink	1 - 4
BU4204	Expresstix, french toast	1 - 4
BU4205	Carsan'wich, croissant	1 - 4
BU4206	Chicken Chassis, chicken tenders	1 - 4
BU4207	Indianapolis Racer, apple pie	1 - 4
Point of Purchase		
BU4210	Translite	10 - 20

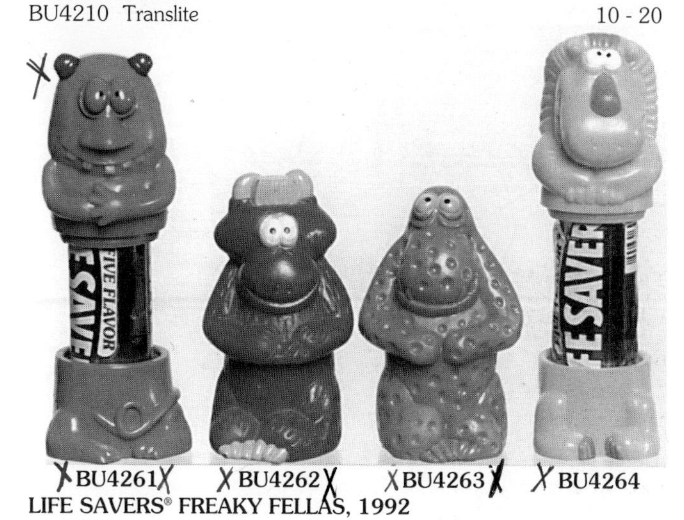

BU4261 BU4262 BU4263 BU4264

LIFE SAVERS® FREAKY FELLAS, 1992

Pull-apart hollow rubber figures were offered during this controversial promotion. During the first 2½ weeks of the offering, a package of Life Savers candy came with each figure. The two ends of the figure could then be placed at either end of the Life Savers pack to elongate the body of the creature. However, due to complaints regarding the Life Savers being unsafe for small children, they were not included during the last part of the promotion. The yellow figure appears to be the hardest to find packaged with the Life Savers candy.

BU4261	Blue	1 - 4
BU4262	Red	1 - 4
BU4263	Green	1 - 4
BU4264	Yellow	1 - 7
Point of Purchase		
BU4269	Door decal	10 - 20
BU4270	Translite	15 - 20

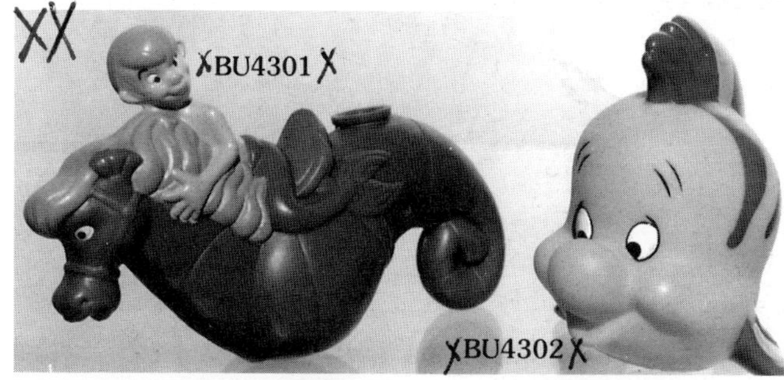

BU4301 BU4302

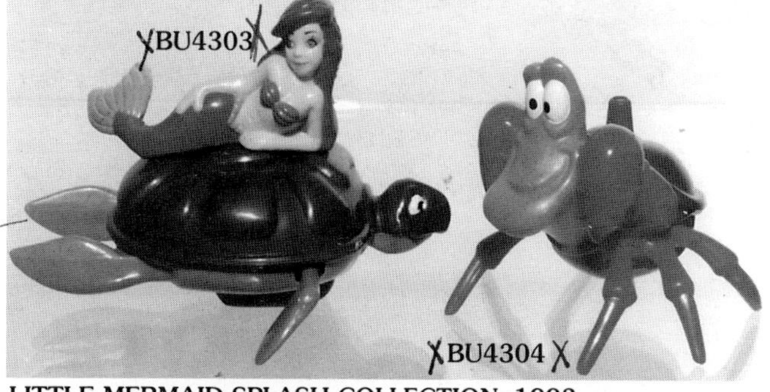

BU4303 BU4304

LITTLE MERMAID SPLASH COLLECTION, 1993

Disney's Ariel and her friends became summer time premiums for the Kids Club. All were water toys except for the wind-up Sebastian.

BU4503 BU4501 BU4502 BU4504

BU4506 BU4507

BU4508 BU4509

BU4301	Urchin Squirtgun Toy, 1 piece	2 - 4
BU4302	Flounder Squirter, 1 piece	1 - 3
BU4303	Ariel Wind-Up, 2 pieces	2 - 4
BU4304	Sebastian Wind-Up, 1 piece	1 - 3
Point of Purchase		
BU4305	Door decal	10 - 20

MAGIC MEAL, 1981

Mystical feats were featured in this "Magic Meal" promotion. Instructions were printed on the sealed clear bags which contained the plastic pieces or on a section of the cardboard punch-out piece. Each premium was featured on the front panel of a uniquely designed box. Other magic tricks were printed on the side panels.

BU4501	Mind-Reading Cube, blue	8 - 10
BU4502	King-Flip, multi-color cards	8 - 10
BU4503	Magic Nails, yellow/orange	8 - 10
BU4504	Mystery Box, Black	8 - 10
Boxes		
BU4506	The Amazing Mind-Reading Cube	3 - 5
BU4507	The Astounding King-Flip	3 - 5
BU4508	The Incredible Magic Nails	3 - 5
BU4509	The Magical Mystery Box	3 - 5

MANY FACES OF ALF, 1988

The space visitor from Melmac was the subject of this over-the-counter offer. The Alf figure was issued as four 12" furry hand puppets dressed in an appropriate outfit. Attached to one of Alf's arms was a cardboard accessory prop(s) to complement the individual outfits. On the back side of the prop was the name of the promotion. A paper record featuring a song based on the theme of each puppet was also included with this offer. A detachable rebate offer from Coleco was on the record. Since these toys were sold over the counter, no boxes were issued.

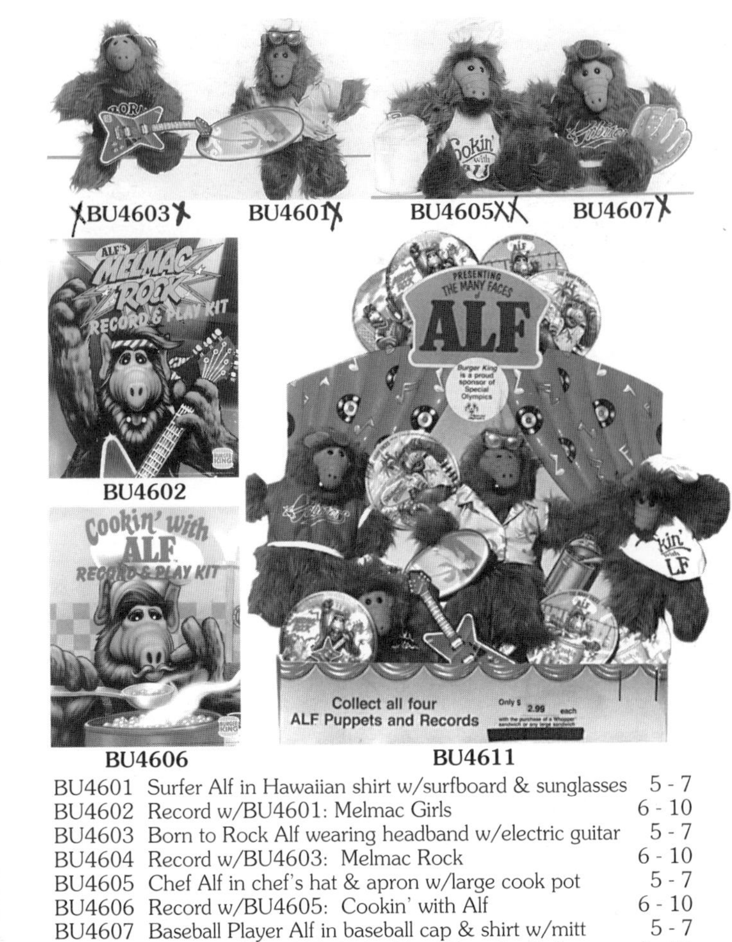

BU4603 BU4601 BU4605 BU4607

BU4602

BU4606 BU4611

BU4601	Surfer Alf in Hawaiian shirt w/surfboard & sunglasses	5 - 7
BU4602	Record w/BU4601: Melmac Girls	6 - 10
BU4603	Born to Rock Alf wearing headband w/electric guitar	5 - 7
BU4604	Record w/BU4603: Melmac Rock	6 - 10
BU4605	Chef Alf in chef's hat & apron w/large cook pot	5 - 7
BU4606	Record w/BU4605: Cookin' with Alf	6 - 10
BU4607	Baseball Player Alf in baseball cap & shirt w/mitt	5 - 7
BU4608	Record w/BU4607: Take Me, Alf, to the Ballgame	6 - 10
Point of Purchase		
BU4610	Translite	25 - 35
BU4611	Display	50 - 100

BU4651 BU4652 BU4653 BU4654

MASTERS OF THE UNIVERSE CUPS, 1985

Louisiana Plastics, Inc. of St. Louis, MO manufactured four 5" white plastic cups which featured a full-color wrap-around comic strip.

BU4651	Thunder Punch He-Man Saves the Day	4 - 6
BU4652	He-Man & Roboto to the Rescue	4 - 6
BU4653	Spydor Stalking Enemies of Skeletor	4 - 6
BU4654	He-Man Takes on the Evil Horde	4 - 6
Boxes		
BU4656	There is Power in Friendship	5 - 10
BU4657	Everyone is Good at Something	5 - 10
BU4658	There is Strength in Numbers	5 - 10
BU4659	Things Aren't Always as They Seem	5 - 10

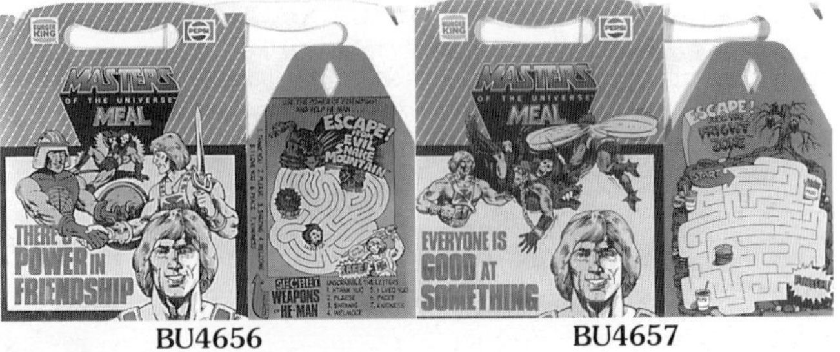

BU4656 BU4657

BU4658 BU4659

Point of Purchase

BU4660	Translite	20 - 40
BU4661	Tray Liner	1 - 2

MASTERS OF THE UNIVERSE II, 1987

Assorted premiums relating to the TV cartoon series were issued in this promotion. However, little is known regarding them.

BU4671	Secret Ring	3 - 7
Boxes		
BU4676	Music is the Key to the Universe	5 - 8
BU4677	Half the Battle	5 - 8
BU4678	A Strong Will	5 - 8
BU4679	Time for Action	5 - 8
Point of Purchase		
BU4680	Translite	20 - 40

BU4703 BU4701 BU4702

BU4706 (front and back)

MATCHBOX CARS, 1987

Metal 3" cars from Matchbox were packaged in sealed bags imprinted with the Burger King logo.

BU4701	Red Ferrari	4 - 7
BU4702	Yellow Corvette	4 - 7
BU4703	Blue 4x4, Mountain Man on cab top	4 - 7
BU4704	Ford LTD Police Car	4 - 7
Boxes		
BU4706	Fire Station/Car Wash/Gas Station/Burger King	3 - 6
Point of Purchase		
BU4710	Translite	20 - 40

BU4741 BU4742 BU4743 BU4744

McGRUFF CARES FOR YOU, 1991

A McGruff licensed product of the National Crime Prevention Council was created expressly for Burger King. Four 16-page songbooks and 20-minute audio cassettes have surfaced, but it is unknown if these were actually a kid's meal premium or an over-the-counter item. Each booklet contained the song lyrics and safety tips. The booklets and cassette boxes were numbered and color coordinated.

BU4741	Set #1, dark golden yellow	3 - 6
BU4742	Set #2, burnt orange	3 - 6

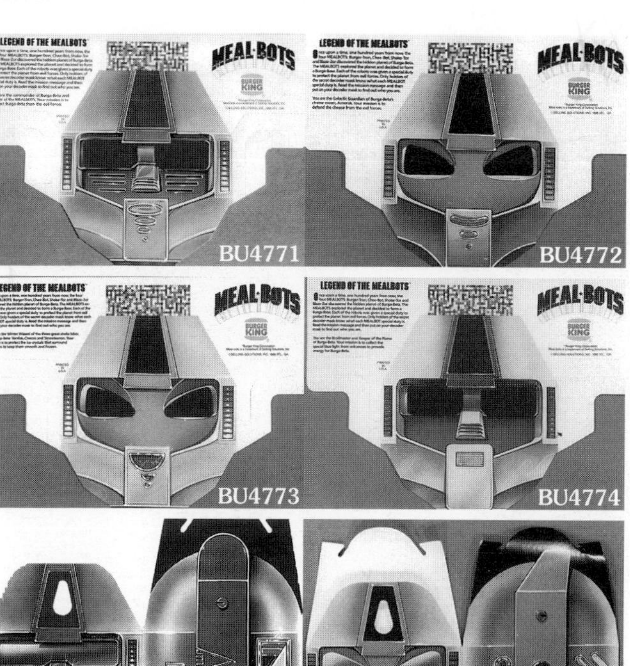

BU4771 BU4772 BU4773 BU4774

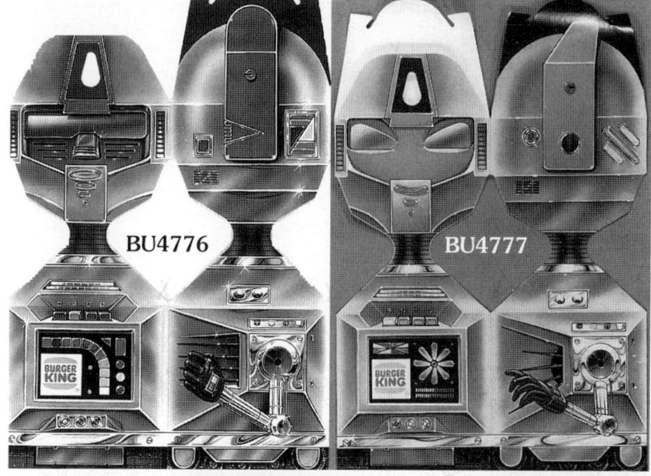

BU4776 BU4777

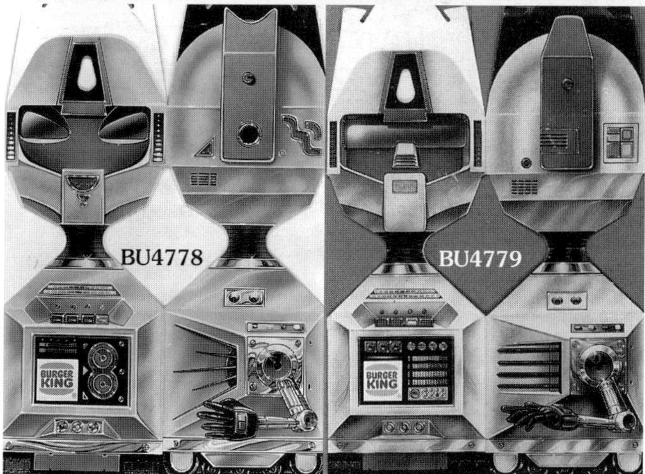

BU4778 BU4779

BU4743	Set #3, purple	3 - 6
BU4744	Set #4, red	3 - 6

MEAL-BOTS, 1986

The premium was a punch-out cardboard Meal-bot mask. By using the decoder lenses built into the mask, a child could read coded messages. Full-figure boxes were the second part of this promotion.

BU4771	Burger-Tron/Commander, blue	3 - 4
BU4772	Chee-Bot/Galactic Guardian, orange	3 - 4
BU4773	Shake-Tor/Winter Wizard, yellow	3 - 4
BU4774	Blaze-Zor/Broilmaster, green	3 - 4
Boxes		
BU4776	Burger-Tron/Commander, blue	5 - 10
BU4777	Chee-Bot/Galactic Guardian, orange	5 - 10
BU4778	Shake-Tor/Winter Wizard, yellow	5 - 10
BU4779	Blaze-Zor/Broilmaster, green	5 - 10
Point of Purchase		
BU4750	Translite	20 - 40

BU4864 BU4861 BU4870 BU4867

BU4861-70

MICKEY'S TOONTOWN DISNEYLAND, 1993 BU4876

Each premium included an illustrated cardboard quarter-section of the map of Mickey's Toontown, a cardboard attraction stand-up, and a 2" plastic wind-up vehicle.

BU4861	Goofy, green truck w/Bounce House & map section	3 - 7
BU4864	Donald tug boat w/Roller Coaster & map section	3 - 7
BU4867	Mickey/Minnie red roadster w/houses & map section	3 - 7
BU4870	Chip 'n Dale street car w/City Hall & map section	3 - 7
Point of Purchase		
BU4875	Door decal	15 - 25
BU4876	Translite	10 - 15

BU4901 BU4902

MINI SPORTS GAMES, 1993

Various sports balls and equipment were featured during this Kids Club offering.

BU4903

BU4904

BU4901	Football	1 - 3
BU4902	Basketball w/Hoop	1 - 3
BU4903	Inflatable Soccer Ball	1 - 3
BU4904	Catch Mitts w/Ball	1 - 3
Point of Purchase		
BU4911	Door decal	15 - 25

BU5251 BU5252 BU5253 BU5254

BU5256

BU5257

BU5258

BU5260

NERFULS, 1989

Nerfuls were rubber balls with "hats" and a base to give them a solid "footing." These elements could be mixed to create new Nerfuls.

BU5251	Officer Bob, purple face	1 - 5
BU5252	Bitsy Ball (girl), yellow face	1 - 5
BU5253	Fetch (dog), blue face	1 - 5
BU5254	Scratch (cat), orange face	1 - 5
Boxes		
BU5256	A Trip to Nerfuls Beach	3 - 6
BU5257	Fun at Nurferville	3 - 6
BU5258	A Day at Nerfuls Park	3 - 6
Point of Purchase		
BU5260	Translite	15 - 30
BU5261	Display	40 - 60

PILOT PAK, 1988

Styrofoam airplanes manufactured by Tiger Inc. of Ventura, CA were featured during this kid's meal. Each plane had a 7" wing span with details painted in red and gold on the white styrofoam punch-out pieces. Four specially designed boxes used with this offering became airplanes themselves.

BU6341	Two-Seater	5 - 6
BU6342	Sunburst Stripes	5 - 6
BU6343	Checkerboard	5 - 6
BU6344	Airliner	5 - 6
Boxes		
BU6346	Yellow & Red Jumbo Jet	4 - 8
BU6347	Red Airplane w/Yellow Propeller	4 - 8

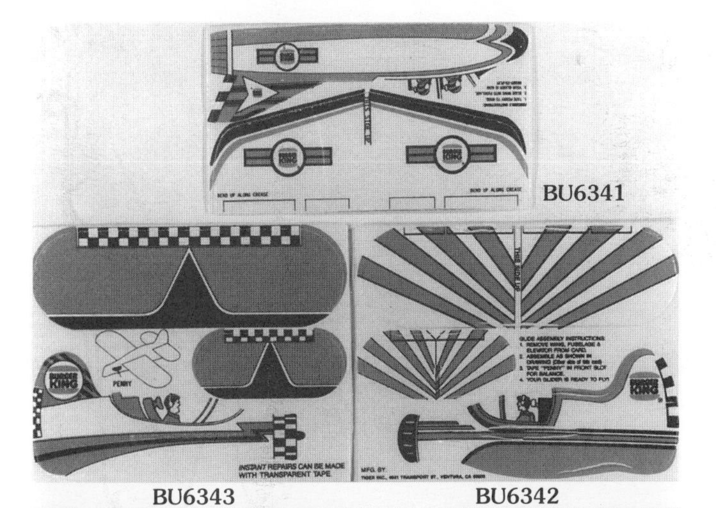

BU6341

BU6343 BU6342

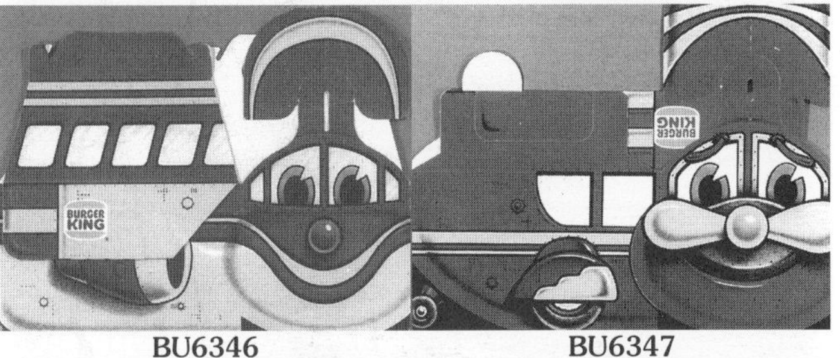

BU6346 BU6347

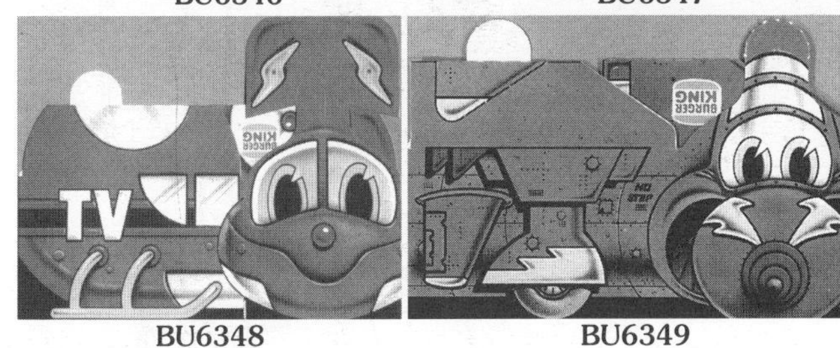

BU6348 BU6349

BU6348 Purple Helicopter 4 - 8
BU6349 Blue Military Jet 4 - 8
Point of Purchase
BU6350 Translite 15 - 30

BU6391 BU6392 BU6393 BU6394

PINNOCHIO SUMMER INFLATABLES, 1988

A tie-in with the re-release of Disney's classic *Pinnochio*. The promotion featured small inflatable vinyl toys of characters from the film .

BU6391 Pinnochio Beach Ball 1 - 4
BU6392 Jiminy Cricket Flyer 1 - 4
BU6393 Monstro the Whale 1 - 4
BU6394 Figaro Bobber 1 - 4
Point of Purchase
BU6399 Door decal 15 - 25
BU6400 Translite 10 - 15

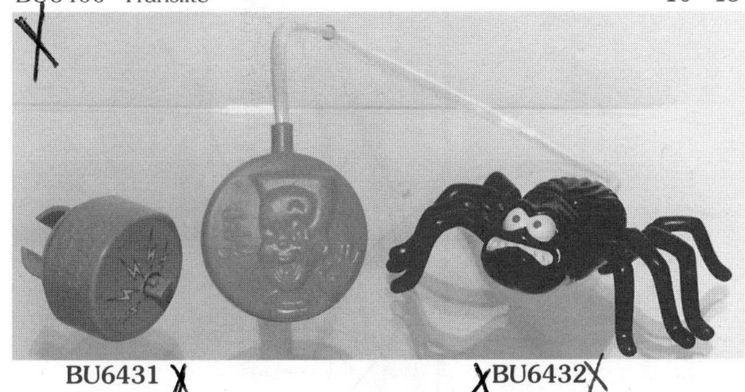

BU6431 BU6432

BU6433 BU6434 BU6435

PRANKSTERS, 1994

A set of five gags featuring the Kid's Club characters. A comic strip insert piece was included with each premium.

BU6431 Boomer's Buzzer 2 - 4
BU6432 Jaws' Jumping Spider 2 - 4
BU6433 Kid Vid's Squirting Channel Changer 2 - 4
BU6434 Lingo's Snake 2 - 4
BU6435 I.Q.'s Whoopee Cushion 2 - 4
Point of Purchase
BU6440 Door Decal 10 - 15

BU6461 BU6462

BU6463 BU6464

BU6466 BU6467

PURRTENDERS, 1988

The Hallmark cats who liked to become other animals were featured in this kid's meal promotion. The two 2½" plastic toys rode on tiny plastic wheels. These came packaged in a sealed clear bag with a 1½" x 2" paper insert which showed how to operate the toy. The bank and storybook are hard to find.

BU6461 Free Wheeling Cheese Rider 2 - 5
BU6462 Flip-Top Car 2 - 5
BU6463 Radio/Bank (yellow) 4 - 8
BU6464 Storybook: *Ice Escapades* 3 - 6
Boxes
BU6466 Holiday Fun at the Pet Shop 3 - 6
BU6467 Holiday Fun at the Train Station 3 - 6

BU6468 BU6469

BU6468 Holiday Fun at the Bakery 3 - 6
BU6469 Holiday Fun at the Lodge 3 - 6
Point of Purchase
BU6470 Translite 15 - 30

BU6821 BU6822 BU6823

BU6824 BU6825 BU6826

RECORD BREAKERS, 1989

Friction driven race cars patterned after the popular Hasbro toy were used as premiums for this promotion. The name of the car was painted on the body. All six cars come with or without the "Record Breakers" logo imprinted on the car.

BU6821 Accelerator 3 - 6
BU6822 Dominator 3 - 6
BU6823 Indy 3 - 6
BU6824 Shockwave 3 - 6
BU6825 Fastlane 3 - 6
BU6826 Aero Afterburner 3 - 6
Point of Purchase
BU6830 Translite 10 - 20

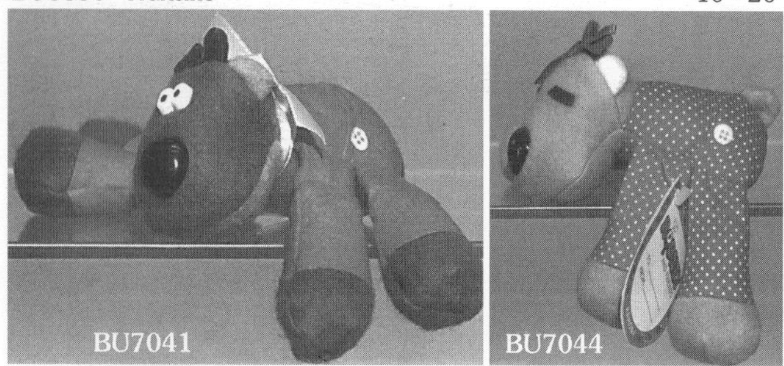

BU7041 BU7044

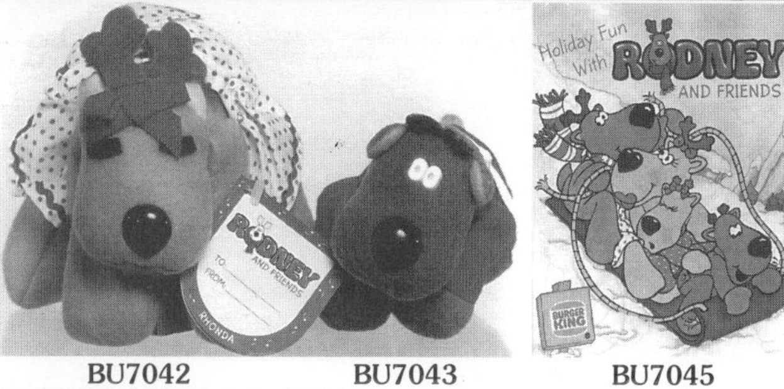

BU7042 BU7043 BU7045

RODNEY & FRIENDS, 1986

Plush reindeer with floppy legs were issued during this Christmas promotion. Each had a folded paper gift tag attached which was imprinted on the front with "Rodney and Friends."

BU7041 Rodney 4 - 7
BU7042 Rhonda 4 - 7
BU7043 Randy 4 - 7
BU7044 Ramona 4 - 7
BU7045 Booklet: *Holiday Fun with Rodney & Friends* 3 - 5

BU7046 BU7047

BU7048 BU7049

Boxes
BU7046 Holiday Fun & Games 5 - 8
BU7047 Holiday Decorating 5 - 8
BU7048 Holiday Fun at the Toy Store 5 - 8
BU7049 Holiday Sweets & Treats 5 - 8
Point of Purchase
BU7050 Translite 10 - 20

BU7201 BU7202

BU7203 BU7204

BU7201 BU7202 BU7203 BU7204

SAVE THE ANIMALS, 1993

These were 25" x 15" tri-fold cardboard albums with 15 trading cards. Each week featured a different category of endangered species.

BU7201	1 - Mammals w/red cards #1-15	2 - 5
BU7202	2 - Birds w/yellow cards #16-30	2 - 5
BU7203	3 - Reptiles and Amphibians w/green cards #31-45	2 - 5
BU7204	4 - Fish w/blue cards #46-60	2 - 5
Point of Purchase		
BU7210	Translite	15 - 30
BU7211	Door decal	25 - 45

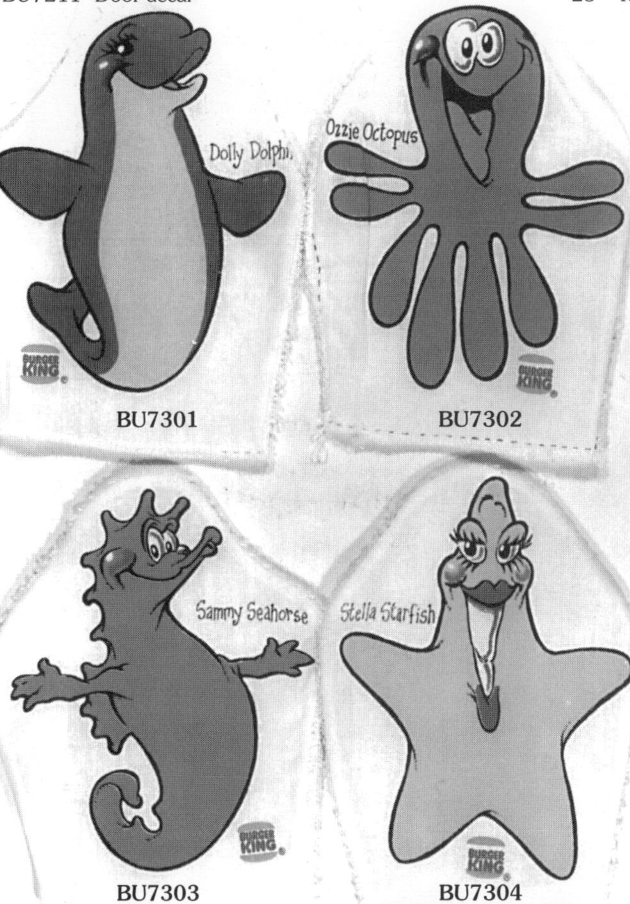

BU7301 BU7302 BU7303 BU7304

BU7311 BU7312

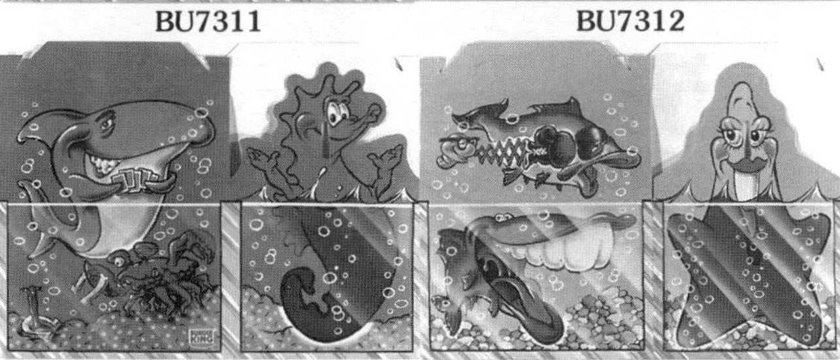

BU7313 BU7314

SEA CREATURES, 1989

Cartoon-style illustrations of four sea creatures were printed on this series of kid's bath mitts. Each whimsical character appeared on a corresponding box.

BU7301	Dolly Dolphin	4 - 6
BU7302	Ozzie Octopus	4 - 6
BU7303	Sammy Seahorse	4 - 6
BU7304	Stella Starfish	4 - 6

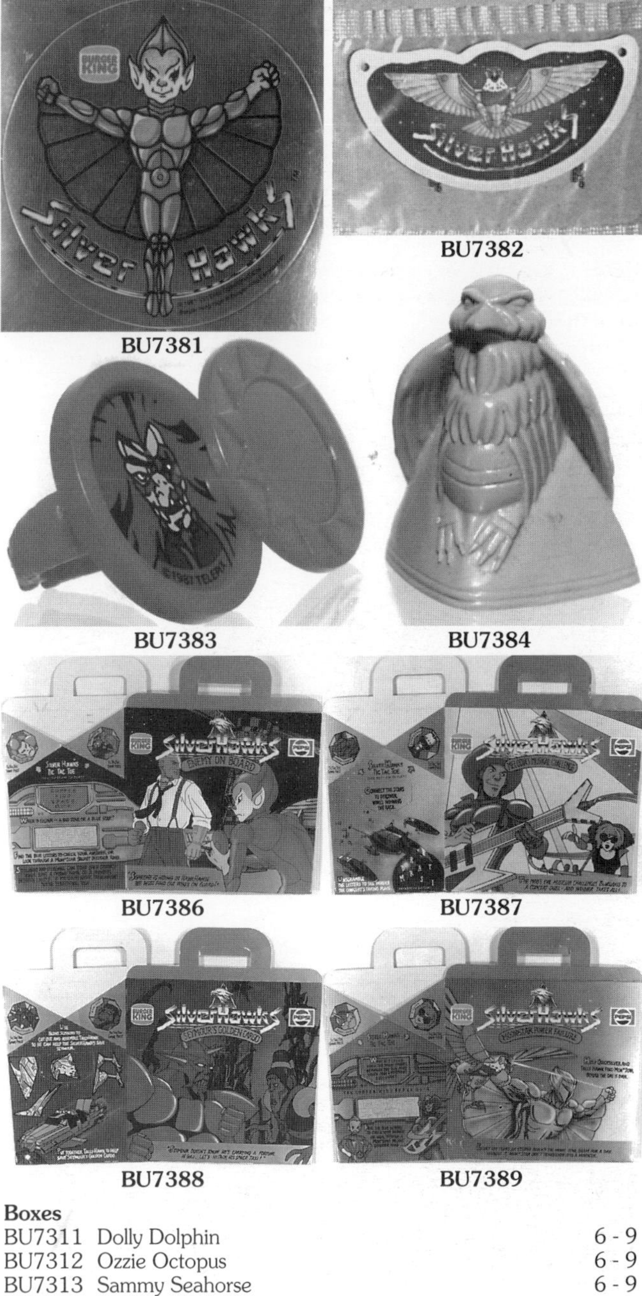

BU7381 BU7382 BU7383 BU7384 BU7386 BU7387 BU7388 BU7389

Boxes		
BU7311	Dolly Dolphin	6 - 9
BU7312	Ozzie Octopus	6 - 9
BU7313	Sammy Seahorse	6 - 9
BU7314	Stella Starfish	6 - 9

SILVERHAWKS, 1987

The SilverHawks were human characters who could employ the powers of hawks to triumph over evil. The kids TV cartoon program, produced by Telepix Corporation, only lasted two seasons. The box handles were done in metalic silver.

BU7381	Silver Foil Reflective Sticker	3 - 7
BU7382	Flasher Name Plate	3 - 7
BU7383	Decoder Ring	3 - 7
BU7384	Pencil Topper	2 - 6
Boxes		
BU7386	Enemy on Board	4 - 8
BU7387	Melodia's Musical Challenge	4 - 8
BU7388	Seymour's Golden Cargo	4 - 8
BU7389	Moonstar Power Failure	4 - 8
Point of Purchase		
BU7390	Translite	20 - 40
BU7391	Ceiling Dangler (see back cover)	75 - 125

SIMPSONS, 1990

The Simpsons were an animated prime time T.V. fad on the Fox Network in 1990. The nuclear waste family faded fast, but Burger King had 'em while they were hot. Each hollow figure came with a cardboard background.

BU7421 BU7422 BU7423 BU7424 BU7425

BU7421 Lisa w/rabbit, tree & animal scene 2 - 5
BU7423 Homer w/skunk, truck scene 2 - 5
BU7425 Maggie w/turtle, underwater scene 2 - 5
BU7427 Marge w/birds in hair, vultures & rocks scene 2 - 5
BU7429 Bart w/backpack, trees & sleeping bag scene 2 - 5

Point of Purchase

BU7435 Translite 15 - 30
BU7436 Tray Liner 1 - 2

BU7511 BU7512

BU7513 BU7514

BU7516 BU7517

BU7518 BU7519

SPACEBASE RACERS, 1989

Plastic 3"-4" toy versions of vehicles used to explore outer space were the focus of this promotion.

BU7511 Super Shuttle 4 - 8
BU7512 Moonman Rover 4 - 8
BU7513 Starship Viking 4 - 8
BU7514 Cosmic Copter 4 - 8

Boxes

BU7516 Earth & Beyond 5 - 8
BU7517 Lunar Expedition 5 - 8
BU7518 Exploring Deep Space 5 - 8
BU7519 The Search for Alien Life 5 - 8

BU7601 (front and back) BU7602

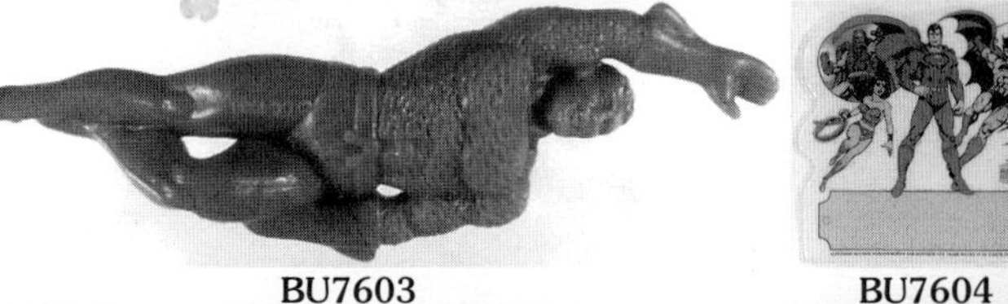

BU7603 BU7604

BU7606 BU7607

BU7608 BU7609

Point of Purchase

BU7520 Translite 18 - 25
BU7521 Banner 15 - 30

SUPER POWERS, 1987

The first of two Super Powers promotions features a Superman/Clark Kent Lenticular Coin, unique Batman toothbrush holder, swimming Aquaman tub toy, and puffy sticker shield picturing arch-villain Darkseid, plus Batman, Superman, and Wonder Woman.

BU7601 Superman Lenticular Coin 6 - 12
BU7602 Batman Toothbrush Holder 5 - 10
BU7603 Aquaman Tub Toy 4 - 8
BU7604 Super Powers Stick-On Door Shield 3 - 7

Boxes

BU7606 The Joker's on a Crime Spree! 5 - 10
BU7607 Make Way for Wonder Woman! 5 - 10
BU7608 The Riddler Runs Rampant! 5 - 10
BU7609 The Penguin is Out of His Cage! 5 - 10

Point of Purchase

BU7610 Translite 25 - 50
BU7611 Mobile w/boxes 35 - 65

SUPER POWERS CUP HOLDER COLLECTION, 1988

Three DC Comics super heroes and a villain were featured in this Super Powers promotion. The figure looked as if it were holding the cup, but was actually like a mug handle for detachable cups which came in at least two sizes.

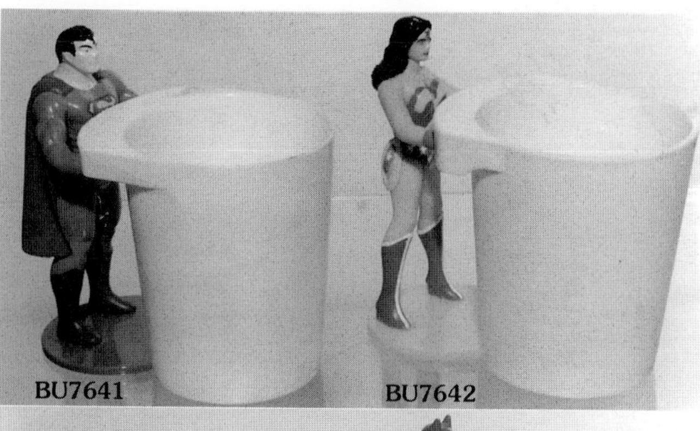
BU7641 BU7642

BU7643 BU7644

BU7650

BU7655

BU7641 Superman, "A" 4 - 6
BU7642 Wonder Woman, "B" 4 - 6
BU7643 Darkseid "C" 4 - 6
BU7644 Batman, "D" 4 - 6
Point of Purchase
BU7650 Translite 15 - 25
BU7655 Display 80 - 100

BU7822 BU7821

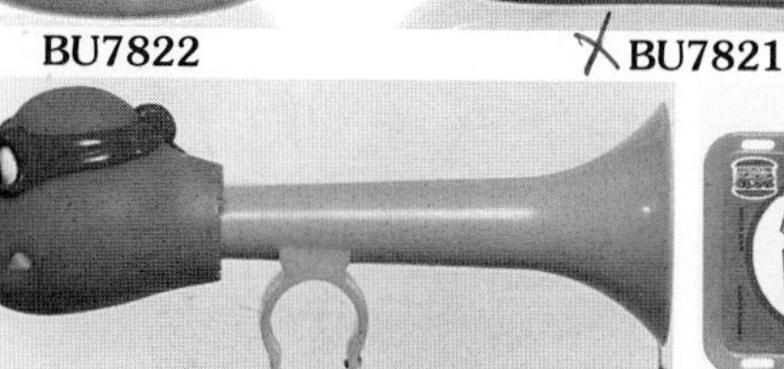

BU7823 BU7824

TEENAGE MUTANT NINJA TURTLES BIKE GEAR, 1993

The second TMNT promotion ran concurrent with the release of their third film, and featured plastic bike accessories.

BU7825

BU7821 Bike Pouch 1 - 3
BU7822 Squeeze Bottle 1 - 3
BU7823 Bike Horn 1 - 3
BU7824 License Plate & Stickers 1 - 3
BU7825 Spoke Sliders 1 - 3
Point of Purchase
BU7827 Door decal 10 - 20

BU7852 BU7851 BU7853

BU7854 BU7856 BU7855

TEENAGE MUTANT NINJA TURTLES RAD BADGES, 1990

Burger King chose *TMNT* to launch their new Kids Club. The kids weren't introduced until later. The *Turtles* were featured on six mechanical badges, four specially priced $5 videos, and a poster promoting their second movie.

BU7861

BU7851 Raphael 2 - 5
BU7852 Leonardo 2 - 5
BU7853 Donatello 2 - 5
BU7854 Michaelangelo 2 - 5
BU7855 Shredder 2 - 5
BU7856 Heroes in a Half Shell 2 - 5
BU7857 The Great Boldini video 3 - 8
BU7858 April Foolish video 3 - 8
BU7859 Sky Turtles video 3 - 8
BU7860 Invasion of the Turtle Snatchers video 3 - 8
BU7861 Give-away poster 5 - 10
Point of Purchase
BU7865 Translite 15 - 30

BU7943

BU7944

THIS IS A BURGER KING TOWN, 1985

A punch-out building promotion.

Boxes
BU7941 Barn, Horse Whirl & Win Game 5 - 8
BU7942 Fire Station, Engine & Fireman 5 - 8
BU7943 Restaurant 5 - 8
BU7944 Apartment, Safety & Door signs 5 - 8
Point of Purchase
BU7950 Translite 20 - 40

BU7985

BU7981 BU7983

BU7982 BU7984

BU7986 BU7987

BU7988 BU7989

THUNDERCATS, 1986

The *ThunderCats* TV series was the theme of this promotion.

BU7981	Snarf Straw Holder	3 - 7
BU7982	Plastic Cup/Bank	3 - 7
BU7983	Secret Message Ring	3 - 7
BU7984	Light Switch Plate	3 - 7
BU7985	X-O-Graphic Medallion on String	3 - 7
Boxes		
BU7986	Snarf's Challenge	5 - 10
BU7987	Jaga the Wise	5 - 10
BU7988	ThunderCats on Patrol	5 - 10
BU7989	Cat's Lair Under Attack	5 - 10
Point of Purchase		
BU7990	Translite	20 - 40

BU8061 BU8062

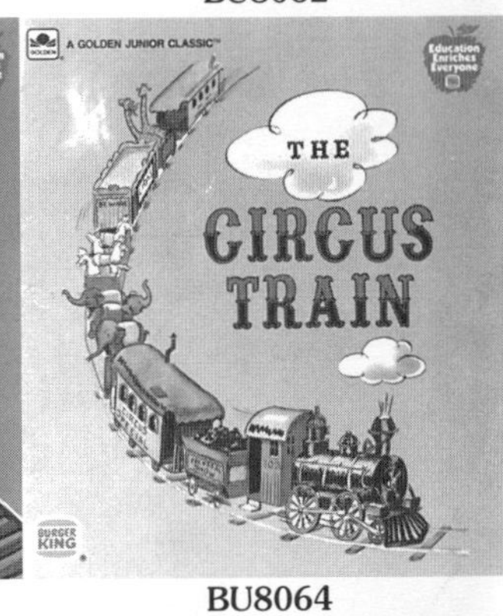

BU8063 BU8064

BU8066 BU8067

TRAK-PAK, 1988 BU8068

Soft cover 6½" x 7¼" Golden Junior Classic books with stories about trains were the premiums in this promotion. The boxes which contained the meal were designed as train engines.

BU8061	The Train to Timbuctoo	4 - 5
BU8062	Roundabout Train	4 - 5
BU8063	My Little Book of Trains	4 - 5
BU8064	The Circus Train	4 - 5
Boxes		
BU8066	Green	4 - 8
BU8067	Red	4 - 8
BU8068	Blue	4 - 8
BU8069	Orange	4 - 8
Point of Purchase		
BU8070	Translite	18 - 36

WALT DISNEY WORLD 20th ANNIVERSARY PARADE, 1991

This ambitious program to celebrate the 20th Anniversary of Walt Disney World featured miniature plastic versions of three-story floats

BU8521 BU8522 BU8523 BU8525

Combined map sections for BU8521-27

used in the Surprise Parade at the Florida theme park (and the year before in Disneyland's "Party Gras" parade). These wind-up "floats" were guided by raised tracks on four connectible map sections. Neat idea...but sections were packed wrong and production control was bad. In short, when all parts were put together, the tracks didn't work. At the time, Burger King had to set up a special 800 number just to deal with a major miss-matched toy and map section problem.

BU8521	Minnie Mouse Float w/#1 Liberty Square/ Frontierland map section	4 - 8
BU8523	Donald Duck Float w/#2 Fantasyland/ Mickey's Starland map section	4 - 8
BU8525	Roger Rabbit Float w/#3 Adventureland/ Main Street, U.S.A. map section	4 - 8
BU8527	Mickey Mouse Float w/#4 Tomorrowland map section	4 - 8
Point of Purchase		
BU8530	Store Display	20 - 35
BU8531	Translite	10 - 20
BU8532	Door Decal	10 - 20

BU8850 BU8852 BU8853

BU8854 BU8855

WATER MATES, 1991

The figures of I.Q. on a dolphin and Lingo on the jet ski could float or be used as squirters. Snaps and Wheels were seated PVC figures in a boat and hovercraft in this Kids Club promotion. All toys were boat-oriented. There are two variations in the set.

BU8850	Snaps/rowboat (blue shirt)	1 - 3
BU8851	Snaps/rowboat (pink shirt)	2 - 6
BU8852	I.Q. on a dolphin	1 - 3
BU8853	Lingo/Jet Ski (pink Jet Ski & swimwear)	1 - 3
BU8854	Lingo/Jet Ski (green Jet Ski & swimwear)	2 - 6
BU8855	Wheels/hovercraft (gray control portion)	1 - 3
BU8856	Wheels/hovercraft (blue control portion)	2 - 6
Point of Purchase		
BU8860	Translite	10 - 20

BU9301 BU9302

BU9303 BU9304

WIZARD OF FRIES CALCULATORS, 1981

Four "calculator" disks were made for this back-to-school promotion.

BU9301	Addition	2 - 5
BU9302	Subtraction	2 - 5
BU9303	Multiplication	2 - 5
BU9304	Division	2 - 5

BU9581 BU9582

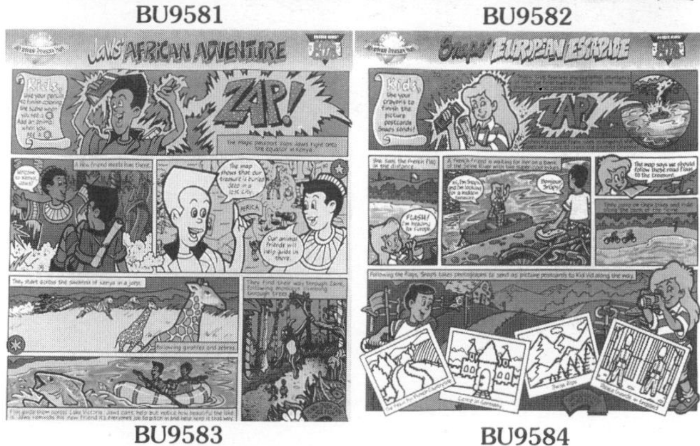

BU9583 BU9584

WORLD TRAVEL ADVENTURE KITS, 1991

New Crayola crayon and marker colors came with adventure stories and maps in this Kids Club series. The Mystery Treasure Map came in the first week, and could be referred to in the other adventures.

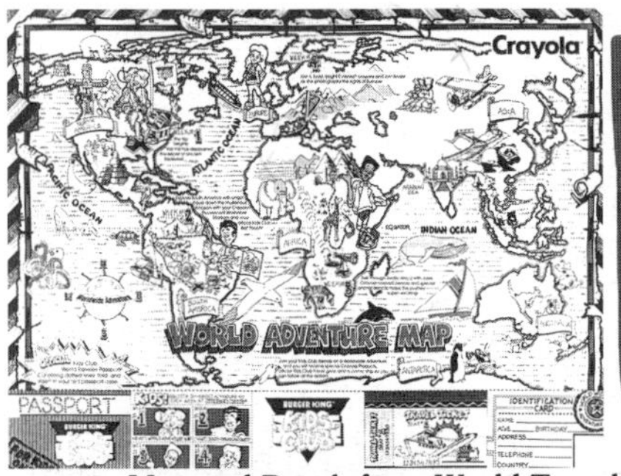

Map and Pouch from World Travel Adventure Kits

BU9691

BU9581	Set #1, Kid Vid's Mystery Treasure Map w/map	2 - 5
BU9582	Set #2, Lingo's South American Quest	2 - 5
BU9583	Set #3, Jaw's African Adventure	2 - 5
BU9584	Set #4, Snap's European Escapade	2 - 5
Point of Purchase		
BU9590	Translite	10 - 20
BU9691	Translite, Drive-up window	10 - 20

CARL'S JR.

This venerable west coast chain has served California, Arizona, Washington, and Oregon for more than 50 years. They have an exceptional kid's meal program for a regional chain, based on their Happy Star character. Premiums dating back to 1986 have been found. Many promotions are undoubtably missing from this section, and some existing entries are incomplete. Carl's Jr. premiums are some of the most sought-after by collectors in areas where they are not available.

Unless the premium was a bucket or other container, all meals are assumed to have been packaged in a bag or box. Only those known are listed.

CA0121 CA0122 CA0123

ADDAMS FAMILY, 1993

The release of *The Addams Family* movie on video cassette and Halloween prompted a tie-in for this kid's meal promotion.

CA0121	Thing Pencil Topper	2 - 4
CA0122	Lurch Stamper	2 - 4
CA0123	Cousin Itt Bubbler	2 - 4
CA0124	Mansion Booklet & Stickers	3 - 5

CA0124 CA0129

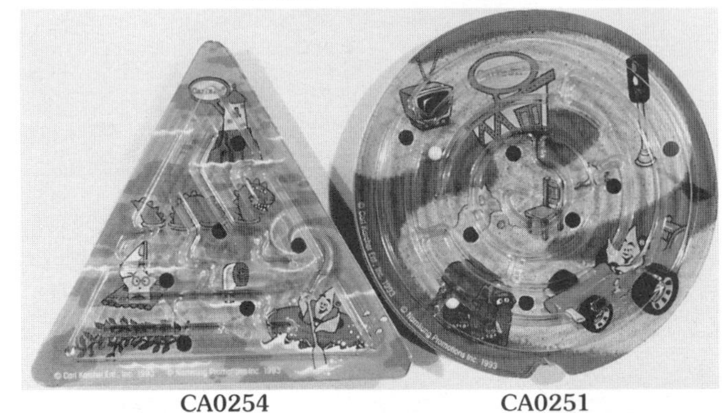

CA0254 CA0251

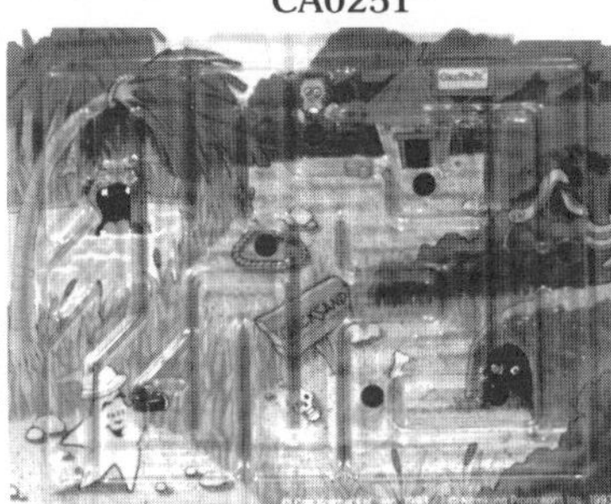

CA0252 CA0253

CA0129	Sack	1 - 2
Point of Purchase		
CA0130	Translite	15 - 25

AMAZING MAZES, 1993

Premiums were double-sided hand-held maze games. The maze graphics were printed on stiff cardboard. The plastic covering created the "tunnels" through which the white balls traveled toward the winning center spot. Holes punched in various locations permitted the balls to "fall through" to the different maze created on the opposite side.

CA0251	Car Maze (round)	2 - 4
CA0252	Space Maze (star)	2 - 4
CA0253	Jungle Maze (rectangular)	2 - 4
CA0254	Water Maze (triangular)	2 - 4
CA0260	Sack	1 - 2

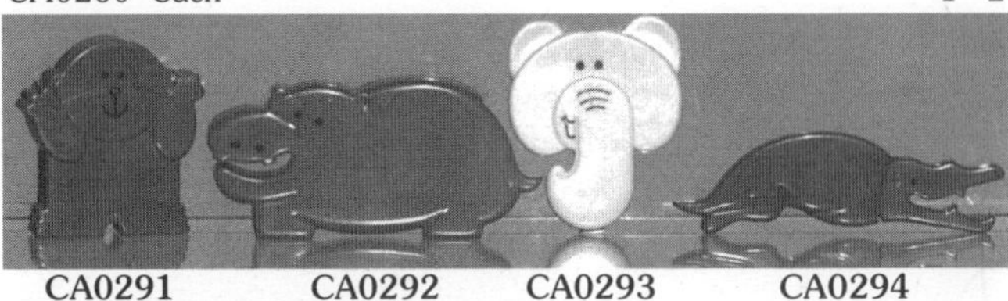

CA0291 CA0292 CA0293 CA0294

ANIMAL OFFICE SUPPLIES, 1987

Desk accessories in the shape of animals were featured during this Carl's Jr. offering. The alligator's head was the cap to the body-shaped felt-tip pen. A tape dispenser came in the shape of a hippo. Paper clips could be placed in the holder shaped like a brown bear and the pink elephant formed a pair of scissors.

CA0291	Brown Bear Paper Clip Holder	4 - 6
CA0292	Blue Hippo Tape Dispenser	4 - 6
CA0293	Pink Elephant Scissors	4 - 6
CA0294	Green Alligator Pen	4 - 6

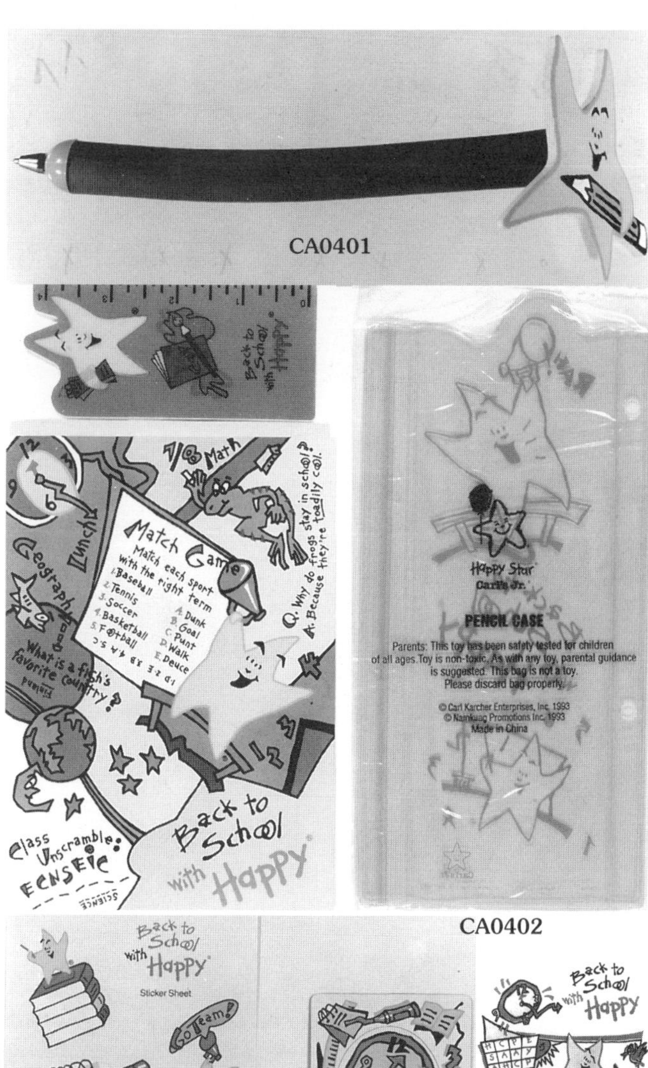

CA0401

CA0402

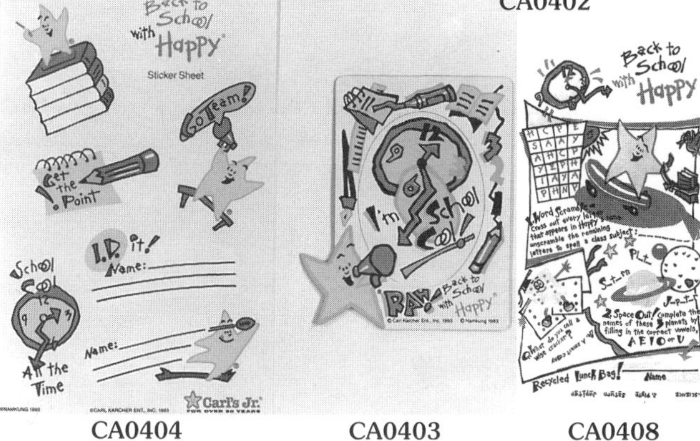

CA0404 CA0403 CA0408

BACK TO SCHOOL, 1993

Back to school for the 1993-94 school year. was the occasion for some nifty supplies from Carl's Jr.

CA0401	Bendy Pen	2 - 4
CA0402	Pencil Case	2 - 4
CA0403	Magnet Picture Frame for locker & memo magnet	2 - 4
CA0404	Folder, Sticker Sheet, Ruler/Bookmark	2 - 4
CA0408	Back to School with Happy Sack	1 - 2

CA0601 CA0605

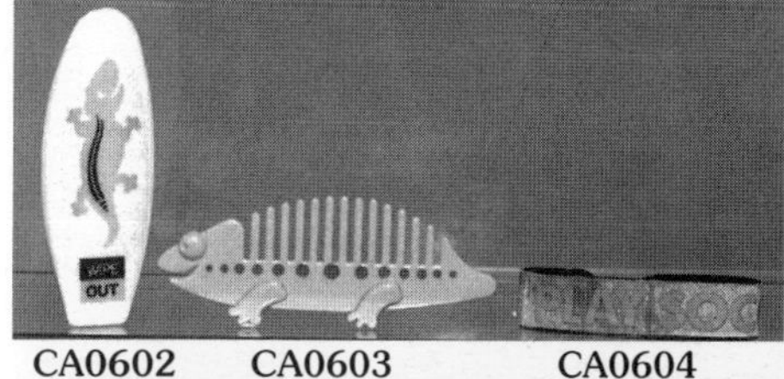

CA0602 CA0603 CA0604 CA0604

BEACH CREATURES, 1990 CA0610

Beach Creatures Surf-prizes came with this summertime Happy Star Meal. Each had a surfing catchphrase such as "Wipe-Out," "Cowabunga," "Dig It," etc. as part of the graphic design.

CA0601	Beach Ball	2 - 5
CA0602	Squirter	2 - 5
CA0603	Comb w/Case	2 - 5
CA0604	Beach Tote w/Friendship Bracelet	2 - 5
CA0605	Flying Disc	2 - 5
Point of Purchase		
CA0610	Translite	15 - 30

CA1021 CA1022 CA1023 CA1024

CAMP CALIFORNIA, 1992

Camp California was featured both in this promotion and a similar one done by White Castle. The Surf Disk is marked Carl's Jr.

CA1021	Surf Disk	2 - 5
CA1022	Squirter	2 - 5
CA1023	Spinner Thrower	2 - 5
CA1024	Mini Volleyball	2 - 5
Point of Purchase		
CA1030	Translite	10 - 20

CAMP CARL'S JR, 1989

Plastic camping equipment was featured during this Happy Star promotion.

CA1061	"Pen Knife" Utensil Set	2 - 5
CA1062	Valuables Holder	2 - 5

CA1030

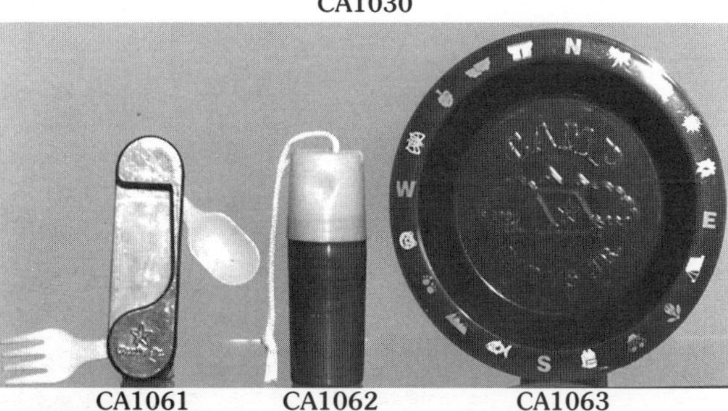

CA1061 CA1062 CA1063

CA1064 CA1065 CA1066

CA1063	Plate (green, yellow or orange)	2 - 5
CA1064	Canteen	2 - 5
CA1065	Small Oval Cup	2 - 5
CA1066	Camp Cookbook	2 - 5

Point of Purchase

CA1070	Translite	15 - 25

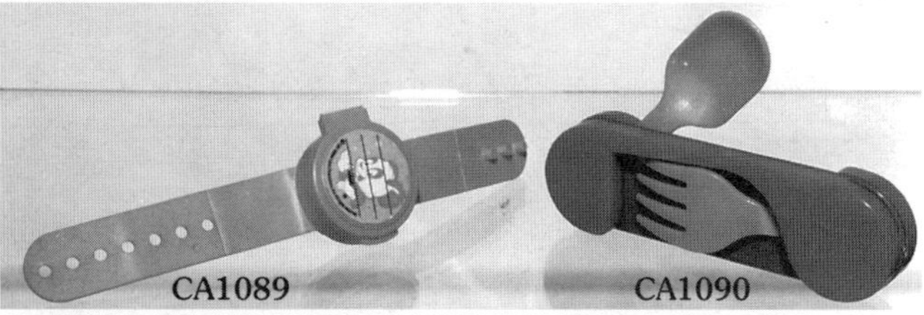

CA1089 CA1090

CAMPING WITH WOODY WOODPECKER & PALS, 1991

The premiums are very similar to those issued during the 1989 Camp Carl's Jr. promotion. The Pen Knife Utensil Kit was identical to CA1061 except the center piece was blue instead of green and the imprints on the ends of the knife were of Splinter and Knothead with the name of this promotion.

CA1089	Andy Panda wrist container	6 - 8
CA1090	"Pen Knife" Utensil Kit	6 - 8

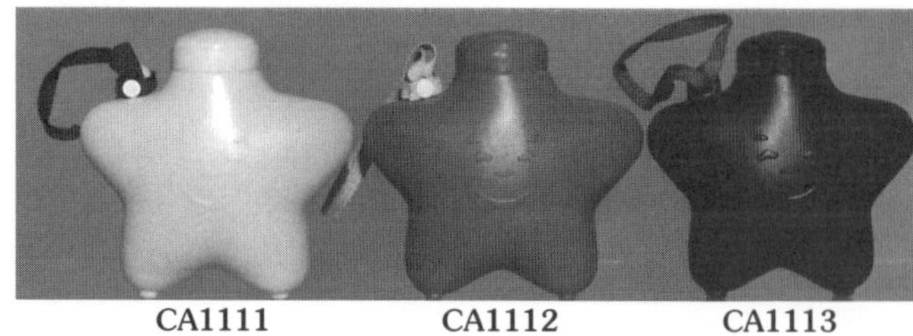

CA1111 CA1112 CA1113

CANTEENS, 1989

Star-shaped plastic canteens having faces and screw-on lids were issued as kid's meal premiums. Each of the 4½" drink holders were identical except for color.

CA1111	Yellow	3 - 5
CA1112	Pink	3 - 5
CA1113	Purple	3 - 5
CA1114	Green	3 - 5

CA1201 CA1202 CA1203

CA1205

CIRCUS FANTASY DISNEYLAND, 1987

Carl's Jr. and The Walt Disney Company teamed up for a Disneyland Circus Fantasy offering. These were 3" plastic drinking cups with various Disney characters

CA1201	Mickey, Minnie, Goofy, two circus clowns	5 - 10
CA1202	Mickey as a lion tamer	5 - 10
CA1203	Minnie balancing on a ball	5 - 10

Box

CA1205	Disneyland Circus Fantasy	6 - 8

CRAZY DOODLERS, 1994

Various types of doodling equipment was featured in this Happy Star Meal. Each came with a sheet of Crazy Doodlers paper.

CA1451	Crayons w/holder	1 - 3
CA1452	Marker	1 - 3

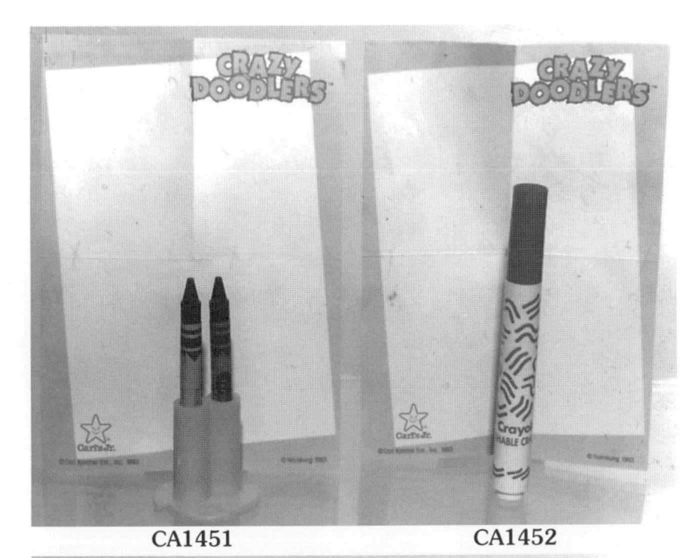

CA1451 CA1452

CA1453 CA1454

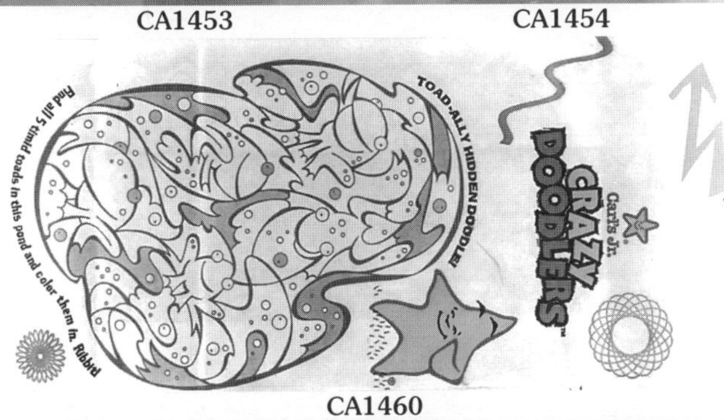

CA1460

CA1741 CA1742 CA1743

CA1453 Doodletop 1 - 3
CA1454 Spiral Wheel 1 - 3
CA1460 Sack 1 - 2

DINO-POUR BOTTLE TOPPER, 1992

A dinosaur head measuring 3½" x 3" could be used as a catsup squeeze bottle top. Each top was identical except for the color. Had "Heinz" name on the back of each neck.

CA1741 Yellow Head 3 - 6
CA1742 Green Head 3 - 6
CA1743 Purple Head 3 - 6

CA1751 CA1752 CA1753

CA1754 CA1755 Sticker Sheet

DINOSTARS, 1987

Flat solid-color interlocking plastic pieces fit together to create a 4" - 5½" dinosaur. This is a stock promotion. Carl's Jr. added a 3" x 5" sheet of stickers of the 6 dinosaurs.

CA1751 Tyrannosaurus 2 - 5
CA1752 Brontosaurus 2 - 5
CA1753 Woolly Mammoth 2 - 5
CA1754 Stegosaurus 2 - 5
CA1755 Triceratops 2 - 5
CA1756 Pteranodon 2 - 5
Point of Purchase
CA1760 Translite 20 - 40

CA2101 CA2102 CA2103

EASTER TAPES, 1989

Cassette tapes of children's stories given out during the 1989 Easter season. One side of the white cassette told the featured story and the other side had songs and activities if the story did not fill both sides. Each cassette had a different colored label with a sketch of animals.

CA2101 The Velveteen Rabbit 4 - 6
CA2102 The Little Rabbit Who Wanted Red Wings 4 - 6
CA2103 The Tale of Peter Rabbit/Chicken Little 4 - 6
Point of Purchase
CA2110 Translite 15 - 25

CA2211 CA2212 CA2213

CA2215 CA2214

FENDER BENDER 500, 1990

Vehicles, approximately 2" each, uniquely designed to coordinate with the Hanna-Barbera character drivers were featured. Hardee's ran the same promotion in the East.

CA2211 Yogi Bear & Boo Boo 2 - 5
CA2212 Dick Dastardly & Mutley 2 - 5
CA2213 Huckleberry Hound & Snagglepuss 2 - 5
CA2214 Quick Draw McGraw & Bobba-Louie 2 - 5
CA2215 Magilla Gorilla & Gator 2 - 5
Point of Purchase
CA2219 Mobile Display 20 - 30
CA2220 Translite 15 - 25

CA2344 CA2342 CA2343 CA2341

50th ANNIVERSARY, 1991

CA2347

To celebrate this special anniversary, premiums during this promotion featured the Carl's Jr. Happy Star logo surrounded by a ribbon banner with "50th Anniversary."

CA2341 Carl Jr. Groovi-Van Cardboard Puzzle 2 - 5
CA2342 Plastic Puzzle 2 - 5
CA2343 Book – *Cruisin'* 2 - 5
CA2344 Baseball 2 - 5
Box
CA2347 50 Happy Star Years 1 - 3
Point of Purchase
CA2350 Translite 15 - 30

FLYIN' AWAY, 1993

Happy Star in various modes of flight was the theme in this innovative promotion.

CA2525 Happy's Sky Blimp 2 - 4
CA2526 High Flyin' Happy 2 - 4
CA2527 Happy's Flight Log 2 - 5
CA2528 Happy's Flip-Out Flyer 2 - 4

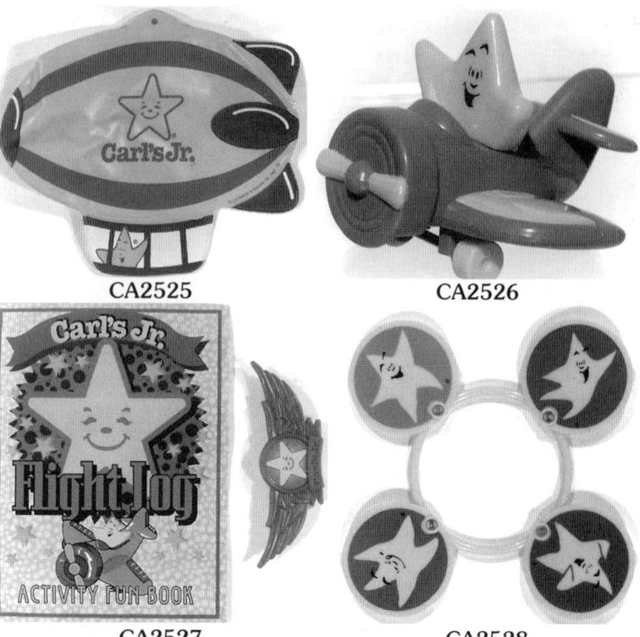

CA2525 CA2526

CA2527 CA2528

CA3061 CA3062 CA3063

CA3064 CA3065 CA3066

CA3070

Sack
CA2530 Flyin' Away 1 - 2
Point of Purchase
CA2535 Translite 15 - 30

FUN HOUSE FACES, 1990

Rubber creature face puppets measuring 4" x 3½" could be manipulated by utilizing the 4 finger holes in the back. Each premium came with a pack of Sunkist Fun Fruits – the first three creatures listed came with Spooky Fruit; the last three with Animals Fruit.

CA3061 Franklin, green 2 - 5
CA3062 Petey Pumpkin, orange 2 - 5
CA3063 Glenda Ghost, white 2 - 5
CA3064 Barney Bear, turquoise 2 - 5
CA3065 Tina Tiger, orange 2 - 5
CA3066 Rudy Rabbit, yellow 2 - 5
Point of Purchase
CA3070 Translite 15 - 30

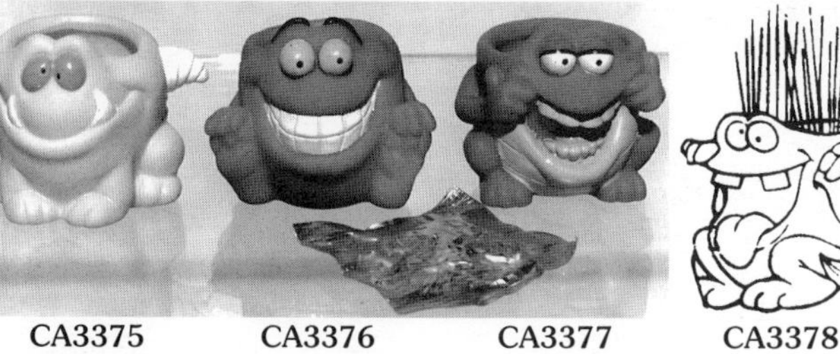

CA3375 CA3376 CA3377 CA3378

HAIR DUDES, 1993

A small packet of ryegrass seeds was placed in the hollowed out portion of each soft rubber creature during this Happy Star Kid's Meal. The seeds were to be sown in the 2" planters so that as the grass grew, "hair" would appear. Also done by Sonic in 1994.

CA3375 Horned Dude, yellow 2 - 4
CA3376 Toe Grasping Dude, orange 2 - 4
CA3377 Pull Back the Mouth Dude, blue 2 - 4
CA3378 Tongue Sticking Out Dude, green 2 - 4

HALLOWEEN, 1989 CA3405

This Halloween's Happy Star Meal offering included a packet of Sunkist Spooky Fruits and a special Halloween book.

CA3401 Molly's Monsters 2 - 5
Point of Purchase
CA3405 Translite 20 - 40

HALLOWEEN BUCKETS, 1993

Two plastic buckets depicting Happy as assorted monsters.

CA3421 Happy w/Pumpkins 3 - 5
CA3422 Haunted House 3 - 5

HAPPY'S HOCKEY LEAGUE, 1994

A hockey-based promotion.

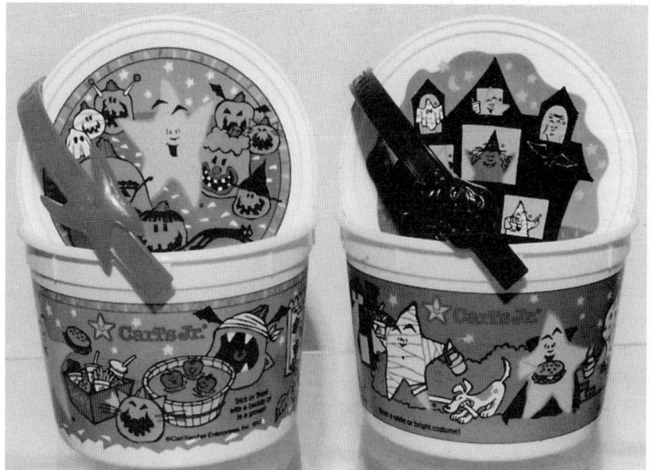

CA3421 CA3422

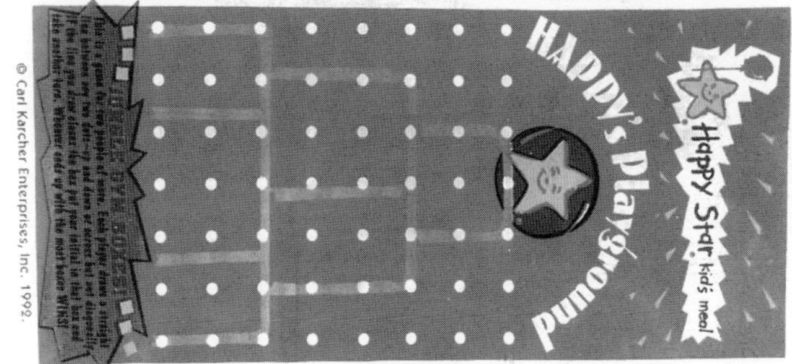

CA3450

CA3431 Mini Megaphone w/sticker sheet 2 - 4
CA3432 Sports Sipper 2 - 4
CA3433 Sliding Puck 2 - 4
CA3434 Goal For It activity book w/sticker sheet 2 - 4

HAPPY'S PLAYGROUND

The only evidence of this promotion found was the sack.

CA3450 Sack 1 - 2

CA3522 CA3525 CA3527

ICE-POP MAKERS, 1987

Popsicles could be formed in the shape of the Carl's Jr. Star, the Kool-Aid Kids and Kool-Aid Pitcher by using the molds with reusable clip-on sticks offered during this Happy Star meal deal. The Happy Star mold came in blue, purple and green; while the Kool-Aid Kid mold came in purple and orange.

CA3522 Happy Star 4 - 5
CA3525 Kool-Aid Kid 4 - 5
CA3527 Red Guy w/Sunglasses 4 - 5
Point of Purchase
CA3530 Translite 30 - 50

LIFE SAVERS ROLL 'EM, 1990

The popular 5 flavors of Life Savers candy became rolling "cars" which could be connected via an interlocking "hole" and "peg" configuration. Each rolled on 4 small rubber wheels and had "Life Savers" embossed on each side. The drink came in a corresponding color cup.

CA4001 Cherry w/cup 3 - 6
CA4002 Pineapple w/cup 3 - 6

CA4001 CA4002 CA4003 CA4004 CA4005

CA4001-5 snapped together

Cup from CA4001

CA4003	Orange w/cup	3 - 6
CA4004	Lemon w/cup	3 - 6
CA4005	Lime w/cup	3 - 6

Point of Purchase

CA4020	Translite	15 - 30

CA4331 CA4332

CA4332 CA4332

LITTLE CRITTER BOOKS, 1986

Western Publishing's Golden Look-Look books by Mercer Mayer were offered for premiums. Each 8" x 8" book had the Carl's Jr. logo on the back cover.

CA4331	Just Me and My Babysitter	3 - 5
CA4332	Just Me and My Dad	3 - 5
CA4333	Just Me and My Little Sister	3 - 5
CA4334	Just Grandma and Me	3 - 5
CA4335	Just for You	3 - 5
CA4336	All by Myself	3 - 5

Point of Purchase

CA4340	Translite	30 - 50

M&M's CHRISTMAS BOOK ORNAMENTS, 1989

These 5" x 4" 5-page heavy cardboard die-cut shaped books had a tie-in to the candy manufacturer. A gold loop was placed through a hole punched in the upper left corner of the book so it could be used as a tree ornament. M&M characters appeared throughout each story.

CA4851 CA4852

CA4853 CA4854

CA4851	The Perfect Snowman	4 - 5
CA4852	A Happy Note	4 - 5
CA4853	Timmy's Tree Trimmers	4 - 5
CA4854	The One That Almost Got Away	4 - 5

CA4881 CA4882 CA4883 CA4884

MIX 'N MATCH DINOS, 1993

Each of the four dinos in this promotion came bagged in two or three sections which were interchangeable with others in the series. The decoration was unique to Carl's Jr., but the same figures were used by Denny's and White Castle.

CA4881	Pterry, yellow	2 - 4
CA4882	Bronto, green	2 - 4
CA4883	Rex, purple	2 - 4
CA4884	Steggy, pink	2 - 4

Sack

CA4889	Mix 'N Match Dinos	1 - 2

Point of Purchase

CA4890	Translite	15 - 30

CA4921 CA4922 CA4923 CA4924

MONSTER DAYS, 1988

These hollow rubber 4-legged fanged monsters had shackles around their front feet. The premiums measured 2½" - 4".

CA4921 Monster lying down, pink 2 - 4
CA4922 Monster lying down, purple 2 - 4
CA4923 Monster lying down, orange 2 - 4
CA4924 Monster standing, blue 2 - 4

Point of Purchase

CA4930 Translite 20 - 40

CA4889

CA5056

CA5051 CA5052

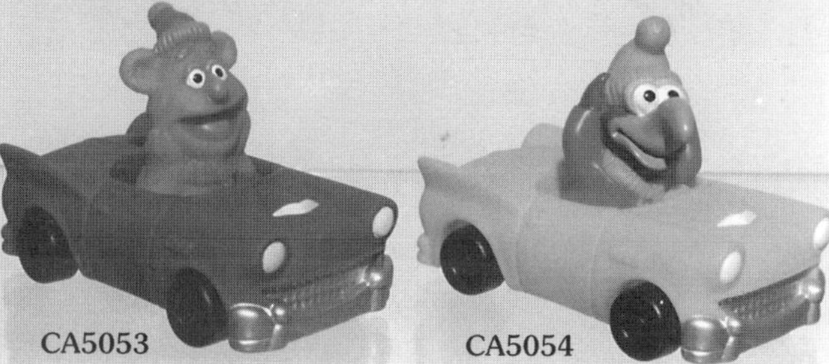

CA5053 CA5054

MUPPET PARADE OF STARS,

Hollow molded Muppet PVCs. Each was removable from its car.

CA5051 Kermit 3 - 5
CA5052 Miss Piggy 3 - 5
CA5053 Fozzy 3 - 5
CA5054 Gonzo 3 - 5

Sack

CA5056 Muppet Parade of Stars 1 - 2

MY PET MONSTER, 1986

Golden Look-Look books with the Carl's Jr. logo on the back cover. There may have been others in this series.

CA5271 Meet My Pet Monster 3 - 5
CA5272 My Pet Monster Goes to School 3 - 5

REAL GHOSTBUSTERS, 1991

A tie-in with *The Real Ghostbusters* and Halloween '91, Carl's distributed buckets and stickers as part of each Happy Star kid's meal.

CA5271 CA5272

CA6501 CA6502

CA6505

CA6501 Slimer bucket w/Slimer sticker 2 - 6
CA6502 Ghostbuster logo bucket w/Ghostbuster logo sticker 2 - 6

Point of Purchase

CA6505 Translite 15 - 30

REFRIGERATOR MAGNETS, 1988

Food items with large magnets on the back were the premiums in this Happy Star meal.

CA6761 Hamburger - notepad 3 - 5
CA6762 Hot Dog 3 - 5
CA6763 Fries - eraser 3 - 5
CA6764 Chocolate Chip Cookie - felt-tip pen 3 - 5

CA6761 CA6763 CA6764

CA6821 CA6823

CA6824 CA6825

REPTILE INFLATABLES, 1991

These vinyl inflatables were reptile-shaped, measuring 4"-8". This was one of the Carl's Jr. 50th anniversary promotions. The 50th Anniversary I.D. appeared on the premium bags.

CA6821	Alligator	2 - 4
CA6822	Snake	2 - 4
CA6823	Turtle	2 - 4
CA6824	Lizard	2 - 4
CA6825	Box	1 - 3
Point of Purchase		
CA6830	Translite	15 - 30

CA7002 CA7001 CA7003

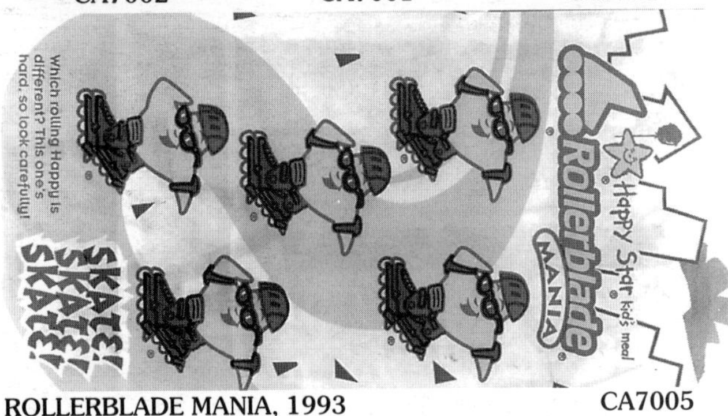

CA7005

ROLLERBLADE MANIA, 1993

Rollerblading was the theme for the varied array of premiums given in this Happy Star promotion.

CA7001	Roller-Cubes	2 - 5
CA7002	Safe Skatin' Happy	2 - 5
CA7003	Rollerblade Snap To It key chain	2 - 5
CA7004	The Rollerblade Chase Game Book	2 - 5
Sack		
CA7005	Rollerblade Mania	1 - 2
Point of Purchase		
CA7010	Translite	15 - 30

CA7262

SAND MOLDS, 1986

Brightly colored 7" plastic sand pails/buckets came with fish and seashell stickers. Each had a snap-in white handle.

CA7261	Yellow	2 - 3
CA7262	Blue	2 - 3
CA7263	Green	2 - 3

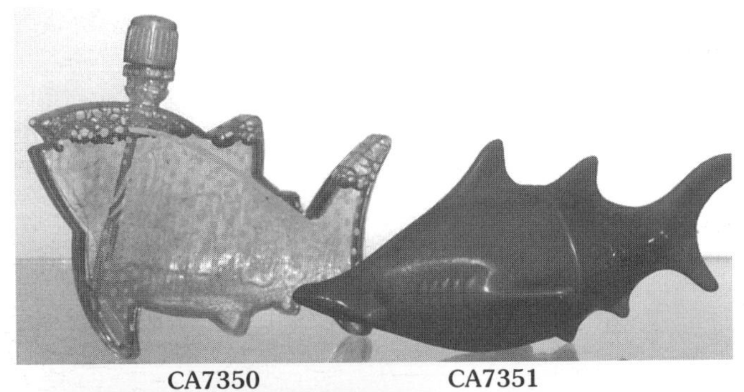

CA7350 CA7351

Trading cards from Shark!

Stikers from CA7351

CA7352 CA7353

SHARK!, 1993

Four shark-themed items were used for this promotion.

CA7350	Bubble Blower	3 - 5
CA7351	Hammerhead, purple w/Stickers	2 - 4
CA7352	Inflatable	2 - 4
CA7353	Cup w/top	2 - 4
Sack		
CA7360	Sack	1 - 2

A submarine takes Babar and his family under the English Channel to France.
BABAR'S WORLD TOUR
BABAR's Gondola Ride
BABAR'S WORLD TOUR
ARBY'S ADVENTURE MEAL
The back of this Arby's Adventure Meal Box shows a fun scene from Babar's World Tour!
ARBY'S ADVENTURE MEAL
LOONEY TUNES
"WHO'S KITTEN WHO?"
Duck Dodgers in the 24½th Century
Why don't we just follow the letters, S-S-Sir?
Good Knight Bugs Bunny
DOG-GONE WILD!
N-N-No!!! I don't want a dog! N-N-Now stay out of my corn field!
ARBY'S PRESENTS
HOLIDAY ADVENTURE MEAL WITH PUNCH-OUT GIFT TAGS
TIS THE SEASON TO BE JOLLY! FA-LA-LA-LA!
BAH HUMBUG
FUN N' GAMES
PORKY PIG'S PICTURE PUZZLE
TWEETY'S TWIDDLY WINKS
Gotcha this time, partner...
Beep Beep!
LOONEY TUNES MOUNTAIN LODGE
DRIVE-IN
NOW PLAYING
the Scarlet Pumpernickel
Daffy Duck
ACADEMY
BIG GAME SUNDAY!
LOONEY TUNES HOLIDAY
ARBY'S NEW ADVENTURE MEAL FEATURING
LOONEY TUNES FRIENDS
ICE CREAM PARLOR
WHIRRR
Arby's
YOUR LOONEY TUNES FRIENDS ARE HERE
MENU
Arby's Super
Beef n' Cheddar
Adventure Meal
Jamocha Shake
Potato Cakes
French Fries
BABAR'S WORLD TOUR
ADVENTURE MEAL
USA
BRAZIL
SOUTH POLE

BIRDFEEDER FUNMEAL Feast
Burger Chef
Replica Camaro Pace Car FUNMEAL Feast
CAMARO Z28
FUNMEAL FEAST
BURGERILLA LENDS A HAND
FANGBURGERS FUNHOUSE
BURGER CHEF & JEFF
In Days of Olde
THE GREAT BURGERINI MAGIC SHOW
MEAL BURGER CHEF & JEFF'S FUN
BLUEBURGER'S PIRATE CREW
BURGER CHEF & JEFF ON SAFARI
PAPER TIGER
CRASH OFFENBURGER RIDES AGAIN!
STAR WARS
TIE FIGHTER
DARTH VADER
CARD GAME
R2-D2 DROID PUPPET
FLIGHT
R2-D2 AND C-3PO ESCAPE FROM IMPERIAL WARSHIP VIA LIFE POD
FUNBURGER
HOTEL
SALOON
Surfchaser
FUN IS A FUNBURGER
SCHOOL BUS
Welcome to Fun Village Playland
ANTIQUES
George's Movers
FUN BURGER
PACE CAR
Burger Chef. KID RACER

Happy Star kid's meal
The Addams Family
Soccer Stars
Happy Star kid's meal
Where's Waldo?
StarRookies
ROSTER
Weird Science
Spooky Pails Sticker Sheet
Spooky Pails Sticker Sheet
Dig It
Cowabunga
A Snuggle & Read Story Book
Illustrated by Jared Lee
A Hippopotamus Ate the Teacher
by Mike Thaler
The Addams Family Mansion
The Addams Family
Camp
Carl's Jr.
Camp
Carl's Jr.
Circus Fantasy
Disneyland
Play Soc
1941-1991
StarRookies Sticker Sheet
StarRookies
StarRookies
StarRookies

Hardee's
THIS WEEK FEATURING
THE MYSTERIOUS ORIGIN OF
CAPTAIN AMERICA!
Hardee's
THIS WEEK FEATURING
THE MYSTERIOUS ORIGIN OF
The Amazing
SPIDER-MAN!
Hardee's
THIS WEEK FEATURING
THE MYSTERIOUS ORIGIN OF
SPIDER-WOMAN!
Hardee's
THIS WEEK FEATURING
THE MYSTERIOUS ORIGIN OF
FIRE-STAR!
Hardee's
THIS WEEK FEATURING
THE MYSTERIOUS ORIGIN OF
The Incredible HULK!
ENTER
3-D THEATRE
DAYS OF
Thunder
FUNMEAL PACK
Hardee's
Funmeal Pack
FENDER BENDER 500
Hardee's
SQUIRTERS
children's meal
Hardee's
HOME ALONe2
LOST IN NEW YORK
DUNCAN'S
Hardee's
Funmeal Pack
MARVEL
SUPER HEROES
LIL' BRO
SMURF
INSIDE
SMURF
CHILDREN'S MEAL
SMURF A Helping Hand To A Friend Today!
Hardee's
SMURF'S
Funmeal Pack
POOH
CORNER
Welcome
To Pooh
Corner
The Disney Channel
Fun with Hobbies!
A HONEY OF A HOBBY!
Pooh's main hobby is, of course, eating and dreaming about honey. Can you find the 12 pots of honey on this box?
Hardee's
CHILDREN'S MEAL
GOLDEN
The Little RED HEN
Who will help me plant this grain of wheat?
The POKY LITTLE PUPPY
Hardee's
CHILDREN'S MEAL
GOLDEN
Little Red Riding Hood
Somewhere on this box there are 3 forest animals hiding from the wolf. Can you find them?
. . . To Grandma's house I go!
The Three Little Pigs
POOH
CORNER
Welcome
To Pooh
Corner
The Disney Channel
Fun with Words!
SEEING DOUBLES
How many words can you make by adding a letter in front of and in back of the double O's?
P OO H
FunWheel
Welcome to Pooh Corner

SILLY PUTTY, 1993

Silly Putty was featured in this 1993 promotion. The plastic containers came in fluorescent colors. The bottom of the container could be used as a mold to stamp "Silly Putty" into the material.

CA7411	Yellow container	2 - 4
CA7412	Green container	2 - 4
CA7413	Orange container	2 - 4
Sack		
CA7419	Sack	1 - 2
Point of Purchase		
CA7420	Translite	10 - 20

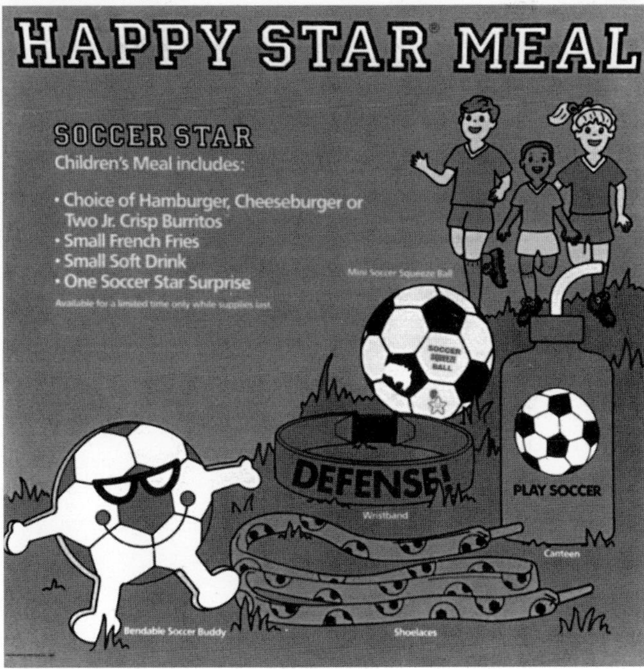

CA7540

SOCCER STAR, 1990

Soccer equipment provided the focus for this kid's meal promotion.

CA7535	Mini Soccer Squeeze Ball	2 - 4
CA7536	Wristband	1 - 3
CA7537	Canteen	3 - 6
CA7538	Shoelaces	2 - 4
CA7539	Bendable Soccer Buddy	3 - 6
Point of Purchase		
CA7540	Translite	10 - 20

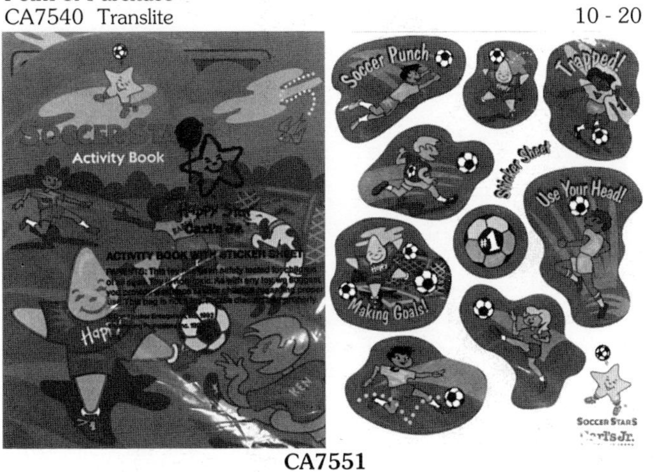

CA7551

SOCCER STARS, 1992

Happy Star was featured as a soccer player to largely repeat the popular 1990 theme.

CA7551	Activity Book w/Sticker Sheet	2 - 5
CA7552	Soccer Ball	2 - 5
CA7553	Shoelace Case w/Mini Laces	2 - 5
CA7554	Schedule Board w/Crayon	2 - 5
Sack		
CA7556	Soccer Stars	1 - 2

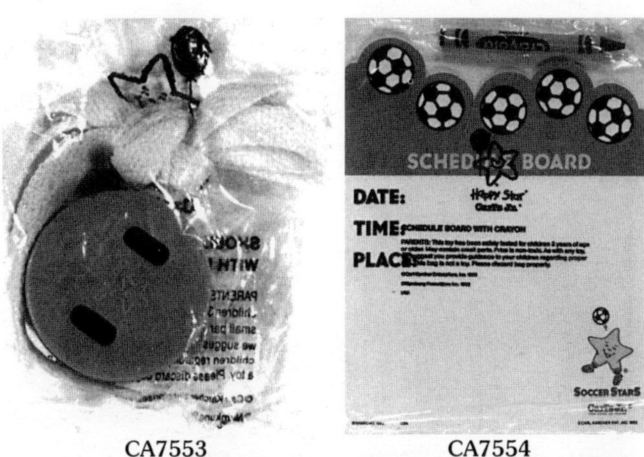

CA7553 CA7554

CA7556 CA7581 CA7582

SPOOKY PAILS, 1992

This Halloween promotion featured 6" diameter plastic pails with black handles and snap-on lids. The lids were molded to look as if slime was "dripping" over the sides. A set of stickers came with each pail.

CA7581	Orange pail w/green lid and stickers	2 - 4
CA7582	Purple pail w/black lid and stickers	2 - 4
Point of Purchase		
CA7590	Translite	10 - 20

CA7601 CA7602

STAR GAZERS, 1988

Telescoping eyeglasses which extended from 1½" to 2¾" were offered during this promotion. Each plastic eyepiece was marked with the Carl's Jr. logo.

CA7601	Blue	3 - 4
CA7602	Red	3 - 4
Point of Purchase		
CA7608	Translite	15 - 25

A HIPPOPOTAMUS ATE THE TEACHER

CA7611 CA7621

STAR OF THE CLASS, 1989

A variety of premiums to reward the "Star of the Class" were offered during this Happy Star back to school promotion.

CA7611	A Hippopotamus Ate the Teacher book	4 - 5
CA7612	Wrist Pouch	3 - 4
Point of Purchase		
CA7618	Translite	15 - 30

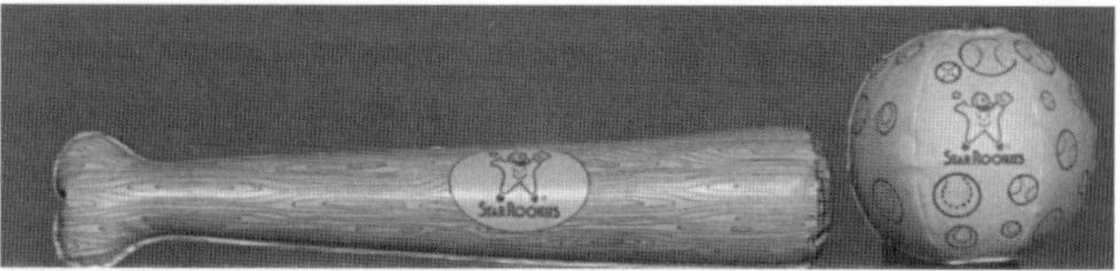

CA7632 CA7631

CA7634 CA7633

CA7638

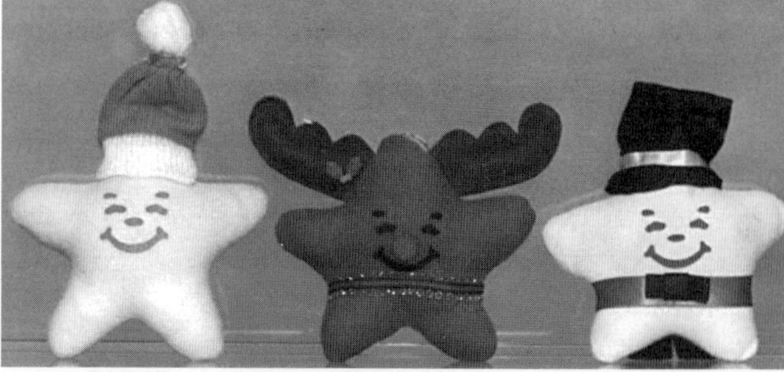
CA7651 CA7652 CA7653

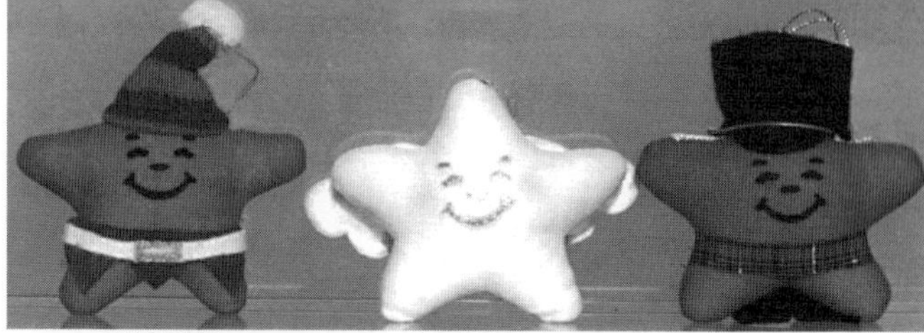
CA7654 CA7655 CA7657

CA7656 CA7664

CA7661 CA7662 CA7663

CA7670

CA7690

STAR RIDER

The license plate found indicates some sort of bike safety promotion.

CA7621	License plate	1 - 3

STAR ROOKIES, 1992

Baseball was the theme for this Happy Star offering. Two items were inflatable toys; the other two supplies for baseball card collecting.

CA7631	Inflatable Ball	2 - 5
CA7632	Inflatable Bat	2 - 5
CA7633	Baseball Card Holder w/Baseball Cards	2 - 5
CA7634	Baseball Card Frame w/Sticker Sheet	2 - 5
Sack		
CA7637	Star Rookies	
Point of Purchase		
CA7638	Translite	10 - 20

STARNAMENTS, 1990

Each 5" stuffed decorated felt star ornament was made of different colored felt with a different holiday accessory.

CA7651	Yellow Star w/stocking hat	2 - 6
CA7652	Tan Reindeer w/antlers	2 - 6
CA7653	White Snowman w/top hat, bow tie & tails	2 - 6
CA7654	Red Elf w/stocking hat	2 - 6
CA7655	White Angel w/wings	2 - 6
CA7656	White Chimney Sweep w/black hat & broom	2 - 6
CA7657	Red Toy Soldier	2 - 6
Point of Purchase		
CA7659	Translite	10 - 20

STARNAMENTS, 1991

This year's hanging stuffed felt stars had cloth tags attached and its own holiday trim.

CA7661	Anniversary Star, yellow w/1941-1991 banner	2 - 5
CA7662	Moose Star, brown w/antlers	2 - 5
CA7663	Holly Star, red w/holly	2 - 5

CA7681 CA7682

CA7683 CA7685 CA7684

CA7664	Twinkle Star, white w/ribbon wings	2 - 5

Point of Purchase

CA7670	Translite	10 - 20

STARNAMENTS, 1992

This year the hanging loop was red rather than gold. Each star had a unique decoration in keeping with the 1990 and 1991 versions.

CA7681	Angel Star, white w/halo & wings	2 - 5
CA7682	Mouse Star, gray w/red hat	2 - 5
CA7683	Toy Soldier Star, red w/drum & black hat	2 - 5
CA7684	Carol Star, yellow w/cap, candle & song book	2 - 5
CA7685	Snow Star, white w/red & green muffler & hat	2 - 5

Sack

CA7689	Starnaments	1 - 2

Point of Purchase

CA7690	Translite	15 - 20

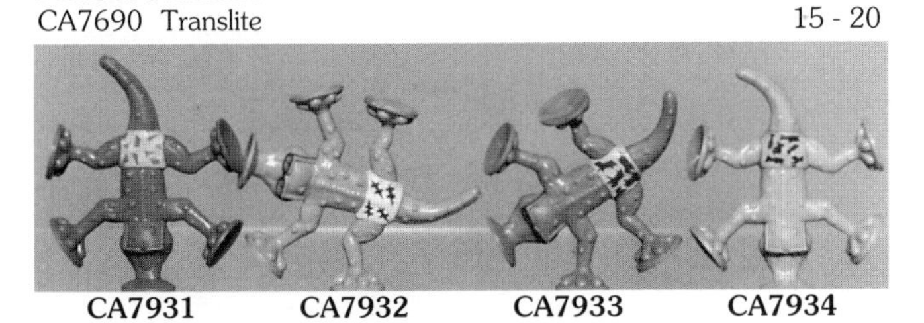

CA7931 CA7932 CA7933 CA7934

STUNT GRIP GECKOS, 1991

Gator-like rubber figures in shorts and sunglasses had suction cups on each foot and on their snouts. This promotion was run at White Castle and Dairy Queen the following year...and Carl's Jr. again in '94.

CA7931	Purple	2 - 4
CA7932	Blue	2 - 4
CA7933	Green	2 - 4
CA7934	Pink	2 - 4

Point of Purchase

CA7940	Translite	15 - 20

CA8913 CA8914

WEIRD SCIENCE, 1992

Scientific principles were illustrated and explained via the premiums used in this promotion.

CA8911	Frisbee	2 - 5
CA8912	Rainbow Stickers	2 - 5

CA8919 CA9021 CA9022

CA9023 CA9024

CA9026 CA9730

CA8913	Red Top w/covers	2 - 5
CA8914	Green Prism Viewer	2 - 5
CA8919	Weird Science sack	1 - 2

Point of Purchase

CA8920	Translite	15 - 20

WHERE'S WALDO, 1992

The popular "hiding" character was featured in this promotion. Hardee's did a similar promotion in the East using 4 straw buddies.

CA9021	Straw Buddy, PVC figure	2 - 5
CA9022	Pencil Watcher, PVC figure	2 - 5
CA9023	Booklet – Incredible Activity Kit	2 - 5
CA9024	Glow-in-the-Dark Switch Plate	2 - 5
CA9026	Where's Waldo? sack	1 - 2

Point of Purchase

CA9030	Translite	15 - 20

YOUNG EXECUTIVE

Every child could be like mom or dad with the premiums from this Happy Star Meal. The book was written and illustrated by Amy Schwartz. Each business card featured the Happy Star logo with space for writing the child's name and "title." These came with a plastic carrying case. "While You Were Out Playing" message Post-it Notes came with a standard pencil.

CA9721	Book, *Bea and Mr. Jones*	4 - 5
CA9722	Business Card Case w/Business Cards	4 - 5
CA9723	Post-it Notes & Pencil	4 - 5
CA9724	1990 Monthly Planner	4 - 5
Point of Purchase		
CA9730	Translite	20

CA9951 CA9955

CA9952 CA9953

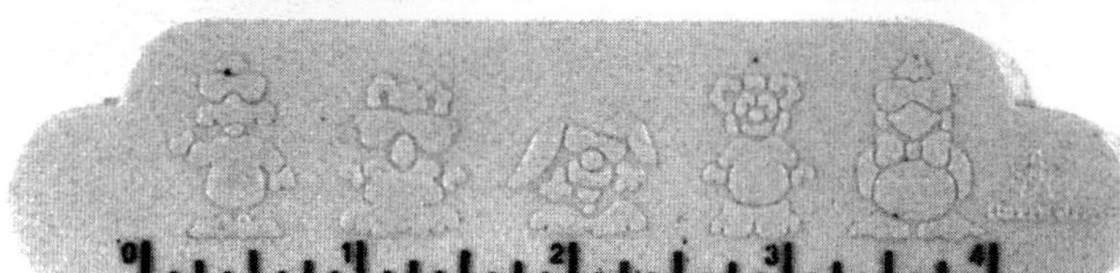

ZOO CREW, 1990

CA9954

Office/school supplies were issued during this kid's meal promotion; this offering had an animal theme. The vinyl pencil case had a ziplock closing and was marked in white ink with the Happy Star logo.

CA9951	Blue Bear Claw Pencil Case	3 - 4
CA9952	Clip w/Rabbit	3 - 4
CA9953	Clip w/Bear	3 - 4
CA9954	Ruler, purple or yellow	3 - 4
CA9955	Mini-Frisbee w/Stickers	3 - 4
Point of Purchase		
CA9960	Translite	15 - 20

CHICK-FIL-A

Chick-fil-A, headquartered in Atlanta, operates mainly mall locations in 31 states and free-standing Chick-fil-A Dwarf House restaurants in four Southern states. College campus and drive-thru only locations are also found. There is usually a new kid's meal each quarter, with nothing given when supplies run out. Premiums tend to be wholesome and occasionally have a moral bend. One cassette tape was recalled because of its "non-family" story theme. The name of the Chick-fil-A kid's promotion is the Nugget Meal.

CH0300 CH0301

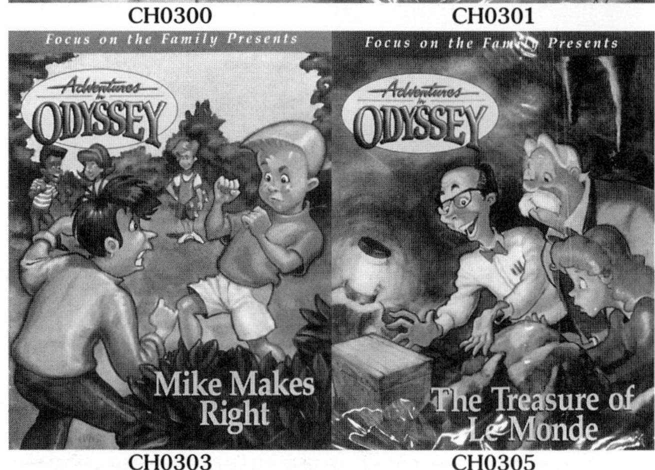

CH0303 CH0305

ADVENTURES IN ODYSSEY BOOKS, 1991

Booklets which contained story episodes involving kids and a special place called Whit's End were issued as premiums during this Nuggets Meal for Kids. Each 4" x 5" booklet contained 24 pages which had a story with a positive value lesson printed on the left hand page. Storyline drawings to be colored were on the facing page.

CH0300	All's Well With Boswell	2 - 3
CH0301	Isaac the Courageous	2 - 3
CH0302	Suspicious Minds	2 - 3
CH0303	Mike Makes Right	2 - 3
CH0304	A Matter of Obedience	2 - 3
CH0305	The Treasure of Le Monde	2 - 3
CH0306	Last Great Adventure of Summer	2 - 3

CH0321 CH0322 CH0323

ADVENTURES IN ODYSSEY CASSETTE TAPES, 1993

Audio tapes produced by Focus on the Family of Colorado Springs promoting similar video tapes by mail. The tape "Father's Day" was pulled because it dealt with a divorced father.

CH0324 CH0325 CH0326

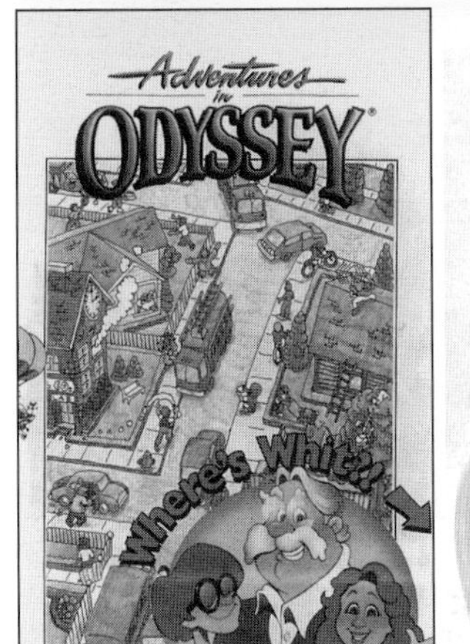

CH0330

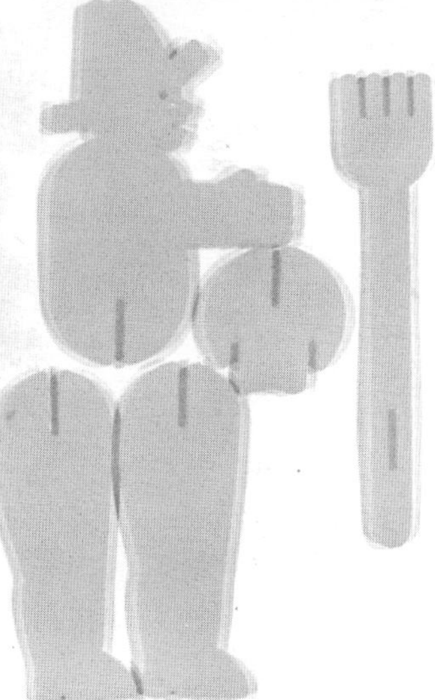

CH0901

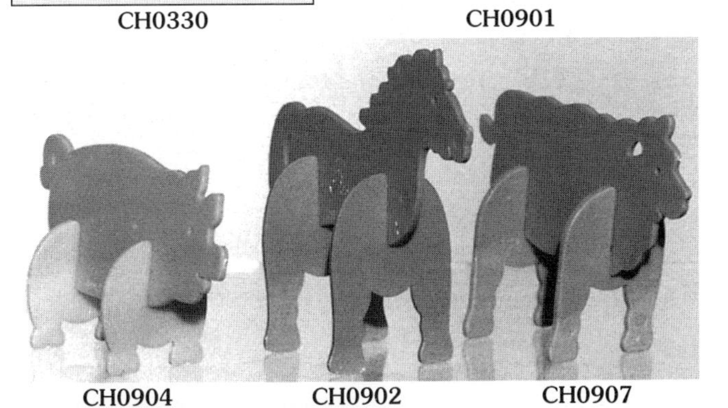

CH0904 CH0902 CH0907

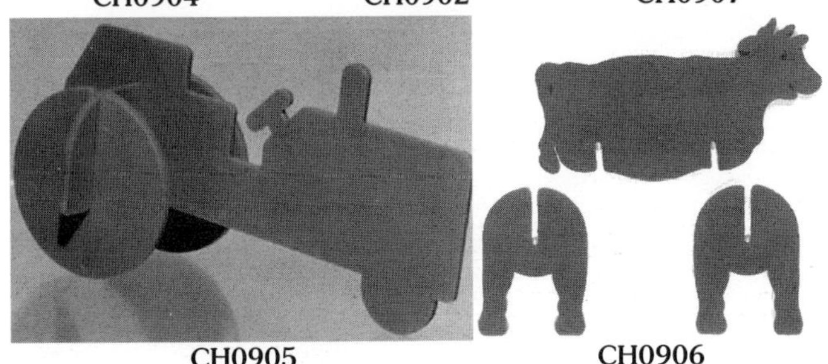

CH0905 CH0906

CH0321	The Ill-Gotten Deed	2 - 4
CH0322	This Is Chad Pearson?	2 - 4
CH0323	Wishful Thinking	2 - 4
CH0324	A Test for Robyn	2 - 4
CH0325	Father's Day	3 - 6
CH0326	Suspicious Minds	2 - 4
CHO310	Where's Whit? Sack	1 - 2

BARNYARD BUDDIES, 1992

The farm became the focus during this promotion. Solid-color plastic pieces had slots cut into them so the 2-4 pieces slid onto a main body shape to create an animal or farm necessity. The body of each premium was imprinted with the Chick-fil-A logo.

CH0908

CH0901	Farmer	1 - 4
CH0902	Horse	1 - 4
CH0903	Goat	1 - 4
CH0904	Pig	1 - 4
CH0905	Tractor	1 - 4
CH0906	Cow	1 - 4
CA0907	Sheep	1 - 4
Box		
CA0908	Barn	1 - 3

CH1101 CH1102

CH1103 CH1104

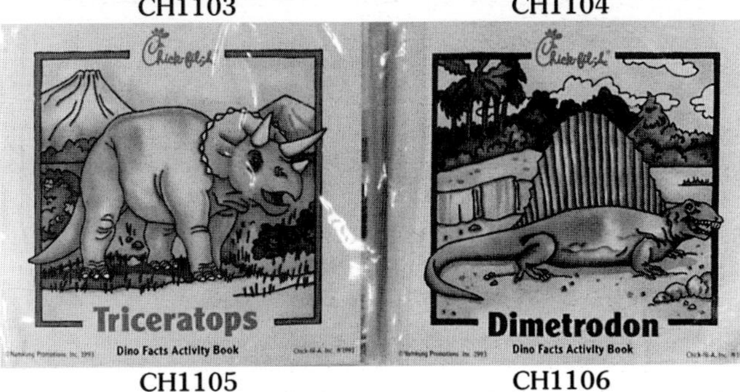

CH1105 CH1106

BLOCK-A-SAURUS, 1994

This promotion included a series of six dinosaur "kits" comprised of embossed flat plastic pieces. Each one included a folder with facts about the dinosaur and a painted background for the prize.

CH1101	Brachlosaurus	3 - 4
CH1102	Tyrannosaurus	3 - 4
CH1103	Parasaurolophus	3 - 4
CH1104	Stegosaurus	3 - 4

CH1110 CH1303 CH1304

CH1301 CH1302 CH1305

CH1310 CH1311

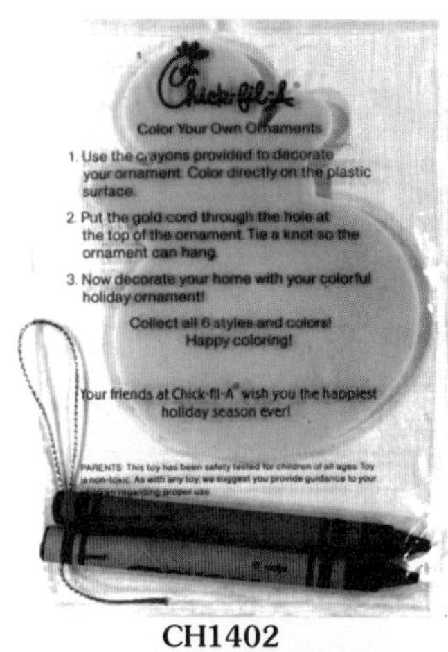

CH1402

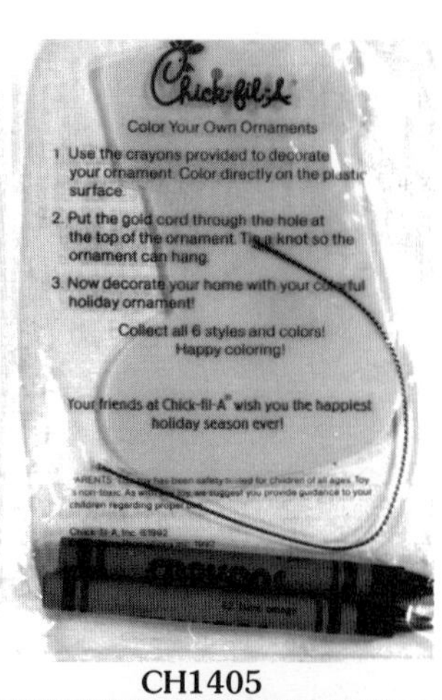

CH1405

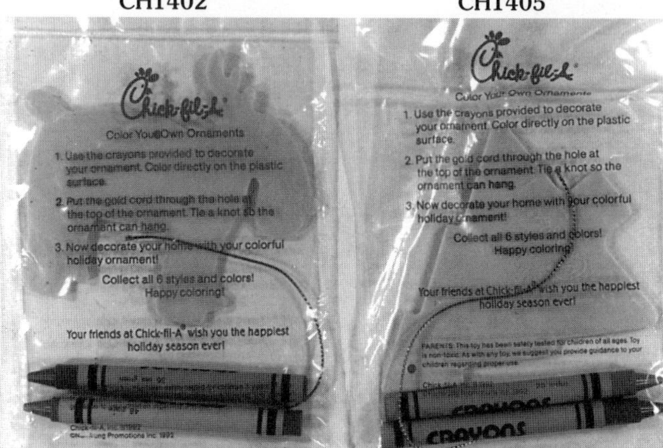

CH1403 CH1406

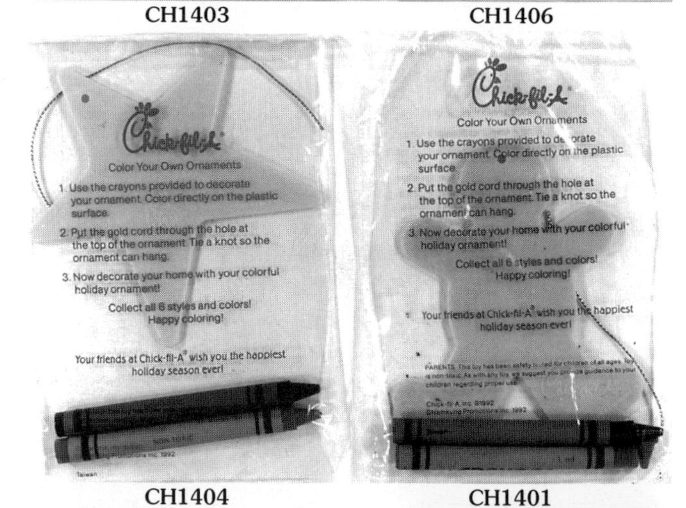

CH1404 CH1401

CH1105	Triceratops	3 - 4
CH1106	Dimetrodon	3 - 4
CH1110	Sack	1 - 2

THE BUSY WORLD OF RICHARD SCARRY, 1993

A sand pail, 2 sand tools, and 3 sand molds were used for this ambitious program.

CH1300	Beach Bucket	2 - 4
CH1301	Huckle Cat Shovel	3 - 6
CH1302	Lowly Worm Rake	3 - 6
CH1303	Hilda Hippo mold	3 - 6
CH1304	Sergeant Murphy mold	3 - 6
CH1305	Mr. Fumble mold	3 - 6
Point of Purchase		
CH1310	Translite	15 - 25
CH1311	Display	25 - 50

CHICKEN LITTLE STORY BOOK

A special version of this item from the Grosset & Dunlap Pudgy Pal Board Book series was printed with the Chick-fil-A logo on the back.

CH1350	Chicken Little story book	4 - 6

COLOR YOUR OWN ORNAMENTS, 1992

This Christmastime offering had "color yourself" plastic ornaments in various holiday shapes. Each 4" premium was a different solid color with the Chick-fil-A logo and came with 2 crayons – no 2 colors the same in any premium package.

CH1401	Gingerbread Man	1 - 4
CH1402	Snowman	1 - 4

CH1350

CH1408

CH1510

CH1403	Reindeer	1 - 4
CH1404	Star	1 - 4
CH1405	Stocking	1 - 4
CH1406	Christmas Tree	1 - 4

Sack

CH1408	Sack showing all 6 ornaments	1 - 2

DOODLES KID'S CUPS

A set of four cups depicting animals at play.

CH1501	Camping scene	2 - 3
CH1502	Playground scene	2 - 3
CH1503	Fitness scene	2 - 3
CH1504	Sidewalk scene	2 - 3

Point of Purchase

CH1510	Display	20 - 30

CH2201 CH2202

IT'S A KID'S WORLD, 1988

Two boxes have been found from this promotion.

CH2201	Journey Across the World	4 - 6
CH2202	The Kids of America	4 - 6

NOAH'S ARK, 1991

For this promotion, stock slotted animals were featured. The box designed for this offering folded out into the shape of the ark.

CH2800	Monkey	2 - 4
CH2801	Giraffe	2 - 4
CH2802	Elephant	2 - 4
CH2803	Zebra	2 - 4
CH2804	Lion	2 - 4
CH2805	Hippopotamus	2 - 4
CH2806	Ostrich	2 - 4
CH2807	Water Buffalo	2 - 4

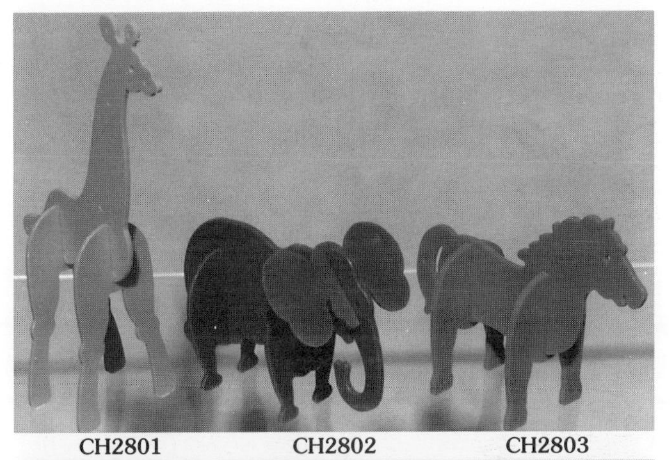

CH2801 CH2802 CH2803

CH2805 CH2806 CH2807

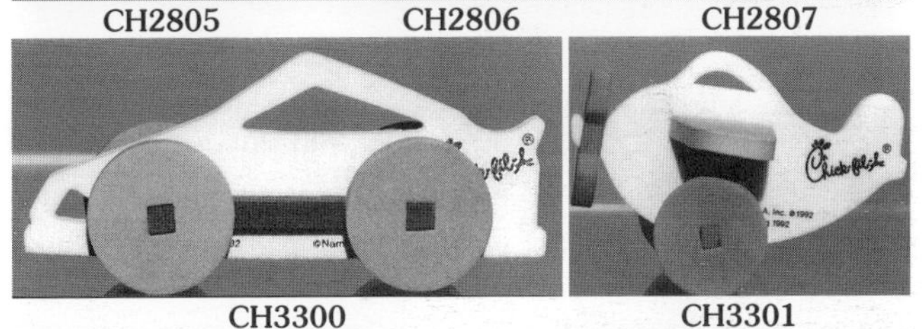

CH3300 CH3301

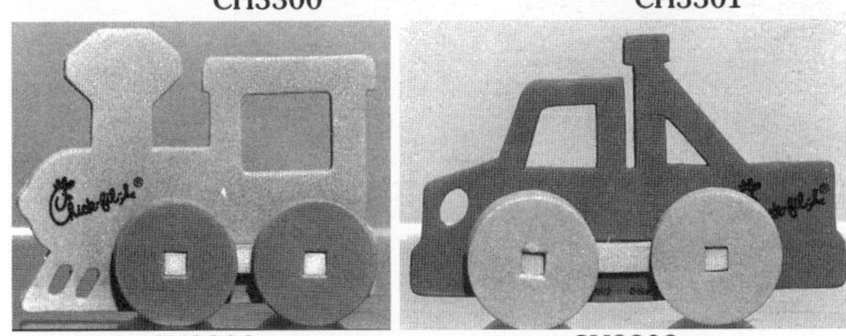

CH3302 CH3303

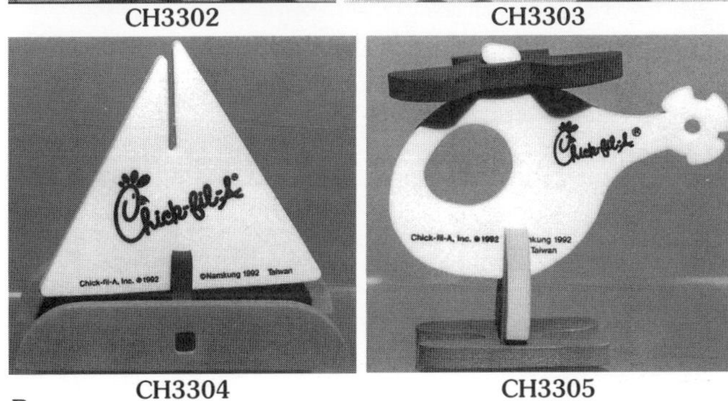

CH3304 CH3305

Box

CH2810	Noah's Ark	3 - 5

ON THE GO, 1993

Multi-colored interlocking foam pieces fit together to form different modes of transportation were issued as premiums. There were many color combinations for each of the premiums. The body of each was imprinted in black ink with the Chick-fil-A logo.

CH3300	Car	1 - 3
CH3301	Plane	1 - 3
CH3302	Train	1 - 3
CH3303	Truck	1 - 3
CH3304	Boat	1 - 3
CH3305	Helicopter	1 - 3

SCHOOL SUPPLIES, 1992
Assorted school-related items made up this promotion.

CH5501	Green ruler/stencil	1 - 3
CH5502	Purple sticker case w/sticker pad	1 - 3
CH5503	Blue vinyl pencil case	1 - 3

DAIRY QUEEN BRAZIER
There are two types of Dairy Queen outlets – one serves mainly ice cream products, while Dairy Queen Brazier units expand on the original concept to serve a variety of fast food meals. Usually only the Brazier stores sell a Treatmeal® which includes collectible toys. There are national programs, but stores may be offering a variety of prizes at any given time. Even when a national promotion runs, distribution is very uneven. Boxes and sacks have been used over the years. Four characters were developed in the early '90s for use in treatmeal packages. They are "The Flavor Friends" — Butterscotch Beaver, Chocolate Chimp, Strawbeary Bear, and Marshmallo Moose. The Dairy Queen Corporation had previously used newspaper comics star Dennis the Menace on sacks, paper cups and other items used for special kid's meal promotions. He was revived in 1993 after several years' absence. Sometimes boxes and sacks were used for the same promotion. Boxes were used until the supply was exhausted, then sacks until the promotion was concluded.

DA0402

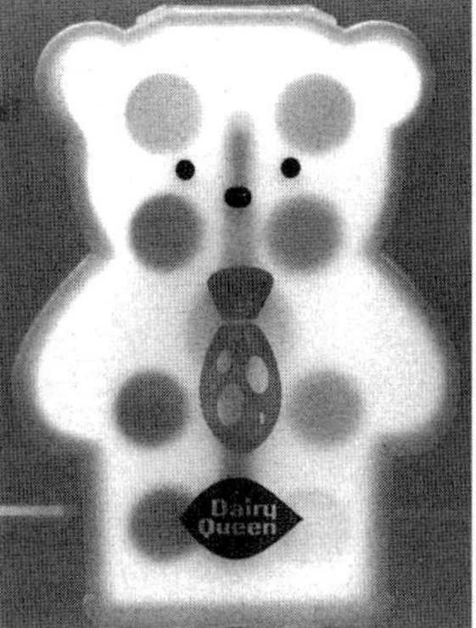

DA0521

BALLS, 1993
Two colorful balls were issued during the year.

DA0401	Hackeysack ball	1 - 3
DA0402	Bloom Ball	1 - 3

BEAR PAINT SET, 1993
A 5" translucent plastic case in the shape of a teddy bear opened to reveal a set of 8 water color paints. A similar set without the Dairy Queen logo was sold in retail toy outlets.

Premium

DA0521	Paint Set	3 - 5

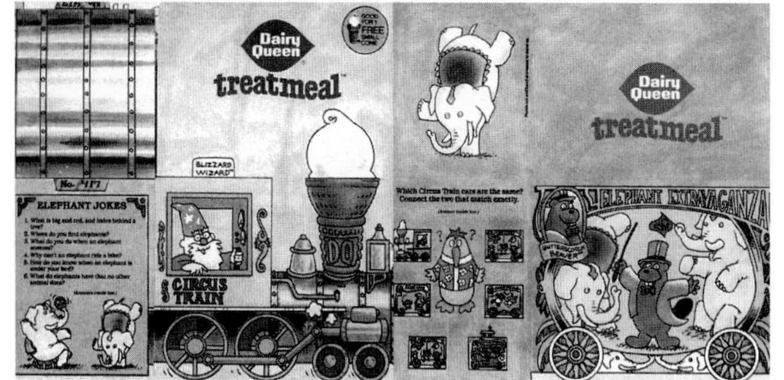

DA1271 DA1272

CIRCUS TRAIN
For this treatmeal™, the box itself became the premium. Each box was a portion of a circus train and featured various punch-outs, jokes, and games to be completed. A different Dairy Queen character was featured on each box. In the upper right corner of the handle portion of each box was a punch-out circle good for 1 free small cone.

Boxes

DA1271	Blizzard Wizard/Engine	3 - 5
DA1272	Butterscotch Beaver/Elephant Extravaganza	3 - 5
DA1273	Chocolate Chimp/Death Defying Daredevils	3 - 5

DA1273 DA1274

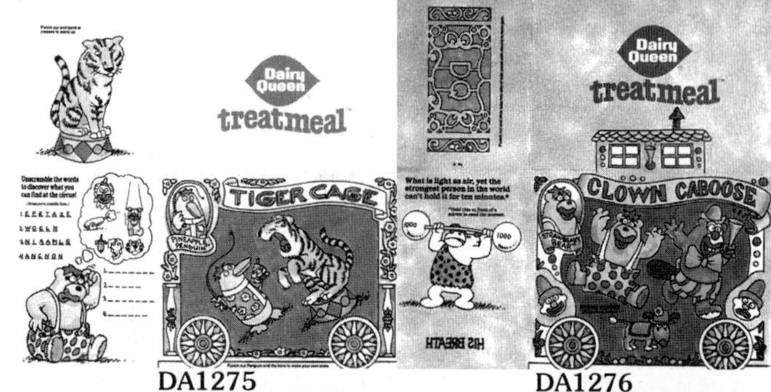

DA1275 DA1276

DA1553 DA1551 DA1554 DA1552

DA1274	Marshmallo Moose/Circus Sideshow	3 - 5
DA1275	Pineapple Penguin/Tiger Cage	3 - 5
DA1276	Strawbeary Bear/Clown Caboose	3 - 5

DENNIS THE MENACE, 1993
To coincide with the June 25th release of the movie *Dennis the Menace*, the premiums for this promotion featured the main characters: Dennis, Joey, Margaret and Ruff. Silk-screened on 6" white cups were at least 3 different cartoon scenes: Dennis water-skiing; Dennis carrying a sundae with Joey and Ruff; and Dennis, Joey and Margaret on bellyboards. Unique 3-D molded plastic character heads were used as snap-on lids for the cups.

DA1551	Dennis, yellow	3 - 6
DA1552	Joey, pink	3 - 6

DA1571 DA1572

DA1573

DA1574

DA1553	Ruff, blue	3 - 6
DA1554	Margaret, pink	3 - 6

DENNIS THE MENACE, 1994

Two cars and two PVC figures with snap-on costumes we used.

DA1571	Dennis Fire Engine	1 - 3
DA1572	Joey Hot Rod	1 - 3
DA1573	Ruff w/costume	1 - 3
DA1574	Margaret w/Astronaut suit	1 - 3

DENNIS THE MENACE COLORING PUZZLES, 1993

Six-piece framed puzzles of Dennis the Menace cartoons with a box of four crayons included with each.

DA1601	Bowling	1 - 2
DA1602	On Jungle Jim	1 - 2
DA1603	Golfing	1 - 2
DA1604	In Row Boat	1 - 2

DINOCARDZ COLLECTOR CARDS, 1993

A set of 26 dinosaur cards, in packs of 5 cards were given.

DA1610	Cards 1-26	1 - 2

DA1623 DA1622

DA1624 DA1621

DQ KIDS

Western characters were issued as "Bendies" in this early promotion.

DA1621	Bad Guy	10 - 15
DA1622	Cowboy	10 - 15
DA1623	Horse	10 - 15
DA1624	Girl	10 - 15

EYE LINERS, 1991

Stiff plastic tubing was shaped into eye glasses. These came with 2 pieces of flexible, clear rubber tubing. When properly connected, one could sip through 1 piece of the rubber tubing and have the liquid travel up through the other piece of rubber tubing, through the eye glass tubing and into the mouth. Wendy's offered a similar premium in their "Funsips" promotion.

DA2271	Glasses	2 - 4

FELT TIP PENS, 1991

Plastic felt tip pens were issued during this promotion. Each 8" pen had a white cap and "Dairy Queen" printed on the barrel.

DA2401	Red barrel pen	2 - 4
DA2402	Brown barrel pen	2 - 4

FLEXIBLOCKS, 1993

Two sets of seven Flexiblocks were used. a similar promotion was used by White Castle

DA2451	4 green/3 yellow	1 - 3
DA2452	4 blue/3 red	1 - 3

DA2501 DA2502

FUNBUNCH FLYERS

Each flying disk had an animal's face imprinted on the top with the character's name imprinted along the lower rim. The Dairy Queen logo also appeared on the disk.

DA2501	Chompanzee	2 - 4
DA2502	Hungrizzly	2 - 4

HAND PUPPETS, 1991

One side of these hand puppets was clear vinyl with the character printed against a white background on the other side.

DA3071	Strawbeary Bear	1 - 2
DA3072	Marshmallow Moose	1 - 2
DA3073	Butterscotch Beaver	1 - 2

HEART CASES, 1994

Plastic heart-shaped cases with heart shaped inside were given.

DA3151	Red Heart	1 - 3
DA3152	Blue Heart	1 - 3
DA3153	Yellow Heart	1 - 3

DA3311 DA3312 DA3313 DA3314

HOLIDAY BENDIES, 1993

Three and one half-inch tall rubber bendie figures of two reindeer and two Santas were given in these holiday meals.

DA3311	Reindeer with Yellow Bell/Green Mittens	2 - 4
DA3312	Reindeer with Green Scarf/White Mittens	2 - 4
DA3313	Santa, Eyes Closed	2 - 4
DA3314	Santa, Eyes Opened	2 - 4

DA3371

DA4301

DA3903 DA3904 DA3901

INFLATABLE BEACH BALL

The Dairy Queen logo appeared on an inflatable beach ball.

DA3371	Beach Ball, red, blue and white	3 - 4

KRAZY FORK, KNIFE, AND SPOON, 1993

Squiggly plastic tableware sets, molded in four different colors.

DA3901	Shocking Pink	1 - 3
DA3902	Aqua Green	1 - 3
DA3903	Regal Purpal	1 - 3
DA3904	Turquoise Blue	1 - 3

MAGIC SPRING, 1993

A rainbow-colored slinky toy, suction ball, and cup were given.

DA4301	Magic Spring, Suction Ball, or Cup, each	2 - 4

MIX 'N' MATCH DINOS, 1993

Four prehistoric rubber take-apart dinosaurs with "Dairy Queen" printed in white on the bottom of one foot. The promotion was also used by Denny's, Carl's Jr., and White Castle.

DA4881	Pterry — Yellow	2 - 4
DA4882	Bronto — Green	2 - 4
DA4883	Rex — Purple	2 - 4
DA4884	Steggy — Pink	2 - 4

DA5701

NOISE MAKERS, 1993

A 3" plastic cylinder with end caps housed a noise maker which made a duck-like sound when shaken. This premium came in iridescent colors with a large Dairy Queen logo on the side.

DA5701	Green	2 - 4

DA5949 (as robot and number)

NUMBER TRANSFORMERS, 1993

Simple 2" x 2" numeric cubes transformed into robots and came in three colors.

DA5941	#1	2 - 4
DA5942	#2	2 - 4
DA5943	#3	2 - 4
DA5944	#4	2 - 4
DA5945	#5	2 - 4
DA5946	#6	2 - 4
DA5947	#7	2 - 4
DA5948	#8	2 - 4
DA5949	#9	2 - 4
DA5950	#10	2 - 4

DA6671 DA6672 DA6673

PICTIONARY, 1991

The adult drawing/guessing game was simplified into a child's version for this treatmeal® promotion. Each premium pack included several pieces which made up the game.

DA6671	Butterscotch Beaver Moon Adventure	1 - 4
DA6672	Marshmallo Moose Blizzard Adventure	1 - 4
DA6673	Strawbeary Bear Circus Adventure	1 - 4

DA6701 DA6702

PLAYING CARDS, 1993

A variation on the popular children's card game, Old Maid, was created using Dennis the Menace characters and DQ food items. All pieces punched out of a cardboard strip which also included a put-together box for holding the miniature cards.

DA6701	A•B•C Flash Cards	2 - 3
DA6702	Fish	2 - 3
DA6703	Crazy Eights	2 - 3
DA6704	Old Maid	2 - 3

DA6703 DA6704

DA6722 DA6741

PLUSH FLAVOR FRIENDS, 1985

Plush stuffed animals of the Flavor Friends were offered in 1985. These 5" characters came with a paper sticker which showed the name of the character. Some materials are different.

DA6721	Butterscotch Beaver	4 - 6
DA6722	Marshmallo Moose	4 - 6
DA6723	Strawbeary Bear	4 - 6
DA6724	Chocolate Chimp	4 - 6

PLUSH FLAVOR FRIENDS, 1991

Plush 5" stuffed dolls of the Flavor Friends were again issued in 1991 with the kid's meal.

DA6731	Butterscotch Beaver	6 - 8
DA6732	Marshmallo Moose	6 - 8
DA6733	Strawbeary Bear	6 - 8
DA6734	Chocolate Chimp	6 - 8

PLUSH KANGACHEW, 1990

A stuffed kangachew was offered in 1990. The character wears a bandanna and has a red Dairy Queen logo appeared on its pouch.

DA6741	Kangachew	5 - 7

POP ROCKETS, 1993

Plastic 3-piece rockets came with color decals of DQ characters. As the plunger was pushed down, the top section of the rocket flew off.

DA6791	Strawbeary Bear, yellow	1 - 3
DA6792	Marshmallo Moose, red	1 - 3
DA6793	Butterscotch Beaver, blue	1 - 3

PRISMASCOPE, 1991

Spyglass-shaped viewers in four colors which had a prismatic lens were premiums for this promotion.

DA6851	Red Viewer	2 - 4

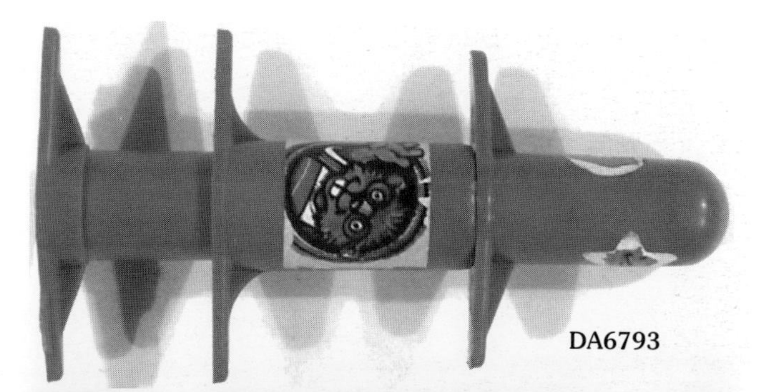

DA6793

DA6853 DA6952

DA6852	Blue Viewer	2 - 4
DA6853	Yellow Viewer	2 - 4
DA6854	Green Viewer	2 - 4

PULLBACK RACERS, 1993

Premiums offered here were 1½" pullback plastic cars with the Dairy Queen logo on the roof.

DA6951	Red Racer	2 - 4
DA6952	Powder Blue Racer	2 - 4
DA6953	Pink Racer	2 - 4
DA6954	Yellow Racer	2 - 4
DA6955	Light Green Racer	2 - 4
DA6956	White Racer	2 - 4

DA7215

RADIO FLYER, 1991

Miniature 4" red plastic Radio Flyer wagons were distributed in a promotion in conjunction with the release of the movie *Radio Flyer*. The Dairy Queen version has the logo on only one side of the wagon.

DA7215	Wagon	4 - 7

DA7271 DA7272 DA7273

REFRIGERATOR MAGNETS, 1991

Each magnet had its own shape and a picture of a different character. A banner over the character had its name and the DQ logo.

DA7271	Strawbeary Bear	2 - 4
DA7272	Marshmallo Moose	2 - 4
DA7273	Chocolate Chimp	2 - 4
DA7274	Butterscotch Beaver	2 - 4

DA7401 DA7402 DA7403

DA7404 DA7405 DA7406

DA7408 DA7409

ROCK-A-DOODLE, 1992

Characters from the animated film *Rock-A-Doodle* were featured as 2½"-3¾" PVC figures.

DA7401	Patou the Dog	3 - 6
DA7402	Edmond the Cat	3 - 6
DA7403	Chanticleer the Rooster	3 - 6
DA7404	The Grand Duke of Owl	3 - 6
DA7405	Peepers the Mouse	3 - 6
DA7406	Snipes the Magpie	3 - 6
Sacks		
DA7408	Chanticleer on car	1 - 3
DA7409	Chanticleer on hay mound	1 - 3

ROCKIN' TOPPERS, 1993

Soft rubber pencil topper with a gummy, clinging surface. These came in four colors: green, blue, yellow, and orange, and walk down a wall.

DA7430 DA7621 DA7622 DA7623

DA7430	Rockin' Topper	1 - 3

SIDEWALK CHALK, 1992

Pieces of chalk embossed with the shape of Flavor Friends faces.

DA7621	Marshmallo Moose	1 - 4
DA7622	Chocolate Chimp	1 - 4
DA7623	Strawbeary Bear	1 - 4

DA7651 DA7652 DA7653

SILLY PUTTY, 1991

Containers of Silly Putty with Flavor Friends mold tops.

DA7651	Chocolate Chimp, green	2 - 4
DA7652	Marshmallo Moose, blue	2 - 4
DA7653	Strawbeary Bear, pink	2 - 4

SPORTS BANDS, 1993

Terry cloth sports bands with the Dairy Queen logo.

DA7841	Headband, green	1 - 2
DA7842	Wristband, blue	1 - 2

STICKERLAND DINOSAUR STICKER PUZZLES

Color stickers which could be assembled to form a dinosaur picture.

DA7901	Apatosaurus	1 - 2
DA7902	Euoplocephalus	1 - 2
DA7903	Triceratops	1 - 2

DA7921 DA7923

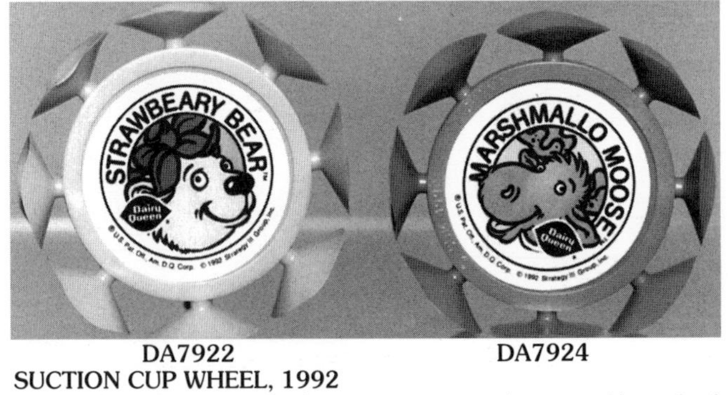

DA7922 DA7924

SUCTION CUP WHEEL, 1992

The Ninja throwing star idea was incorporated into a rubber wheel with 8 suction cups all the around. Each Flavor Friend had its own color disk featured on the center sticker.

DA7921 Chocolate Chimp, green 2 - 4
DA7922 Strawbeary Bear, red 2 - 4
DA7923 Butterscotch Beaver, yellow 2 - 4
DA7924 Marshmallo Moose, blue 2 - 4

SUMMER SPORTSBAND

Terrycloth sportsbands were offered in this promotion.

DA8001 Wristband 1 - 2
DA8002 Headband 1 - 2

DA8151

DA8152

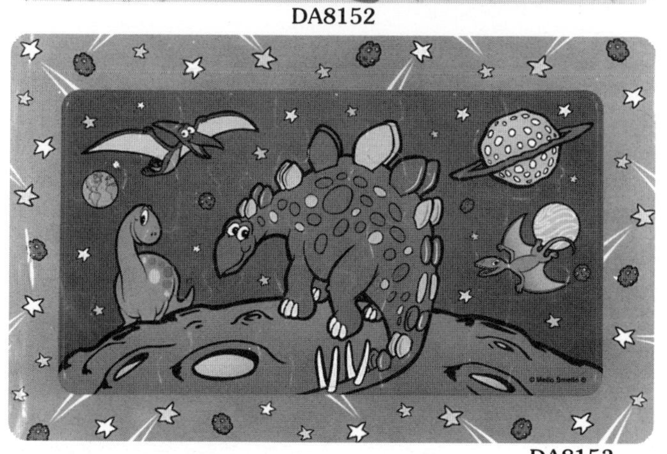

DA8153

SUPERSAURUS PUZZLES, 1993

Five by eight inch 15 piece cardboard tray puzzle with pictures of colorful cartoon dinosaur scenes made by Mello Smello.

DA8151 Purple Border 1 - 2
DA8152 Yellow Border 1 - 2
DA8153 Blue Border 1 - 2

TOM & JERRY, 1993

Tom and Jerry were featured during this national promotion which coincided with the July release of the new Tom & Jerry movie. A pair of stampers, 2 pull-back racers, and 2 squirters were used.

DA8351 Sizzling Stamper, Tom 2 - 5
DA8352 Sizzling Stamper, Jerry 2 - 5
DA8353 Summer Cruiser, Tom 2 - 5

DA8356 DA8355 DA8351 DA8352 DA8353 DA8354

DA8354 Summer Cruiser, Jerry 2 - 5
DA8355 Squirter, Tom 2 - 5
DA8356 Squirter, Jerry 2 - 5

Sack

DA8360 Tom & Jerry 1 - 3

DA8360 DA9846 DA9847

TRAIN SET, 1993

Train set of 4 cars. A similar set was used by White Castle and Sonic. This version was red and white with the Dairy Queen Logo.

DA7931 Engine 4 - 5
DA7932 Coal Car 4 - 5
DA7933 Box Car 4 - 5
DA7934 Caboose 4 - 5

UNDERWATER FUN, 1994

An activities booklet featuring an underwater theme and stickers.

DA9501 Activity book w/sticker sheet 1 - 2

DA9849 DA9850

MISCELLANEOUS TREATMEAL PREMIUMS, SACKS & BOXES

The following items are known to exist.

DA9846 Kangachew sticker set 1 - 2
DA9847 Hungrizzley sticker set 1 - 2

DA9851

DA9852 DA9853

DA9854 DA9855

DA9849 Treatmeal sack 1 - 2
DA9850 Treatmeal sack, memory game 1 - 2
DA9851 Pineapple Penguin's Wheel of Neat Treats 1 - 3
DA9852 Jungle Match 1 - 3
DA9853 Riddle Rhyme 1 - 3
DA9854 Funbunch Munch (air) 1 - 3
DA9855 Funbunch Munch (water) 1 - 3

DENNY'S

This national chain of sit-down restaurants has had a short and varied record with kid's meal premiums. The concept has been tinkered with and has evidently not produced the desired results. This successful technique has been re-written to work for a broader restaurant. Yearly rather than monthly themes are used. New premium items average more like one a month rather than one a week. They have been designed around presenting the kid's menu rather than a traffic building, and have lacked the variety and new interest power to be successful...but they have done some great premiums, especially for collectors interested in the Flintstones (used the two major years of kid's meal experimentation) and the Jetsons (used in 1992).

ADVENTURE SEEKERS, 1993

This promotion was used for the entire year of 1993. It consisted of a vinyl pouch; an 8-page booklet with a kid's menu, facts and games, and a birthday club application; and a paper toy. Each pouch was used for about five weeks.

DE1001 The Mysterious Madame X/Secret Spy Decoder 1 - 3
DE1002 Out of This World/Paint a Postcard 1 - 3
DE1003 Diggin' the Dinosaurs/Dinosaur sticker sheet 1 - 3
DE1004 Mystery of the Mummy's Message/Red lens charm 1 - 3
DE1005 Trouble in Transylvania/Create-a-Costume game 1 - 3
DE1006 Red Beard's Revenge/Magic Treasure Finder 1 - 3
DE1007 Trouble in Rattlesnake Gulch/Motion Maker 1 - 3
DE1008 The Lost Tribe Trek/Indian Stickers 1 - 3
DE1009 Spellbound/Spellbound Specs 1 - 3
DE1010 Legend of the Lamp/Create-a-Genie Stickers 1 - 3

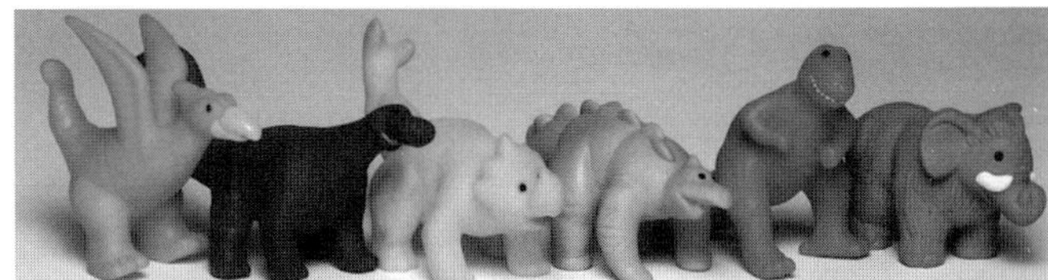

DE1821 DE1823 DE1822 DE1825 DE1826 DE1824

DINO-MAKERS, 1991

These rubber creatures had 2 or 3 pull-apart body pieces. All pieces were interchangeable with other premiums in the series, so many unusual variations could be created. Versions of this promotion were also used by Carl's Jr., Dairy Queen, and White Castle.

DE1821 Pterodactyl, orange 1 - 3
DE1822 Triceratops, yellow 1 - 3
DE1823 Brontosaurus, blue 1 - 3
DE1824 Woolly Mammoth, purple 1 - 3
DE1825 Stegosaurus, lime green 1 - 3
DE1826 Tyrannosaurus, fuchsia 1 - 3

FLINTSTONES DINO-RACERS, 1991

Tiny turnable Flintstone figures on top of pullback creatures.

DE2301 Fred on a Tor-Toi-Saurus 2 - 4
DE2302 Barney on a purple dinosaur 2 - 4

DE1001

DE1002

DE1003

DE1004

DE1005

DE1006

DE1007

DE1008

DE1009

DE1010

DE2301 DE2302 DE2303

DE2304 DE2305 DE2306

DE2303	Betty on a blue dinosaur	2 - 4
DE2304	Pebbles on an aqua triceratops	2 - 4
DE2305	Bamm-Bamm on a yellow dinosaur	2 - 4
DE2306	Dino on a woolly mammoth	2 - 4

DE2331 DE2332 DE2333 DE2334 DE2335 DE2336

FLINTSTONES FUN SQUIRTERS, 1991

Six rubber squirters in the shape of a Flintstones character's head were offered during this promotion.

DE2331	Fred w/phone	1 - 4
DE2332	Barney w/wrist-sundial	1 - 4
DE2333	Wilma w/camera	1 - 4
DE2334	Pebbles w/swim ring	1 - 4
DE2335	Bamm-Bamm w/soda & ice cream cone	1 - 4
DE2336	Dino w/flowers	1 - 4

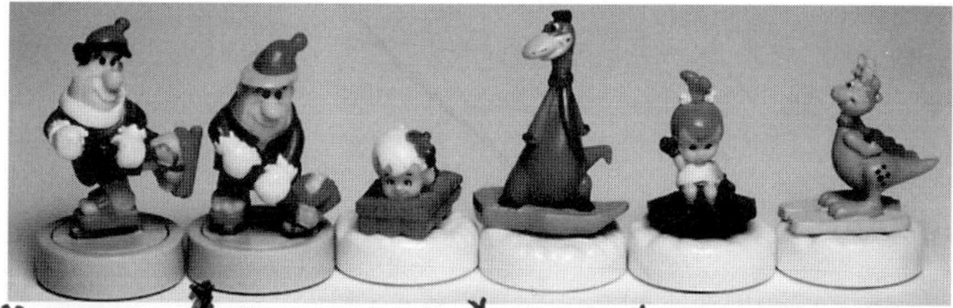

DE2361 DE2362 DE2363 DE2364 DE2365 DE2366

FLINTSTONES GLACIER GLIDERS, 1990

Flintstone cartoon characters as 1½-2" PVC figures on white or powder blue plastic bases which rolled on metal ball bearings.

DE2361	Fred ice skating, blue base	2 - 4
DE2362	Barney playing hockey, blue base	2 - 4
DE2363	Bamm-Bamm on sled, white base	2 - 4
DE2364	Dino, white base	2 - 4
DE2365	Pebbles on saucer, white base	2 - 4
DE2366	Hoppy on skis, white base	2 - 4

FLINTSTONES MINI-PLUSH TOYS, 1989

For the 1989 Christmas holiday, Denny's featured two-packs of 3½-Flintstone figures as a tie-in with the video *How the Flintstones Saved Christmas*. Dino and Hoppy were all fabric; the others had vinyl heads.

DE2391	Fred & Wilma	4 - 8

DE2393

DE2399

DE2392	Barney & Betty	4 - 8
DE2393	Dino & Hoppy	4 - 8
DE2394	Pebbles & Bamm-Bamm	4 - 8

Point of Purchase

DE2399	Display	75 - 100

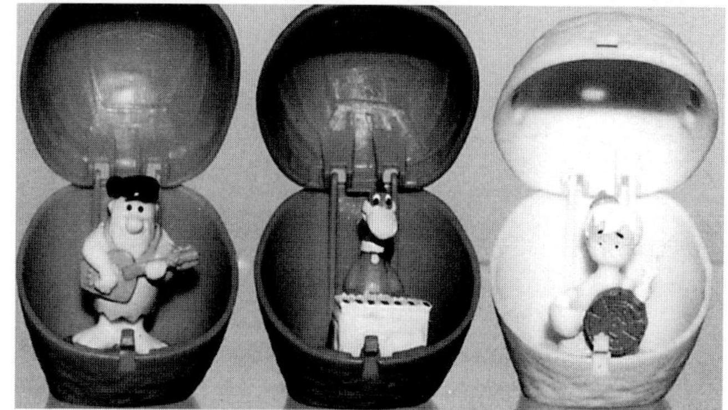

DE2421 DE2422 DE2423

FLINTSTONES ROCK N' ROLLERS, 1991

Plastic 2½" hinged rock shapes opened to reveal 2" PVC Flintstone characters playing musical instruments.

DE2421	Fred w/guitar, fuchsia rock	3 - 6
DE2422	Dino w/piano, blue rock	3 - 6

DE2424 DE2425 DE2426

DE2451 DE2452 DE2453

DE2454 DE2455 DE2456

DE2423	Bamm-Bamm w/drums, yellow rock	3 - 6
DE2424	Barney w/sax, lime green rock	3 - 6
DE2425	Pebbles w/tambourine, purple rock	3 - 6
DE2426	Mastodon w/keyboard, orange rock	3 - 6

FLINTSTONES STONE-AGE CRUISERS, 1991

Premiums consisted of a 2 pieces toy plastic vehicle and figures of Flintstone characters. The figures could be placed in the "seat" of each vehicle or used as finger puppets.

DE2451	Fred, bluish green car	2 - 5
DE2452	Dino, turquoise log boat	2 - 5
DE2453	Bamm-Bamm, orange car	2 - 5
DE2454	Wilma, red car	2 - 5
DE2455	Pebbles, purple bird	2 - 5
DE2456	Barney, yellow motorcycle w/sidecar	2 - 5

DE2483 DE2482 DE2481

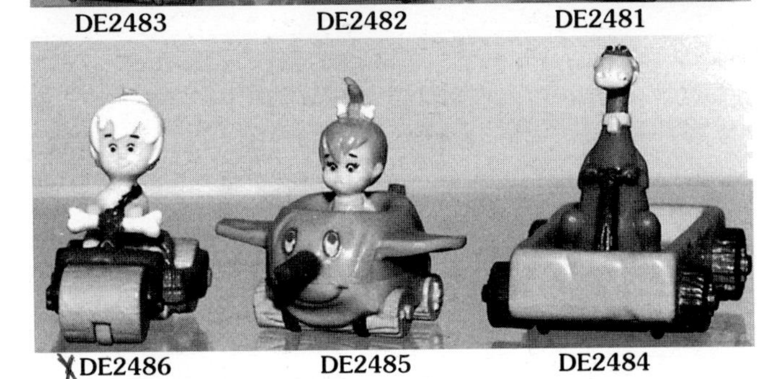

DE2486 DE2485 DE2484

FLINTSTONES VEHICLES, 1990

Plastic prehistoric vehicles with Flintstone characters driving. Each 2"-2½" premium rolled on tiny plastic wheels.

DE2481	Fred in stone roller	2 - 5
DE2482	Barney in dug-out tree	2 - 5
DE2483	Wilma in stone racer	2 - 5
DE2484	Dino in wagon	2 - 5
DE2485	Pebbles in a tree/stone helicopter	2 - 5
DE2486	Bamm-Bamm on a tri-stoner	2 - 5
Point of Purchase		
DE2489	Display	75 - 100

DE3751 DE3752

DE3753 DE3754

DE3755 DE3756

JETSONS CRAYON FUN GAME, 1992

A 6" x 6½" storybook with a crayon game on the back was created by folding a laminated piece of cardboard into thirds. Each book featured a story about one character from the Jetsons cartoon series. Six reusable clinging vinyl accessory pieces were incorporated into the story when pressed in place on the laminated storyboard.

DE3751	Elroy	2 - 3
DE3752	George	2 - 3
DE3753	Rosie	2 - 3
DE3754	Jane	2 - 3
DE3755	Judy	2 - 3
DE3756	Astro	2 - 3

JETSONS GO BACK TO SCHOOL, 1992

A wide variety school supplies were used for the 1992-1993 back to school year promotion.

DE3781 DE3782

DE3783 DE3785

DE3784

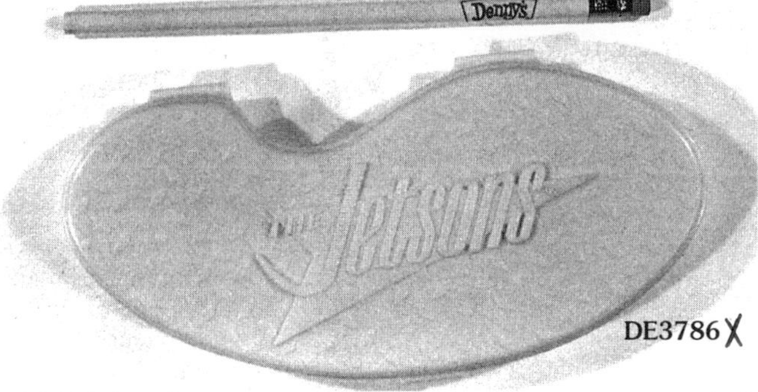

DE3786

DE3781	Mini Dictionary	1 - 3
DE3782	Stencils	1 - 3
DE3783	Cosmic Communicator Magic Slate	1 - 3
DE3784	Rosie Pencil Topper & Pencil	1 - 3
DE3785	Paper Folder	1 - 3
DE3786	Space Case w/Pencil	1 - 3

JETSONS PLANETS, 1992

Planets were made into rubber balls for this promotion. Each 2½" to 4" rubber ball was stamped with a different Jetsons character.

DE3792 DE3791

DE3793 DE3794

DE3796 DE3795

DE3791	Glow-in-the-dark Moon w/Astro	2 - 5
DE3792	Earth w/Jane	2 - 5
DE3793	Mars w/Elroy	2 - 5
DE3794	Saturn w/George	2 - 5
DE3795	Jupiter w/Judy	2 - 5
DE3796	Neptune w/Rosie	2 - 5

DE3814 DE3813 DE3812

DE3815 DE3816 DE3811

JETSONS PUZZLE ORNAMENTS, 1992

Premiums issued during this promotion could serve a dual purpose: games of skill or as a holiday ornament. Available in green or purple.

DE3811	#1, Rosie, diamond-shape casing	1 - 3
DE3812	#2, Judy, diamond-shape casing	1 - 3
DE3813	#3, Jane, round casing	1 - 3
DE3814	#4, George, round casing	1 - 3
DE3815	#5, Astro, square casing	1 - 3
DE3816	#6, Elroy, square casing	1 - 3

JETSONS SPACE TRAVEL FUN BOOKS, 1992

These 5⅛" x 7⅝" activity books contained games, riddles and facts. A package of 3 crayons was included with each.

DE3841	Book #1	1 - 3
DE3842	Book #2	1 - 3
DE3843	Book #3	1 - 3
DE3844	Book #4	1 - 3
DE3845	Book #5	1 - 3
DE3846	Book #6	1 - 3

Crayons form DE3841-6

DE3841 DE3842 DE3843 DE3844 DE3845 DE3846

DE3871 DE3872 DE3873

DE3874 DE3875 DE3876

JETSONS SPACECARDS, 1992

Round trading cards presenting various space-related facts became the focus for this kid's meal offering. Each 2½" round plastic case came with round cards, one of which was an x-ograph.

DE3871	Astronomers, aqua case	2 - 4
DE3872	Constellations, green case	2 - 4
DE3873	Mission Crews, yellow case	2 - 4
DE3874	Spacecraft, pink case	2 - 4
DE3875	Phenomenon, purple case	2 - 4
DE3876	Planets, orange case	2 - 4

DE9803

DE9801

DE9802

JETSON'S MISCELLANEOUS

The following items are known to exist for Jetsons, and were probably used with more than one promotion.

DE9801	Kellogg's Cereal Box w/Free Jetsons Meal promo	1 - 3
DE9802	Table Tent	1 - 2
DE9803	Movie Premium (Kool-Aid)	2 - 4

DOMINO'S

Domino's does not have a kid's meal program, but there have been a number of premiums based on the "Noid" character. Since these were targeted specifically at children, they are included here.

DO5451 DO5452 DO5453

DO5460

AVOID THE NOID, 1988

The PVC figures issued for 1988 were of a lighter reddish-orange rubber material than those issued in 1987 (see DO5481). This time the Noid was featured in a variety of action poses.

DO5451	Noid w/jackhammer	2 - 4
DO5452	Noid w/boxing gloves	2 - 4
DO5453	Noid as a magician	2 - 4

Point of Purchase

DO5460 Pressure-Sensitive "Avoid the Noid" stickers

CHRISTMAS ORNAMENT, 1988

Issued for the 1988 Christmas season was a clear plastic disc with a metal loop at the top. This ornament had a silk-screened picture of the face of the Noid looking through a holly wreath.

Premium

DO5470	Christmas Ornament	3 - 5

KEEP THE NOID OUT, 1987

During 1987, the pizza chain's mascot, The Noid, is a PVC figure.

DO5481	Noid w/both fists raised	2 - 4
DO5482	Noid pulling ears	2 - 4

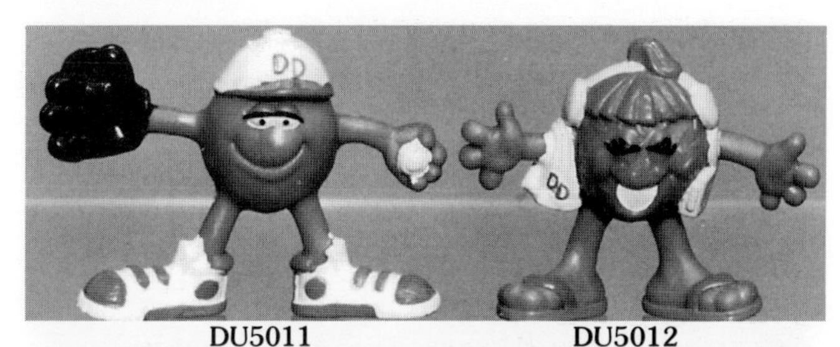

DU5011 DU5012

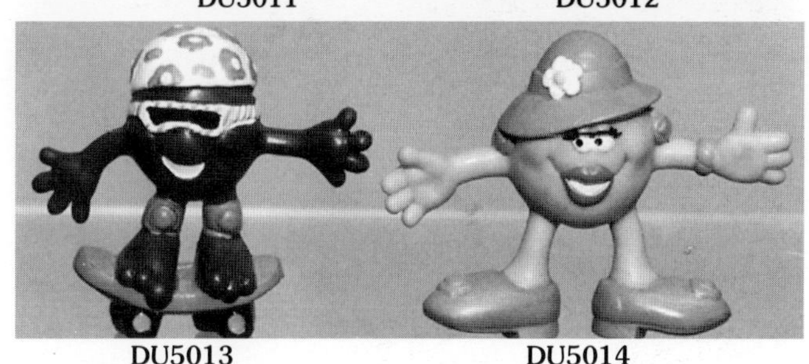

DU5013 DU5014

DO5483	Noid w/bomb	2 - 4
DO5484	Noid sitting w/Domino's Pizza box	2 - 4

NOID FIGURE, 1987

A 6" rubber figure of the Noid character could be purchased the pizza chain.

DO5491	Noid, 6"	6 - 8

NOID BOOKMARK, 1989

DO5501	Bookmark	8 - 12

DUNKIN' DONUTS

This national, primarily breakfast operation doesn't offer a regular kid's meal promotion, but has done a couple of special items worthy to be included in this book.

CAPTAIN PLANET ACTION FIGURES, 1992

Three-inch articulated figures from the children's TV show. They came in a "Munch Box" depicting the figures with ecology messages.

DU1011	Linka	5 - 10
DU1012	Captain Planet	5 - 10
DU1013	Duke Nukem	5 - 10
DU1014	Hoggish Greedly	5 - 10
Box		
DU1015	Munch Box	3 - 5

MUNCH-KINS, 1989

PVC bendy figures in the shape of doughnuts with arms and legs were issued during this promotion.

DU5011	Baseball Player	5 - 8
DU5012	Doughnut w/walkman	5 - 8
DU5013	Doughnut on Skateboard	5 - 8
DU5014	Female w/hat & purple shoes	8 - 10

DO5481 DO5482 DO5483

DO5484 DO5501

DO5491

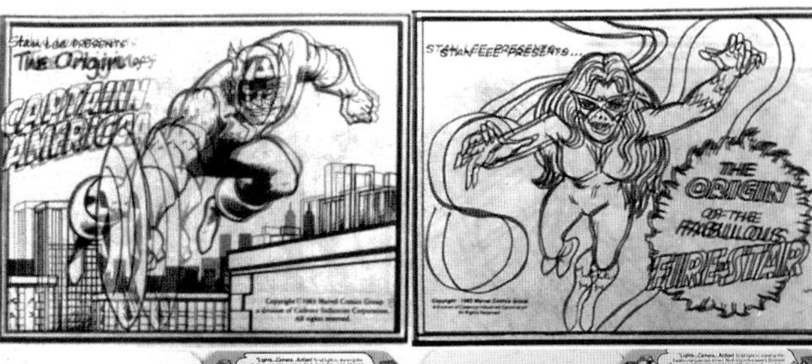

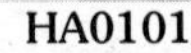

HA0101 HA0102

HA0103 HA0104

HA0105

HARDEE'S

The first Hardee's restaurant opened in Rocky Mount, North Carolina in May of 1961, where its Home Office remains. They acquired Sandy's Systems, an Illinois-based midwest regional chain of 200 restaurants, in 1972, 650 Burger Chef restaurants in 1982 and the 648 Roy Rogers restaurants in 1990. They are the third largest hamburger chain operating in 41 states (everywhere but the west coast) and foreign countries.

They tried many stand alone kids promotions with Gremlin Storybook Records. The year began a series of plush promotions, starting with Shirt Tales. The 1984 and 1985 Disney plushes, and the 1986 and 1987 Pound Puppies promotions. Many early Hardee's promotions consisted of "Mealboxes" with associated across-the-counter premiums with the purchase of some other specific food items. The California Raisins, the Tang Trio, and the Waldo Christmas Ornaments are examples.

When Hardee's instituted a weekly kids promotion "Mealboxes" were renamed Funmeals, the name of the first kid's meal, which they acquired with the purchase of Burger Chef. The earliest Funmeals consisted of Mealboxes, but later included premiums. They normally do about 7 promotions per year. Hardee's also has one or two "open windows" each year in which local restaurant selected promotions are used.

3-D ADVENTURE WEEKLY, 1983

Specially-designed boxes were an integral part of this premium offer. The graphics on the box were similar for all 6 boxes. The name on the marquee and the character shown in the left "enter" doorway were different. Inside the box was a printed stage area and punch-out slots through which the 3-D comic was slipped. This was a 10-panel paper strip.

Boxes w/3-D comic strip

HA0101	Captain America	30 - 40
HA0102	Fire-Star	30 - 40
HA0103	Spider-Man	30 - 40
HA0104	The Incredible Hulk	30 - 40
HA0105	Spider-Woman	30 - 40
HA0106	Iceman	30 - 40

HA0150

HA0151

HA0152

HA0153

HA0155 HA0157

ACTIVITY FUN, 1992

Four 4" x 6" paper booklets were given with Funmeal Packs. Each 8-page book centered around a particular theme and kids were invited to color, draw, connect, rub with a coin, find the differences and solve puzzles involving characters of the theme.

HA0150	Dinosaur Activity Fun	2 - 4
HA0151	Jungle Book Activity Fun	2 - 4
HA0152	Peter Pan Activity Fun	2 - 4
HA0153	The Presidents Activity Fun	2 - 4
Sack		
HA0155	Activity Fun	1 - 2
Point of Purchase		
HA0157	Door Decal	8 - 15

HA0611 HA0612 HA0613 HA0614

HA061 HA061

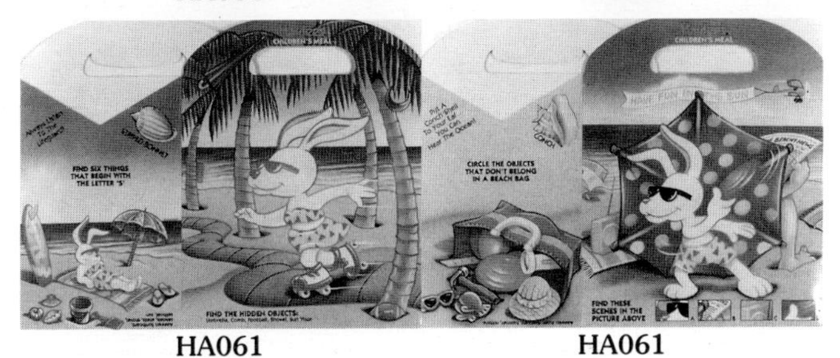

HA061 HA061

BEACH BUNNIES, 1989

Three inch white PVC bunny figures in summertime sport poses were issued with each Children's Meal.

HA0611	Girl w/beachball	2 - 4
HA0612	Boy on skateboard	2 - 4
HA0613	Girl on roller skates	2 - 4
HA0614	Boy w/red frisbee	2 - 4
Box		
HA0616	Girl w/beachball	3 - 6
HA0617	Boy on skateboard	3 - 6
HA0618	Girl on roller skates	3 - 6
HA0619	Boy w/red frisbee	3 - 6
Point of Purchase		
HA0620	Floor Display	20 - 30

BISKITTS, 1983

Hanna Barbera created a storyline regarding Biskitts – animated small dogs living in medieval times. These creature were featured during an Actionmeal promotion. Specially designed boxes contained a fold-out pop-up storybook regarding the adventures of the Biskitts. Inside each box was an additional cardboard piece with punch-out pieces for use in completing the activities described on the box.

HA0701	Right on Target	3 - 6
HA0702	Treasure Chest Quest	3 - 6

HA0701 HA0702

HA1033 HA1034 HA1031 HA1032

HA1039

CALIFORNIA RAISINS, 1987

Marvin Gaye's soul song, "I Heard It Through the Grapevine" resurfaced in a TV promotion for the California Raisin Growers Association. The Claymation-designed signing and dancing raisins featured in the commercial proved to be immensely popular, prompting CALRAB's commissioning of Applause, Inc. to immortalize them in a series of PVC figures. For the 1987 Hardee's California Raisins promotion, 2½" PVCs of four primary characters were issued successively with Children's Meal.

HA1031	Raisin w/microphone	3 - 4
HA1032	Raisin w/saxophone	3 - 4
HA1033	Dancer Raisin, blue sneakers	3 - 4
HA1034	Dancer Raisin w/sunglasses, orange sneakers	3 - 4
Point of Purchase		
HA1038	Translite	15 - 25
HA1039	Display	100 - 150

CALIFORNIA RAISINS, 1988

During the "Grapevine Tour '88", the California Raisins musical group was expanded. Names were given to each new character via a national contest and 2" PVC figures of these six characters were issued during this promotion. A full-color 2½" x 3½" cardboard collector's card was included in each box.

HA1069

HA1051 F.F. Strings 2 - 4
HA1052 Rollin' Rollo 2 - 4
HA1053 Waves Weaver 2 - 4
HA1054 Trumpy Tru Note 2 - 4
HA1055 Captain Toonz 2 - 4
HA1056 S.B. Stuntz 2 - 4

Boxes

HA1061 F.F. Strings, red 3 - 6
HA1062 Rollin' Rollo, lt. orange 3 - 6
HA1063 Waves Weaver, turquoise 3 - 6
HA1064 Trumpy Tru Note, purple 3 - 6
HA1065 Captain Toonz, blue 3 - 6
HA1066 S.B. Stuntz, lt. green 3 - 6

Point of Purchase

HA1068 Translite 10 - 20
HA1069 Door Decal, 2 ft. 15 - 25

HA1071 HA1072 HA1073 HA1074

CALIFORNIA RAISINS, 1988

For this California Raisin promotion, 5" poseable plush figures of the raisin group were offered for $2.19 with the purchase of a dessert item.

HA1075 Microphone 2 - 5
HA1076 Conga Dancer 2 - 5
HA1077 Sunglasses 2 - 5
HA1078 Female Raisin 2 - 5

Point of Purchase

HA1079 Translite 25 - 30

HA1091 HA1092 HA1093 HA1094

CALIFORNIA RAISINS, 1991 HA1100

California Raisins became "The Family of the 90's" as 2-2¼" PVC figures. The insert was a yellow cardboard collector's card with a full color illustration of the character.

HA1091 Benny, the father, w/bowling ball 2 - 5
HA1092 Alotta Stile, the daughter, w/radio 2 - 5
HA1093 Buster, the son, w/skateboard 2 - 5
HA1094 Anita Break, the mother, w/shopping bags 2 - 5

Point of Purchase

HA1096 Translite 15 - 25
HA1097 Door Decal 10 - 20
HA1100 Display 75 - 125

CAMP CALIFORNIA BEACH PATROL, 1993

Premiums featuring Camp California Beach Patrol characters. This promotion was also used by Carl's Jr.

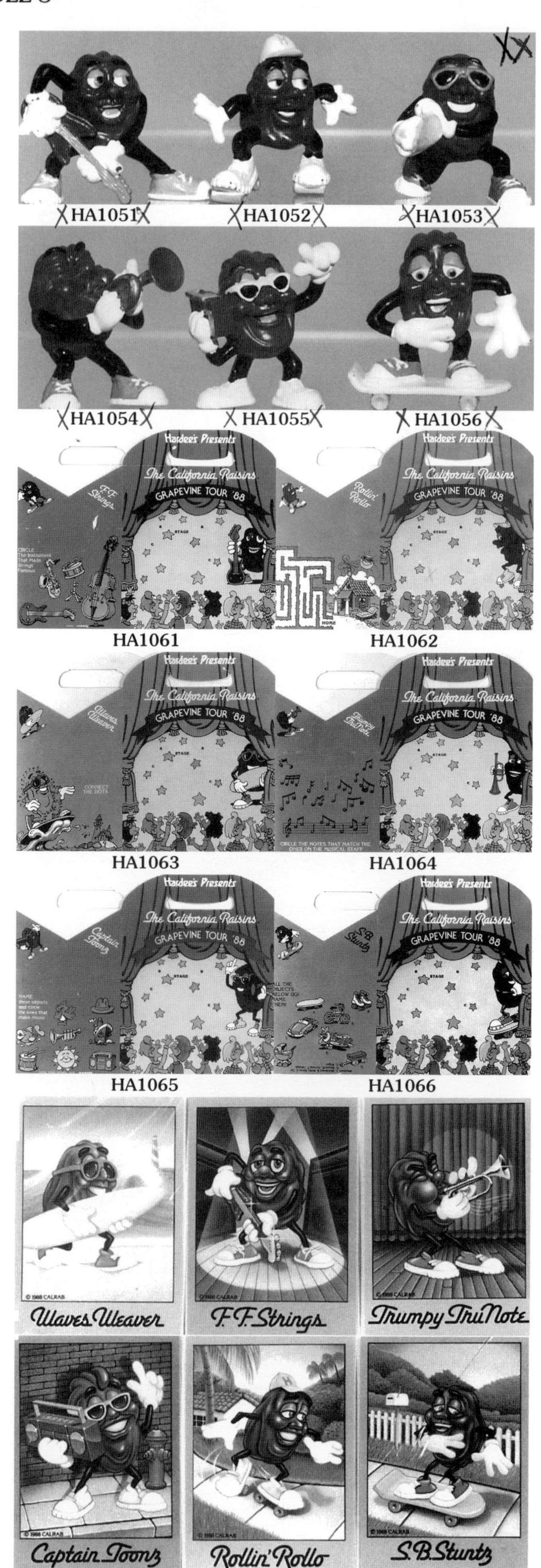

HA1051 HA1052 HA1053

HA1054 HA1055 HA1056

HA1061 HA1062

HA1063 HA1064

HA1065 HA1066

Trading cards from HA1061-HA1066

XHA1201X HA1202 XHA1203X HA1204

HA1205

HA1201

HA1203

HA1442

HA1444

ONE IN EVERY FUNMEAL PACK

BIKE LOCK

BIKE STICKER

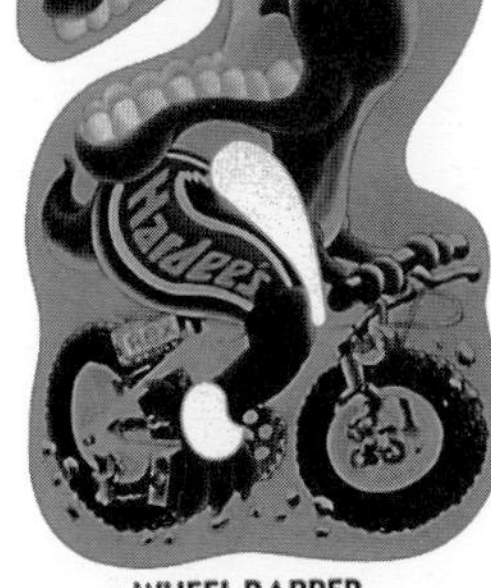

WHEEL RAPPER

© 1992 Hardee's Food Systems, Inc.

LICENSE PLATE

HA1448

HA1201 Lil' Bro Flying Disk 1 - 3
HA1202 Byron Spinner 1 - 3
HA1203 Byron Squirter 1 - 3
HA1204 Shred Mini Volleyball 1 - 3
Point of Purchase
HA1205 Door Decal & Menuboard Lug-On 10 - 15

CYCLIN' GEAR, 1992

Four different cycling Gear toys were issued with the Funmeal promotion.

HA1441 Bike Lock, blue plastic 1 - 3
HA1442 Erasable License Plate 1 - 3
HA1443 Bike Sticker, punch-out 1 - 3
HA1444 Wheel Rapper, punch-out 1 - 3
Sack
HA1445 Cyclin Gear .50 - 1
Point of Purchase
HA1448 Door Decal & Menuboard Lug-On 10 - 15

HA1591 HA1592 HA1594 XHA1593X

HA1596

Days of Thunder cups

HA1598

HA1560

HA1599

HA1561

DAYS OF THUNDER RACERS, 1990

In conjunction with the release of the Paramount movie, *Days of Thunder*, miniature racing cars by Applause were offered as premiums.

HA1591 Week #1, City Chevrolet #46, green & yellow 3 - 5
HA1592 Week #2, Superflo #46, pink & white 3 - 5
HA1593 Week #3, Hardee's #18, orange & blue 3 - 5
HA1594 Week #4, Mello Yello #51, black & green 3 - 5
Box
HA1596 Hardee's Pit Stop 2 - 5
Point of Purchase
HA1598 Translite, showing box 15 - 20
HA1599 Translite, showing cups 15 - 20
HA1600 Translite, showing racers 15 - 20
HA1601 Translite, showing racers 15 - 20

DINOSAUR IN MY POCKET, 1993

Four soft plastic PVC dinosaur figures came with a printed cardboard insert that was used for this promotion.

HA1620 HA1621 HA1622 HA1623 HA1625 HA1627

HA1620	Brontosaurus, yellow	2 - 5
HA1621	Stegosaurus, blue	2 - 5
HA1622	Triceratops, purple	2 - 5
HA1623	Tyrannosaurus, lime green	2 - 5
Sack		
HA1625	Dinosaur in My Pocket	.50 - 1
Point of Purchase		
HA1627	Door Decal & Menuboard Lug-On	10 - 15

HA1701 HA1702

DONALD DUCK PRESENTS

For this Children's Meal, the boxes featured a special reusable wipe-off panel on the back. Various games and punch-outs were also on the box. This promotion was for the Disney channel show, "Donald Duck Presents."

Boxes

HA1701	Adventure!	5 - 15
HA1702	Crazy Stuff!	5 - 15

FENDER BENDER 500, 1990 HA2207

This same promotion ran simultaneously at Carl's Jr. (see CA2211). These 2" hard plastic race cars each with 2 Hanna-Barbera character drivers. Each vehicle rolled on plastic wheels.

HA2201	Dick Dastardly & Mutley	2 - 5
HA2202	Huckleberry Hound & Snagglepuss	2 - 5
HA2203	Yogi Bear & Boo Boo	2 - 5
HA2204	Quick Draw McGraw & Bobba-Louie	2 - 5
HA2205	Magilla Gorilla & Gator	2 - 5
Boxes		
HA2207	Fender Bender 500	1 - 2
Point of Purchase		
HA2210	Translite	10 - 20
HA2211	Ceiling Dangler	15 - 25

HA2210

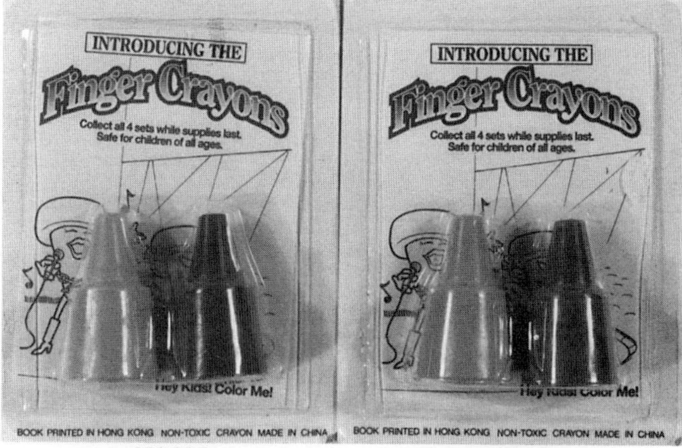

HA230 HA230

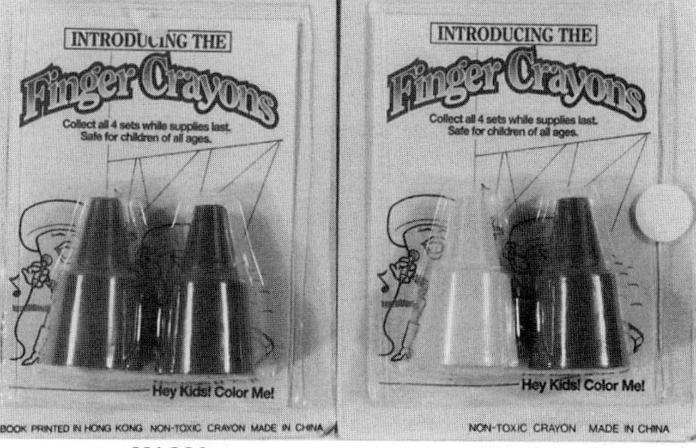

HA230 HA230

FINGER CRAYONS, 1992

Oversized "crayon-thimbles" designed to fit on the end of a finger were issued for this promotion. Each blister pack contained 2 of these 2" tall crayon tips. Originally, a coloring book was included, but due to a safety concern regarding the use of staples, the book was removed from the sealed package. A 2-sided 3¾" x 5" coloring sheet was inserted in place of the book. For this reasons, all known samples of this premium have been slit open and reclosed with a round paper sticker.

HA2301	Pink & Purple	1 - 3
HA2302	Red & Yellow	1 - 3
HA2303	Green & Orange	1 - 3
HA2304	Magenta & Blue	1 - 3
Point of Purchase		
HA2305	Door Decal & Menuboard Lug-On	10 - 15

HA2381 HA2382 HA2383

HA2384 HA2385

HA2391 HA2395

FLINTSTONES FIRST 30 YEARS, 1991

This special 30th anniversary issue featured a Flintstones character plus a small PVC accessory.

HA2381	Dino/Jukebox, green	3 - 6
HA2382	Fred/TV, fuchsia	3 - 6
HA2383	Bamm-Bamm/Pinball Machine, blue	3 - 6
HA2384	Pebbles/Telephone, yellow	3 - 6
HA2385	Barney/Barbecue, orange	3 - 6
Sack		
HA2391	Flintstones First 30 Years	1 - 2
Point of Purchase		
HA2395	Translite	15 - 25

HA2541 HA2542 HA2543 HA2544

GHOSTBUSTERS II, 1989

Ghostbusters II was released in 1989. Several over-the-counter items were offered as well as the specially designed containers for the children's meal. Four noise makers were offered across the counter for $1.79 with the purchase of a dessert or biscuit. Each one emitted two different sounds when the small buttons were pressed. These "ghost blasters" were recalled due to the small parts. Another over-the-counter item was a white plastic tote box. A collector's poster was also given away at the restaurants.

Specially designed vacu-formed plastic containers held the kid's meal. The bottom portion was a solid color and the top was a 3-D molded shape of a ghost or equipment featured in the movie. A sheet of stickers unique to the molded figure came in each box.

HA2547 HA2561

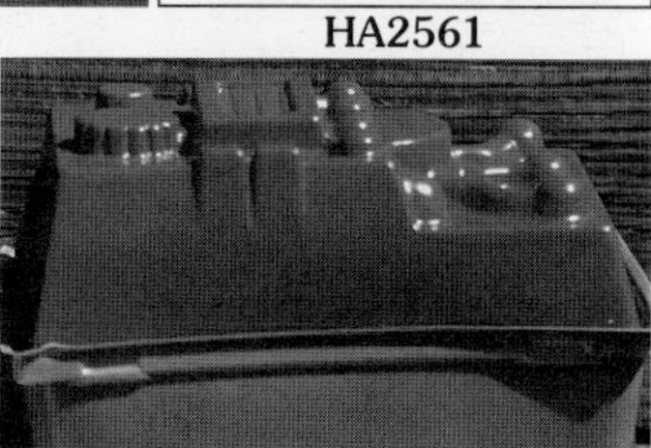

HA2551 HA2552

HA2553 HA2554

SLIME BOO! SLIME
SLIMER, GREEN GHOST

Stickers from HA2553

HA2541	Red Noise Maker, over-the-counter/recalled	7 - 20
HA2542	Gray Noise Maker, over-the-counter/recalled	7 - 20
HA2543	Black Noise Maker, over-the-counter/recalled	7 - 20
HA2544	White Noise Maker, over-the-counter/recalled	7 - 20
HA2547	White Tote Box, over-the-counter	
Boxes		
HA2551	Ectomobile, white w/stickers	5 - 10
HA2552	Gigameter Ghost Detector, blue w/stickers	5 - 10
HA2553	Slimer, green w/stickers	5 - 10
HA2554	Goo E. Ghost, purple w/stickers	5 - 10
Point of Purchase		
HA2560	Translite	15 - 28
HA2561	Collector Poster w/coupons	2 - 5

GREMLIN ADVENTURES, 1984

A series of 5 read-along books and records based on the Steven Spielberg movie *Gremlins* were offered for 89¢ with the purchase of any food item.

HA2821	Gift of the Mogwai	6 - 8
HA2822	Gizmo & the Gremlins	6 - 8
HA2823	Escape from the Gremlins	6 - 8
HA2824	Gremlins - Trapped	6 - 8
HA2825	The Last Gremlin	6 - 8
Point of Purchase		
HA2830	Translite	10 - 20

HA2935 HA3001

GUMMI BEARS, 1992

The premium which came with this Funmeal Pack could be considered dessert. A 1.25 oz bag of Care Bears Gummi Bears candy was placed in each specially designed sack used during this promotion.

HA2935	Gummi Bears Bag	2 - 4

HALLEY'S COMET, 1984

This educational promotion featured a pop-up paper comet with a built-in telescope to spot the real thing which orbits near Earth every 75 years. The box was full of related facts and games, and had a storage slot for the compressed comet/viewer.

HA3001	Halley's Box w/Comet Viewer	15 - 25

HALLOWEEN GLOW-CUPS, 1993

Four and one fourth inch glow-in-the-dark cups with colorful Halloween scenes were the premium of the Halloween season.

HA3111	"Trick or Treat"	1 - 2
HA3112	Wolfman, Dracula, Frankenstein	1 - 2
HA3113	Skeleton with Pumpkin	1 - 2
HA3114	"Happy Halloween"	1 - 2
Point of Purchase		
HA3101	Window Decal	

HA3062 HA3063 HA3061 HA3064

HALLOWEEN HIDEAWAYS, 1989

For this special promotion, Halloween creatures were made into small soft stuffed figures.

HA3261	Black Bat w/Green Tree Stump	2 - 5
HA3262	Green Goblin w/Blue Caldron	2 - 5
HA3263	Black Cat w/Pumpkin	2 - 5
HA3264	White Ghost w/Yellow Bag	2 - 5
Point of Purchase		
HA3270	Translite	15 - 25

HOME ALONE 2, 1992

The video release of the movie *Home Alone 2, Lost In New York* featured four main characters on cups and in Funmeal Packs. Cardboard punch-outs of the character and related items to create a scene were contained in the first box Hardee's had used in years.

HA3323

HA3321

HA3327

Cups from HA3321-HA3327

HA3335

HA3321	Marv, cup and pack	2 - 4
HA3323	Kevin, cup and pack	2 - 4
HA3325	Harry, cup and pack	2 - 4
HA3327	Pigeon Lady, cup and pack	2 - 4
Box		
HA3335	Home Alone 2, Lost in New York	1 - 2

JETSONS, 1984

A "Magic Spaceship™ Decoder" was inside each box. On the box itself, several specially printed areas in scenes involving the Jetsons TV characters could only be read by using the decoder piece.

HA3701	Magic Spaceship Decoder	3 - 5

HA3702

HA4111 HA4112 HA4113 HA4114

Box

HA3702	Exploring Earth	8 - 15

KAZOO CREW SAILORS, 1991

"Can You Kazoo? Our Sailors Do!" read the heading which accompanied the 5" plastic animal figures used to disguise the kazoo.

HA4111	Rabbit, first mate	2 - 5
HA4112	Monkey, look-out	2 - 5
HA4113	Rhino, captain	2 - 5
HA4114	Bear, peg leg	2 - 5
Point of Purchase		
HA4120	Translite	15 - 25
HA4121	Counter Card	8 - 15

HA4341 HA4342

LITTLE LITTLE GOLDEN BOOKS, 1987

Each premium in this Funmeal promotion had its own specially designed box. The theme of each box centered around its tiny Golden Books premium, in which the books were inserted on the outside.

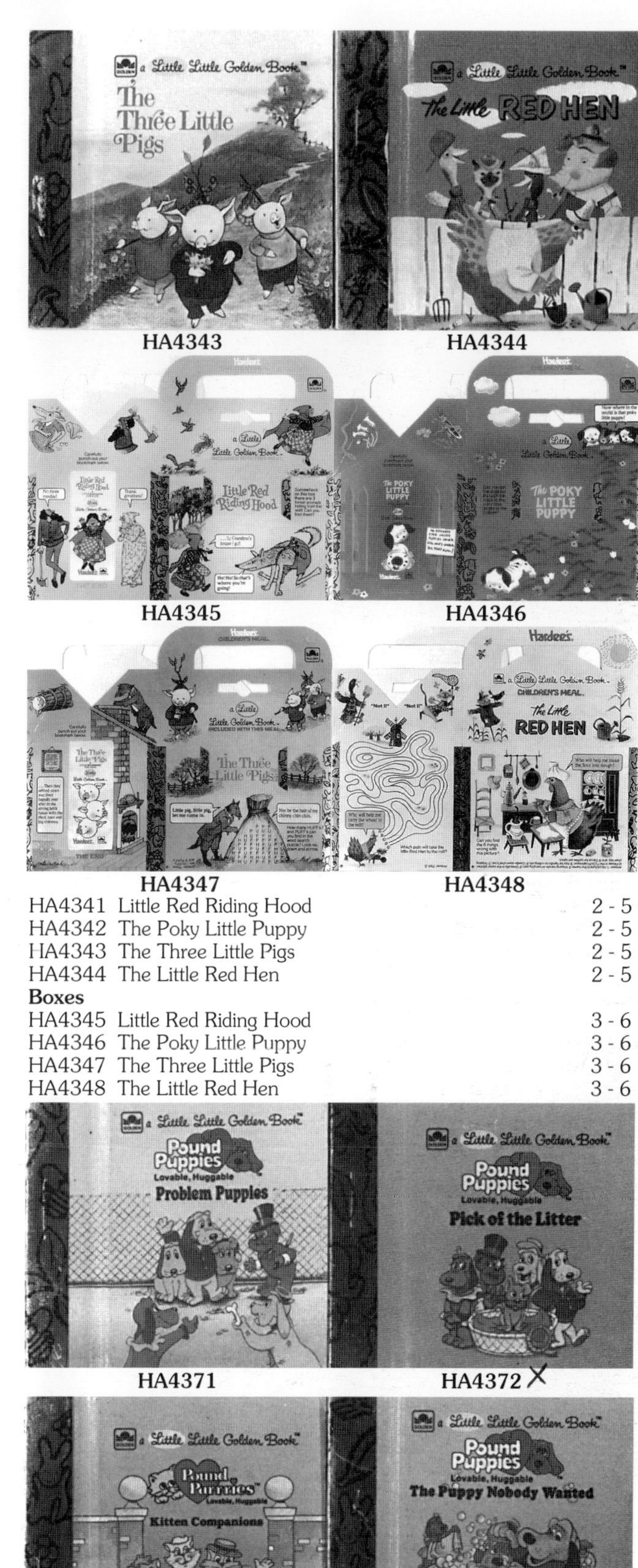

HA4343 HA4344

HA4345 HA4346

HA4347 HA4348

HA4341	Little Red Riding Hood	2 - 5
HA4342	The Poky Little Puppy	2 - 5
HA4343	The Three Little Pigs	2 - 5
HA4344	The Little Red Hen	2 - 5
Boxes		
HA4345	Little Red Riding Hood	3 - 6
HA4346	The Poky Little Puppy	3 - 6
HA4347	The Three Little Pigs	3 - 6
HA4348	The Little Red Hen	3 - 6

HA4371 HA4372 ✗

HA4373 HA4374

LITTLE LITTLE GOLDEN BOOKS, 1987

For this Funmeal promotion, Western Publishing Company furnished Little Little Golden Books were used again.

HA4371	Problem Puppies	2 - 5
HA4372	Pick of the Litter	2 - 5
HA4373	Kitten Companions	2 - 5

HA4375 HA4376

HA4377 HA4378

HA4374 The Puppy Nobody Wanted 2 - 5

Boxes

HA4375	Problem Puppies	1 - 4
HA4376	Pick of the Litter	1 - 4
HA4377	Kitten Companions	1 - 4
HA4378	The Puppy Nobody Wanted	1 - 4

HA4391 HA4392

HA4393 HA4394

HA4396 HA4397

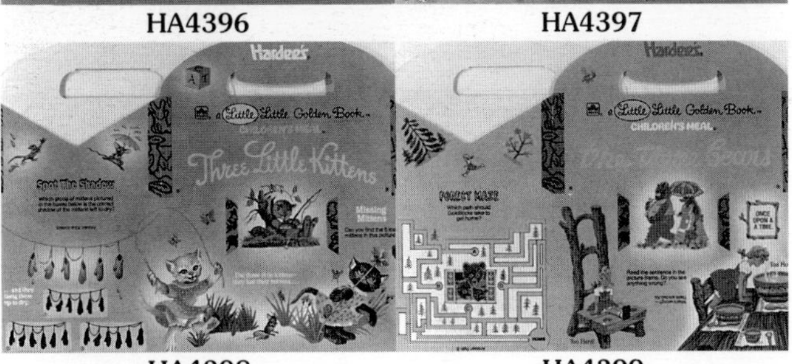

HA4398 HA4399

LITTLE LITTLE GOLDEN BOOKS, 1988

Once again, favorite Little Little Golden Books were used as premiums for a Funmeal promotion. As with the previous promotions, the graphics on each box centered around the featured storybook.

HA4391	The Little Red Caboose	2 - 4
HA4392	Old MacDonald Had A Farm	2 - 4
HA4393	Three Little Kittens	2 - 4
HA4394	The Three Bears	2 - 4
Boxes		
HA4396	The Little Red Caboose	3 - 6
HA4397	Old MacDonald Had A Farm	3 - 6
HA4398	Three Little Kittens	3 - 6
HA4399	The Three Bears	3 - 6

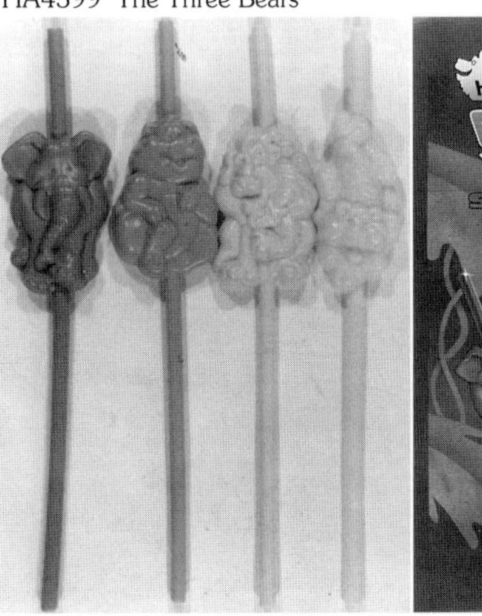

HA4551 HA4552 HA4553 HA4554 HA4558

MAGIC ZOO STRAWS, 1993

Four $8^{1}/_{2}$" tall plastic drinking straws were molded with a different 3-D animal shape located $1^{1}/_{2}$" from one end.

HA4551	Elephant, blue	1 - 2
HA4552	Bear, pink	1 - 2
HA4553	Lion, yellow	1 - 2
HA4554	Tiger, white	1 - 2
Point of Purchase		
HA4558	Door Decal	10 - 15

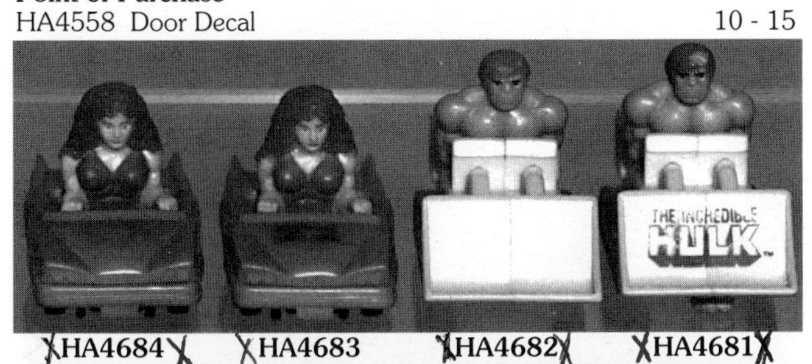

HA4684 HA4683 HA4682 HA4681

HA4687 HA4686 HA4685

MARVEL SUPER HEROES VEHICLES, 1990

Four Marvel Comic's super hero characters were featured as non-removable drivers of colorful 3" plastic vehicles.

HA4681	Hulk/yellow bulldozer, w/The Incredible Hulk logo on the bulldozer scoop	2 - 5
HA4682	Hulk/yellow bulldozer, w/o logo	2 - 5
HA4683	She-Hulk/pink convertible, w/The Sensational She-Hulk logo on the hood	2 - 5
HA4684	She-Hulk/pink convertible, w/o logo	2 - 5

HA4688 HA4689 HA4691

HA4694

HA4695

HA4685	Spiderman/black Supercar, w/spider logo on hood	2 - 5
HA4686	Spiderman/black Supercar, w/o logo	2 - 5
HA4687	Capt. America/white jet ski, w/Capt. America logo hood	2 - 5
HA4688	Doc on the Rocks Cup	3 - 6
HA4689	The Green Team Cup	3 - 6

Box

HA4691	Marvel Super Heroes	1 - 2

Point of Purchase

HA4694	Translite, Fun Meals	15 - 25
HA4695	Translite, cup offer	10 - 15

MISSION FROM MARS, 1991

During this promotion, a fun-sized pack of M&Ms came with each meal along with Martian Money (Zylarks).

HA5321	Zylark note	2 - 4

Sack

HA5324	Bing the Robot	1 - 2

Point of Purchase

HA5325	Door Decal	10 - 15

HA5781 HA5782 HA5783 HA5784

MUPPET CHRISTMAS CAROL FINGER PUPPETS 1993

Two-inch finger puppets of the Muppets as characters from "The Christmas Carol" were given in conjunction with the video release.

HA5781	Kermit	2 - 4
HA5782	Miss Piggy	2 - 4
HA5783	Fozzie	2 - 4
HA5784	Gonzo	2 - 4

Point of Purchase

HA5791	Window Decal	5 - 10

HA6361 HA6362

HA6363 HA6364

POUND PUPPIES, 1986

For $2.19 with the purchase of a food item, kids could take home one of four Pound Puppies offered during this promotion. The 8" puppies were identical to those sold in stores.The box to contain the meal was also designed to resemble a doghouse, but it had punch-out pieces and square openings for the door and a window.

HA6361	Tan w/brown spots	4 - 8
HA6362	Black	4 - 8
HA6363	White w/black spots	4 - 8
HA6364	Gray w/black ears	4 - 8

Boxes

HA6365	Tan Pound Puppy	5 - 9
HA6366	Black Pound Puppy	5 - 9
HA6367	White Pound Puppy	5 - 9
HA6468	Gray Pound Puppy	5 - 9

Point of Purchase

HA6370	Translite	15 - 25

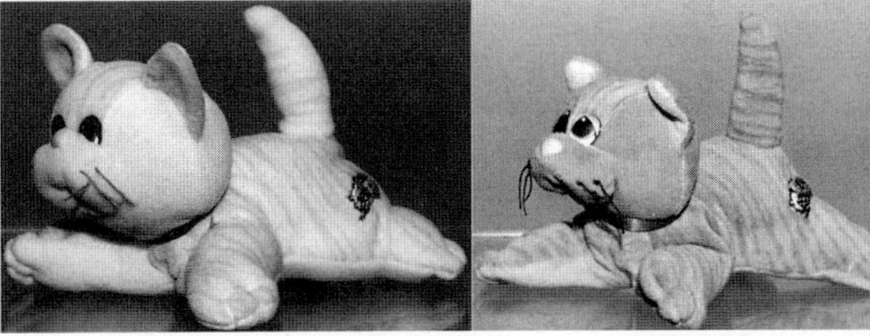

HA6421 HA6422

POUND PUPPIES & PUR-R-RIES, 1987

For this promotion, puppies and kittens were offered as 5"-6" stuffed animals. Each had the Pound Puppy logo embroidered on the hip. These were offered for $2.49 with the purchase of specific food items.

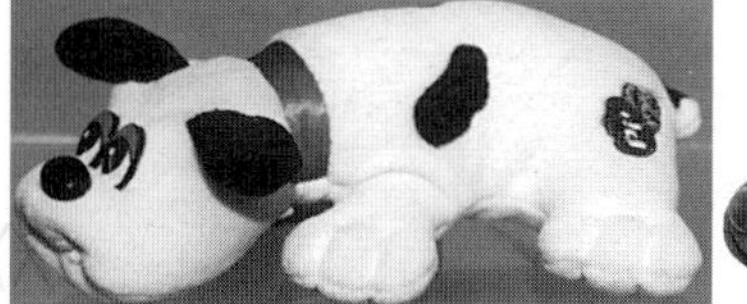

HA6423

HA6424

HA6433 HA6434

HA6421	Pur-R-Rie, white w/gray stripes	5 - 7
HA6422	Pur-R-Rie, brown	5 - 7
HA6423	Bulldog, gray w/brown spots	5 - 7
HA6424	Dalmatian	5 - 7
HA6425	Rumpleskin, brown	5 - 7
HA6433	Box, blue	1 - 3
HA6434	Box, green	1 - 3

Point of Purchase

HA6440	Translite	15 - 25

HA6550

RACER, 1993

A plastic replica of the Hardee's Racer, used as a fill-in premium.

HA6550	Racer, blue or green	3 - 6

HA7101

HA7105

SCOOBY-DOO, 1984

The Hanna-Barbera Scooby-Doo characters were featured on four Mystery Actionmeal boxes for this promotion. A coloring fun book was inserted into the extra "pouch" formed on the front of the box.

Premium

HA7101	Dinosaur Deception Mystery coloring book	5 - 8

Box

HA7105	Dinosaur Deception Mystery	8 - 12

SHIRT TALES, 1983

Premiums for this kid's meal promotion included a "Magic Motion®" Picture Decoder, a storybook involving the Shirt Tales characters, and several different activities to be completed. The fold-out storybook was on the front of each box and specially treated areas on the box could only be unscrambled by moving the picture decoder piece up and down over the areas. A maze game, riddles, and can-you-find activities were printed on the box. Plush figures of the comic book/Hallmark animal characters could be purchased over-the-counter.

HA7326

HA7327

HA7328

HA7329

HA7325

HA7330

HA7320	Magic Motion Picture Decoder	4 - 8

Over-The-Counter

HA7325	Bogey	4 - 8
HA7326	Digger	4 - 8
HA7327	Rick	4 - 8
HA7328	Tyg	4 - 8
HA7329	Pammy	4 - 8

Box

HA7330	The Secret of Hoodwink Hollow	10 - 20

SILLY SACK FUN MEAL, 1990-1991

Stock children's card games were used throughout 1990 and 1991 as a fill-in premium whenever needed by each restaurant.

HA7371	A•B•C Flashcards	2 - 3
HA7372	Fish	2 - 3
HA7373	Crazy Eights	2 - 3
HA7374	Old Maid	2 - 3

Point of Purchase

HA7378	Translite	10 - 20

SKITTLES BACK TO SCHOOL, 1992

Kids could use the premiums offered during this promotion when they returned to school. Each premium was designed to feature the Skittles rainbow. A fun-sized package of Skittles candy came wrapped with the premium in each kid's meal.

HA7390	Rainbow sticker w/candy	1 - 2
HA7391	Rainbow bookmark w/candy	1 - 2
HA7392	Rainbow Circle Tracer w/candy	1 - 2

HA7371 HA7372

HA7373 HA7374 HA7394

HA7436 HA7437

HA7438 HA7439

HA7393	Rainbow Ruler Stencil w/candy	1 - 2
HA7394	Skittles Bag	1 - 2

SMURF CHILDREN'S MEAL, 1987

Special boxes were designed to display the enclosed Smurf PVC figure premium inserted on the inside of the box so the premium showed through the oval hole in the front of the box. Over 100 different Smurf figures were randomly made available to the restaurants.

HA7431	Smurf	2 - 4
Boxes		
HA7436	Smurf a Helping Hand to a Friend Today!	3 - 6
HA7437	Have a Smurfy Day	3 - 6
HA7438	Smurf A Smile and A Surprise Will Come Your Way!	3 - 6
HA7439	Smurf a Song or Play Along	3 - 6
Point of Purchase		
HA7440	Translite	15 - 25

SMURF'S FUNMEAL PACK, 1990

The popular blue-bodied buddies from TV cartoons were featured

HA7471 HA7472 HA7473

HA7474 HA7475 HA7476

HA7478 HA7480

again in 1990 for the Funmeal Pack premium. Each PVC figure was molded onto a colored surfboard with wheels.

HA7471	Little Smurfette on green board	2 - 5
HA7472	Smurfette on purple board	2 - 5
HA7473	Smurf w/green horse life ring on yellow board	2 - 5
HA7474	Smurf standing on a lunch box on top an orange board	2 - 5
HA7475	Papa Smurf on red board	2 - 5
HA7476	Dog on blue board	2 - 5
Boxes		
HA7478	Smurfs Up!	3 - 6
Point of Purchase		
HA7480	Translite, Square	15 - 25
HA7481	Translite, Rectangular	15 - 25

SNOWBALLS, 1994

Squirter toys which change color when filled with water.

HA7491	Girl with Tam	1 - 3
HA7492	Boy w/goggles and snow hat	1 - 3
HA7493	Boy w/hat with flaps	1 - 3
HA7494	Man w/hat and earmuffs	1 - 3

SPEED BUNNIES, 1994

Small single-piece PVC rabbits on skates or skateboards were issued with trading cards in a series of four.

HA7501	Cruiser	2 - 4
HA7502	Dusty	2 - 4
HA7503	Stretch	2 - 4
HA7504	Sunny	2 - 4
Sack		
HA7510	Speed Bunnies	.50 - 1

SQUIRTERS, 1990

Colorful soft plastic water squirters in the shape of food items.

HA7521	Cheeseburger	2 - 4
HA7522	Hot Dog	2 - 4
HA7523	Strawberry Shake	2 - 4
HA7524	French Fries	2 - 4
Boxes		
HA7526	Squirters	3 - 5

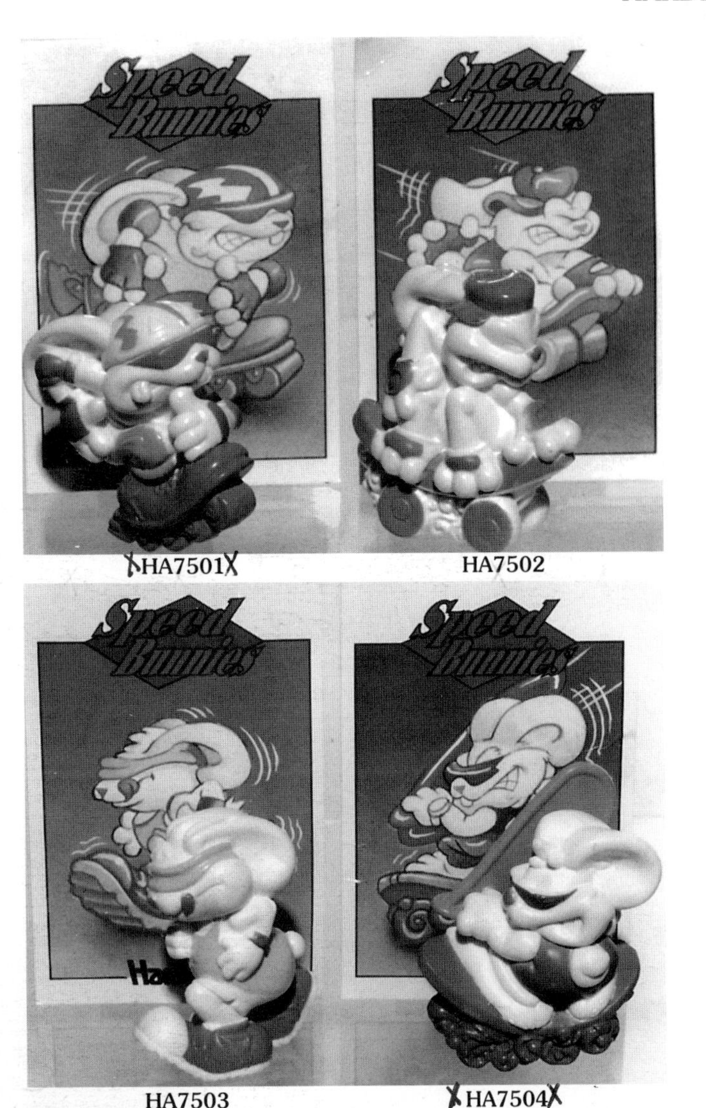

HA7501 HA7502

HA7503 HA7504

HA7510 HA7526

HA7521 HA7522 HA7523 HA7524

Point of Purchase

HA7530 Translite 15 - 25

TANG TRIO, 1989

This Funmeal Pack featured the instant fruit drink Tang characters as 2" PVC figures with corresponding collector's cards.

HA7741 Lance, The Leader 2 - 5

HA7530

HA7742 HA7744 HA7743 HA7741

HA7931 HA7935

HA7742 Awesome Annie, Lip Sync Kid 2 - 5
HA7743 Flap, The Rapper 2 - 5
HA7744 Tag, The Whistler 2 - 5

Point of Purchase

HA7750 Translite 15 - 25

TEDDY GRAHAMS, 3/8/92-4/26/92

During this promotion, a ¾-oz pack of cinnamon-flavored Teddy Grahams came with each kid's meal.

Sack

HA7931 Teddy Grahams 1 - 2

Point of Purchase

HA7935 Translite 10 - 20

TREASURE TROLLS, 1993

Standard Treasure Trolls PVC pencil topper figures came in six different hair colors with four variations of the navel marking (star, diamond, heart and circle), totaling 24 different premiums. Also used by Long John Silvers, Roy Rogers, and Wal-Mart.

HA8131 Red Hair 1 - 2
HA8132 Yellow Hair 1 - 2
HA8133 Blue Hair 1 - 2
HA8134 Pink Hair 1 - 2
HA8135 Purple Hair 1 - 2
HA8136 Green Hair 1 - 2

Sack

HA8139 Treasure Trolls .50 - 1

HA8134 HA8131 HA8133 HA8136 HA8135 HA8134

HA8139 HA8140

Point of Purchase

HA8140 Counter Card & Outdoor Speaker Decal 15

WALDO & FRIENDS HOLIDAY ORNAMENTS, 1991

Nine flat plastic Christmas tree ornaments featuring Waldo and his friends were available for 99¢ per set with any purchase. This was a "stand alone" offer, but some stores may have used them as filler items.

HA8841 Set A - Snowman, Waldo w/Woof, Waldo Watchers 2 - 4
HA8842 Set B - Wizard Whitebeard, Waldo w/Books, Reindeer 2 - 4
HA8843 Set C - Waldo w/Ski Equipment, Woof, Wenda 2 - 4

WALDO & FRIENDS STRAW BUDDIES, 1991

The elusive Waldo and his friends were issued as 2"-2½" PVC straw buddies figures through which a drinking straw could be placed.

HA8881 Waldo 2 - 4
HA8882 Wenda 2 - 4
HA8883 Wizard Whitebeard 2 - 4
HA8884 Woof 2 - 4

WALDO'S TRAVEL ADVENTURE, 1992

Find Waldo on four different premiums.

HA8921 Adventure Travel Journal 1 - 3
HA8922 Postcards 1 - 3
HA8923 Fold 'n Solve Travel Pictures 1 - 3
HA8924 A-mazing-ing Space Adventure 1 - 3

HA8883 HA8881 HA8884 HA8882

HA8921 HA8922

HA8923 HA8924

HA8925 HA8926 HA8991

Sack

HA8925 Where's Waldo? .50 - 1

Point of Purchase

HA8926 Door Decal & Menuboard Lug-On 10 - 20

HA8841

HA8842

HA8843

WALT DISNEY CLASSICS, 1985

Mini plush figures from Disney's classics were offered as self-liquidating premiums as $2.49 each with any meal purchase.

HA8961 Bambi 6 - 10
HA8962 Pinocchio 6 - 10
HA8963 Dumbo 6 - 10
HA8964 Dalmatian Puppy, from *101 Dalmations* 6 - 10
HA8965 Lady, from *Lady & The Tramp* 6 - 10
Point of Purchase
HA8970 Translite 15 - 25

HA8992

HA8995

HA8994 **HA8993**

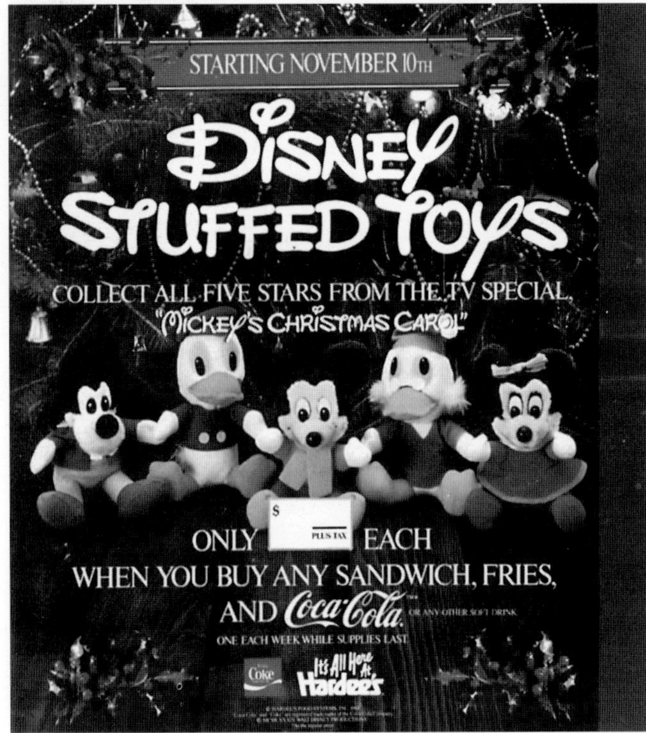

HA8999

WALT DISNEY MICKEY'S CHRISTMAS CAROL, 1984

These Christmas premiums were 7 1/2" stuffed dolls of characters in *Mickey's Christmas Carol*. Each was available for $1.99 with the purchase of specific food items.

HA8991 Minnie as Mrs. Cratchit 6 - 10
HA8992 Mickey as Bob Cratchit 6 - 10
HA8993 Goofy as Jacob Marley 6 - 10
HA8994 Donald as Scrooge's Nephew Fred 6 - 10
HA8995 Uncle Scrooge as Ebenezer Scrooge 6 - 10
Point of Purchase
HA8998 Translite 15 - 25
HA8999 Metal Display Sign 30 - 50

WELCOME TO POOH CORNER, 1986

Four perigraph disks comprised the Fun Wheels issued. The pictures were based on the theme of each Fun Wheel. Boxes used during this promotion carried out the theme of each Fun Wheel. Slots were die cut into one end of the box to hold each Fun Wheel.

HA9020 Fun with Make-Believe! Fun Wheel, purple 5 - 8
HA9021 Fun with Friends! Fun Wheel, green 5 - 8
HA9022 Fun with Hobbies! Fun Wheel, blue 5 - 8
HA9023 Fun with Words! Fun Wheel, yellow 5 - 8
Boxes
HA9024 Fun with Make-Believe! 10 - 15
HA9025 Fun with Friends! 10 - 15
HA9026 Fun with Hobbies! 10 - 15
HA9027 Fun with Words! 10 - 15

HA9401 (front and back)

HA9402 (front and back)

HA9403 (front and back)

HA9404 (front and back)

YOGI BEAR FUNTIME PUZZLES, 1985

Four Actionmeal boxes with punch-out tray puzzles on the back.

HA9401 Spring 20 - 35
HA9402 Summer 20 - 35
HA9403 Autumn 20 - 35
HA9404 Winter 20 - 35

IN3631 IN3632 IN3634 IN3635 IN3636 IN3639

IN3637 IN3638 IN3633 IN3640 IN3660

IN3643 IN3649 IN3650

INTERNATIONAL HOUSE OF PANCAKES

Also known as IHOP, this national chain of sit-down restaurants features breakfast, but also serves lunch and limited dinner favorites. Premiums to attract families with children have been given with kid's meals, but are also usually sold at the cashier's booth.

PANCAKE KIDS, 1991, 1992

In 1991 PVC figures of six pancake characters were issued with a cardboard stage. Different were backdrops was also available for four of them. In 1992 four more PVC figures were added and as supplies depleted, the cardboard stage was replaced with a chartreuse or red plastic lunchbox.

IN3631	Susie Strawberry	2 5
IN3632	Bonnie Blue Berry	2 - 5
IN3633	Chocolate Chip Charlie	2 - 5
IN3634	Harvey Harvest	2 - 5
IN3635	Cynthia Cinnamon Apple	2 - 5
IN3636	Betty Buttermilk	2 - 5
IN3637	Peter Potato	2 - 5
IN3638	Frenchy	2 - 5
IN3639	Von der Gus	2 - 5
IN3640	Rosanna Banana Nut	2 - 5
IN3641	Susie Strawberry Backdrop	2 - 5
IN3642	Bonnie Blue Berry Backdrop	2 - 5
IN3643	Chocolate Chip Charlie Backdrop	2 - 5
IN3646	Betty Buttermilk Backdrop	2 - 5
IN3647	Peter Potato Backdrop	2 - 5
IN3648	Frenchy Backdrop	2 - 5
IN3649	Von der Gus Backdrop	2 - 5
IN3650	Rosanna Banana Nut Backdrop	2 - 5
IN3660	Stage	
Plastic Lunch Boxes		
IN3665	Plastic Lunch Box, red	10 - 15
IN3666	Plastic Lunch Box, chartreuse	5 - 10

PANCAKE KIDS CLOTH DOLLS, 1992

Soft cloth dolls (9"-10" of the Pancake Kids) were sold over the counter.

IN4101	Chocolate Chip Charlie	6 - 8
IN4102	Bonnie Blue Berry	6 - 8
IN4103	Susie Strawberry	6 - 8

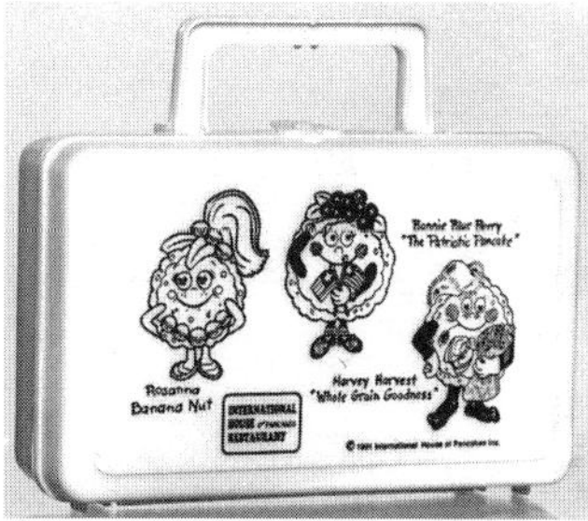

IN3665

IN4101

IN4102

IN4103

IN4321 IN4322

PANCAKE KIDS CRUISERS, 1993

A non-removable Pancake Kid PVC was in the driver's seat of a 2" pull-back racer car. The character's name was imprinted on the back of the head. There are several color variations.

IN4321	Susie Strawberry	2 - 5
IN4322	Betty Buttermilk w/yellow or red hair	2 - 5
IN4323	Harvey Harvest	2 - 5
IN4324	Chocolate Chip Charlie	2 - 5

IN4323 IN4324

IN6810 IN6811

REFRIGERATOR MAGNETS, 1992

The Pancake Kids were featured as 3" refrigerator magnets.

IN6810	Chocolate Chip Charlie	2 - 5
IN6811	Susie Strawberry	2 - 5

JACK IN THE BOX

Jack-in-the-Box is a San Diego-based fast food chain serving Western states. At one time outlets were also located in six major eastern cities, and many early premiums are still found there. The original cast of Jack-in the-Box characters — Jack, Clownie, the Swiss Yodeler, Onion Ring, and Spy — have evolved to the more product-oriented Jumbo Jack, Sly Fry, Betty Burger, Edgar E. Eggroll, and Ollie O. Ring...which are known as the Jack Pack.

Jack-in-the-Box continues to have educational information, puzzles, and games on their kids meal sacks, but rarely are these tied into the promotion at hand. It is also not unusual to find different promotions going from one outlet to another.

JA0253 JA0251

ADVENTURES OF JACK IN THE BOX, early 1980s

Each illustrated booklet came with an Evatone record.

JA0251	Volume 1: Why a House Makes Noise	10 - 15
JA0252	Volume 2:	10 - 15
JA0253	Volume 3: How Pain Helps Us	10 - 15
JA0254	Volume 4:	10 - 15

BACK IN TIME, 1993

Five by eight-inch cardboard tray puzzles with historical themes.

JA0431	Old West	2 - 4
JA0432	Ancient Egypt	2 - 4
JA0433	The Vikings	2 - 4
JA0434	Dinosaur Days	2 - 4
JA0435	Camelot	2 - 4

Sacks

JA0441	Old West	1 - 2

JA0431 JA0433

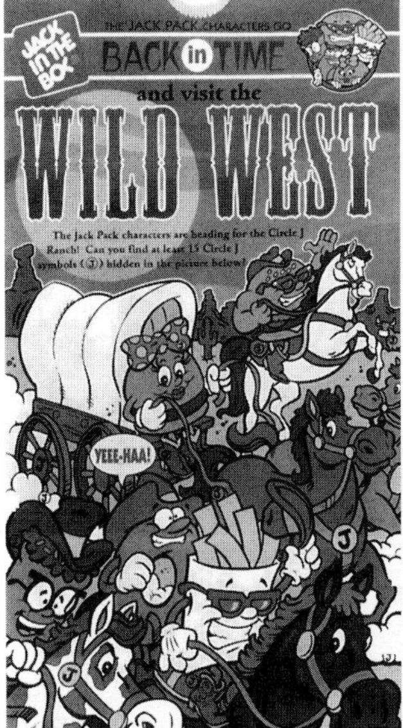

JA0441 JA0443

JA0442 Sack Back

JA0442	Ancient Egypt	1 - 2
JA0443	The Vikings	1 - 2
JA0444	Dinosaur Days	1 - 2
JA0445	Camelot	1 - 2

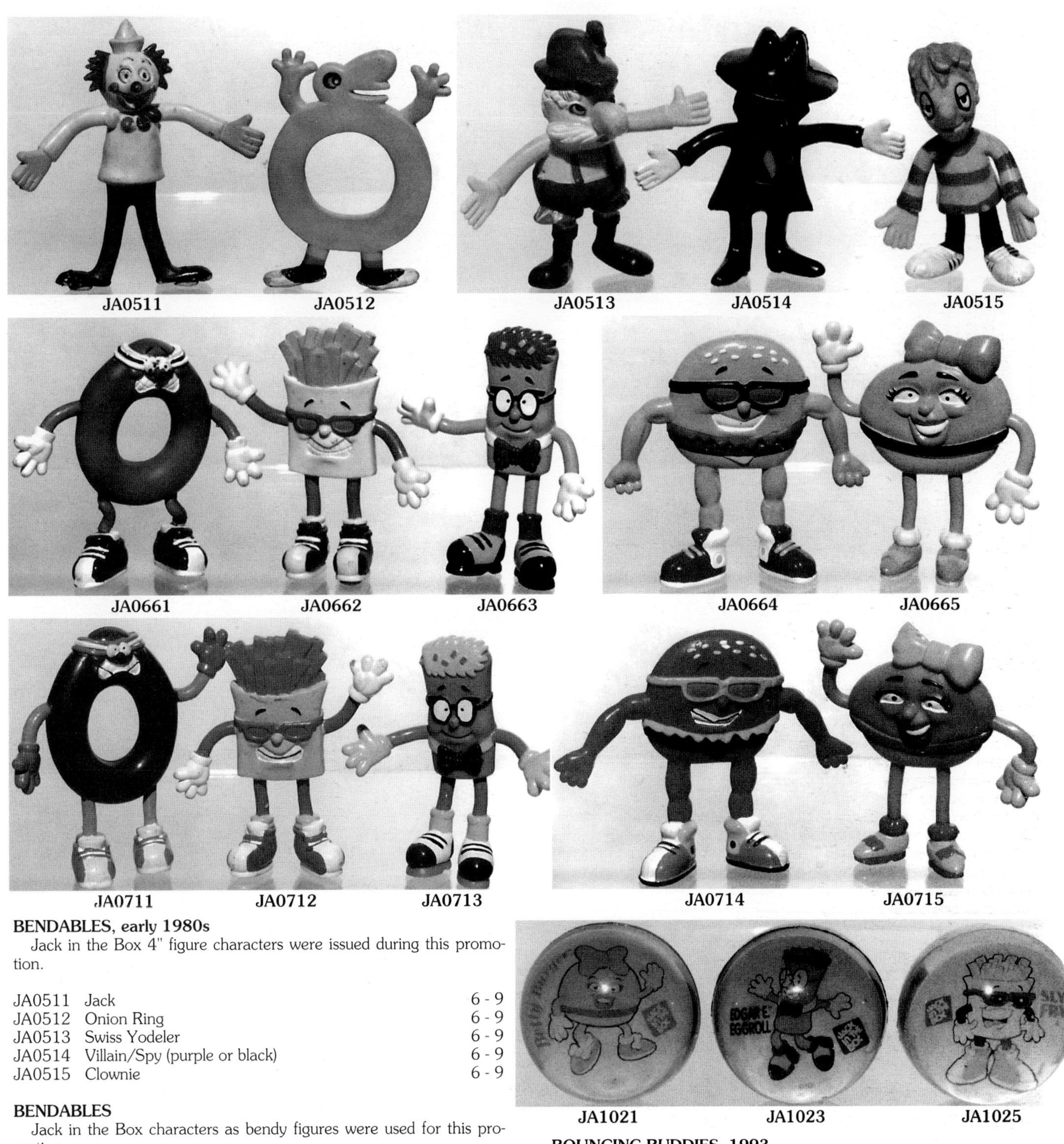

JA0511 JA0512 JA0513 JA0514 JA0515

JA0661 JA0662 JA0663 JA0664 JA0665

JA0711 JA0712 JA0713 JA0714 JA0715

BENDABLES, early 1980s

Jack in the Box 4" figure characters were issued during this promotion.

JA0511	Jack	6 - 9
JA0512	Onion Ring	6 - 9
JA0513	Swiss Yodeler	6 - 9
JA0514	Villain/Spy (purple or black)	6 - 9
JA0515	Clownie	6 - 9

BENDABLES

Jack in the Box characters as bendy figures were used for this promotion.

JA0661	Ollie O. Ring	6 - 9
JA0662	Sly Fry	6 - 9
JA0663	Edgar E. Eggroll	6 - 9
JA0664	Jumbo Jack	6 - 9
JA0665	Betty Burger	6 - 9

BENDABLES, 1991

These are identical to the previous set, but molded in different colors.

JA0711	Ollie O. Ring, purple	6 - 9
JA0712	Sly Fry, red	6 - 9
JA0713	Edgar E. Eggroll, light blue	6 - 9
JA0714	Jumbo Jack, red	6 - 9
JA0715	Betty Burger, pink	6 - 9

JA1021 JA1023 JA1025

BOUNCING BUDDIES, 1993

Hard clear 1½ colored balls contain a flat disk with a character on it.

JA1021	Betty Burger	2 - 4
JA1022	Ollie O. Ring	2 - 4
JA1023	Edgar E. Eggroll	2 - 4
JA1024	Jumbo Jack	2 - 4
JA1025	Sly Fry	2 - 4

CARD GAMES, 1991

Children's card games were offered during this promotion. The cards each measured 1¾" x 2½" and had the Jack in the Box logo on the back.

JA1041	Memory Match	2 - 4
JA1042	Leader of the Pack	2 - 4

JA1041 JA1042 JA1550

JA2331 JA2332 JA2333 JA2334 JA2335

JA3721 JA3722 JA3723 JA3751

JA3771 JA3772 JA3773 JA4501, JA4502

EARTH DAY, 1992

To celebrate the 22nd anniversary of Earth Day this date in 1992, facts and games were featured in an Earth Day booklet.

JA1550	Earth Day fact and game book	2 - 4
Sack		
JA1555	Jack Pack Meal Sack	1 - 2

FINGER PUPPETS, 1992

The Jack Pack characters were issued as finger puppets during this offering. Each comes with accent color variations.

JA2331	Edgar E. Eggroll	5 - 7
JA2332	Betty Burger	5 - 7
JA2333	Jumbo Jack	5 - 7
JA2334	Sly Fry	5 - 7
JA2335	Ollie O. Ring	5 - 7
JA2340	Inventors sack	1 - 2

JACK PACK FOR JUNIORS, 1992

This promotion featured color tray puzzles.

JA3721	Betty Burger & Jumbo Jack	1 - 3
JA3722	Ollie O. Ring, Edgar E. Eggroll & Sly Fry	1 - 3
JA3723	Junior Jack Pack	1 - 3

JACK PACK PUZZLES, 1991

Full-color 9-piece jigsaw puzzles were used.

JA3751	Carousel Scene	2 - 4
JA3752	Speedboat Scene	2 - 4
JA3753	Hiking Scene	2 - 4

JACK PACK PUZZLES, 1992

This promotion was the same format as the '91 Jack Pack Puzzle set, but with different scenes on the puzzles.

JA3771	Road Puzzle	2 - 4
JA3772	Farm Puzzle	2 - 4
JA3773	Undersea Puzzle	2 - 4

JACK PACK STICKERS, 1991

Four by five inch heavyweight paper folder opens to 5" by 8" and contains 2 colorful stickers of the Jack Pack. The inside contains Jack Pack Facts.

JA4411 1 Ollie O. Ring / 2 Betty Burger 1 - 3
JA4412 3 Sly Fry / 4 Edgar E. Eggroll 1 - 3

JACK PACK STICKERS, 1993

Sticker sheets featuring the Jack Pack characters.

JA4501 Set 1 1 - 2
JA4502 Set 2 1 - 2

JA4731 JA4731 JA4731

MAGNETS

Square refrigerator magnets measuring 2⅜" featured the Jack in the Box characters.

JA4731 Edgar E. Eggroll 2 - 5
JA4732 Jumbo Jack 2 - 5
JA4733 Tony Taco 2 - 5
JA4734 Ollie O. Ring 2 - 5

JA4901 JA4902

MINI YO-YOS, 1992

Mini Yo-Yo's about 1" in diameter were offered for each character.

JA4901 Edgar E. Eggroll 2 - 4
JA4902 Betty Burger 2 - 4
JA4903 Sly Fry 2 - 4
JA4904 Ollie O. Ring 2 - 4
JA4905 Jumbo Jack 2 - 4

MAKE-A-SCENE JACK PACK, 1990

A different scene was printed on the back of three 5" x 6" paper sheets. On the front were 20-25 peel-off stickers to be used to complete the scene.

JA4921 Beach Make-A-Scene 2 - 4
JA4922 Space Make-A-Scene 2 - 4
JA4923 Musical Make-A-Scene 2 - 4

NATURE HIKE

A box has been found for this promotion.

JA5010 JA5210

JA5010 Box 8 - 12

PINOCCHIO AND THE EMPEROR OF THE NIGHT

A box has been found for this promotion.

JA5210 Box 8 - 12

JA5401

PRISMASCOPES

Solid Color Prismascopes in 4 or 5 colors were offered. Each has the Jack in the Box logo.

JA5401 Prismascopes, each 1 - 3

PUZZLE MIX-UPS, 1992

Sixteen pressure-sensitive stickers came randomly mixed on a sticker sheet. When removed and placed in correct numerical order on the back of the sticker sheet, a sports scene which featured a Jack Pack character was created.

JA5625 Ollie O. Ring/Sly Fry 1 - 2

SCRATCH AND SMELL STICKERS, 1991

Mello Smello created uniquely treated pressure-sensitive stickers which, when scratched, emitted a special scent. Four sets of stickers were used.

JA6801 Popcorn, Strawberry, Root Beer, Cherry 1 - 2

SIPPER BOTTLE, DINOSAURS

A 5" plastic bottle featuring the Jack Pack characters and dinosaurs.

JA6921 Jumbo Jack and Betty Burger on dinosaurs 4 - 7

SIPPER BOTTLES, SPORTS

Sipper bottles featuring the Jack Pack in various sports scenes.

JA6931 Jumbo Jack and Edgar E. Eggroll 4 - 7
JA6932 Ollie O. Ring 4 - 7
JA6933 Sly Fry, Betty Burger, Edgar E. Eggroll 4 - 7

JA4921

JA4922

JA4923

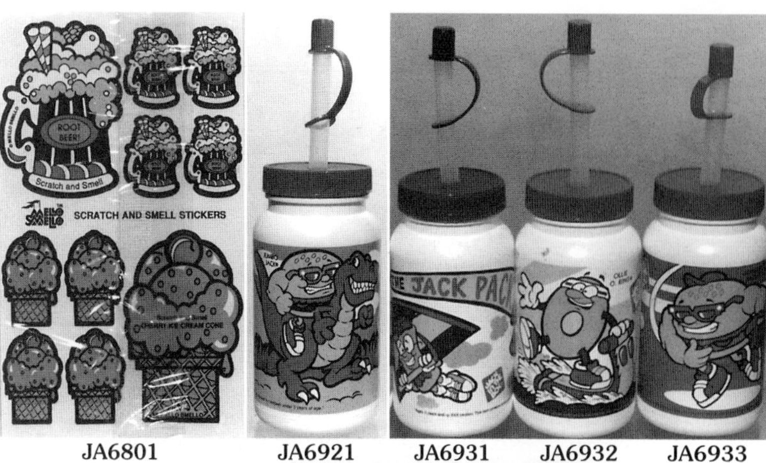

JA6801 JA6921 JA6931 JA6932 JA6933

JA8201

JA9947

WRIST WALLET

An Admark wrist wallet with the Jack in the Box logo.

JA8201 Wrist Wallet	**1 - 3**

ZANY SPACE BUDDIES, 1990

The box featured the promotion name across the top of the handle with "Kid's Meal" and the Jack in the Box logo printed on either side of the opening. Various space related games were printed on the sides of the box. The premium included sticker sets.

JA9941	Set #1	4 - 6
JA9942	Set #2	4 - 6
JA9943	Set #3	4 - 6
Box		
JA9946	Space Creatures Bank	3 - 5
JA9947	Way Out Words	3 - 5

LEE'S FAMOUS RECIPE FRIED CHICKEN

This regional fried chicken franchise was founded in Lima, Ohio, and has had a couple of interesting kid's meal promotions worthy of mentioning. When research on this book began they weren't doing anything. In 1993 up to publication cut-off, some Lee's outlets were simply giving away packages of Skittles candy (probably obtained through Admark) on an ongoing basis. Promotions were not offered by all locations.

CARTOON VIEWERS

Looney Tunes, Walter Lantz, and Mighty Mouse cartoons were used in rapid-advance filmstrip viewers.

LFR2501 Popeye	10 - 15
LFR2502 Bugs Bunny	10 - 15
LFR2503 Porky Pig	10 - 15
LFR2505 Woody Woodpecker	10 - 15
LFR2506 Mighty Mouse	10 - 15

MATCHBOX CARS

Standard Matchbox cars were used in this kid's meal. The only way to tell the car was a premium is to find packaged examples with the Lee's paper insert included.

LFR6700 Matchbox cars, each	1 - 10

Surprise Prize packages from Little Caesars

LITTLE CAESARS

Little Caesars is a midwest pizza outlet headquartered in Detroit. It pioneered the pizza marketing concept of "buy one—get one free," and became famous in its advertising markets for using the same words twice in the company's TV commercials. The Little Caesar mascot thus became known as the Pizza Pizza man... then the Meatsa Meatsa man.

LFR2501 LFR2502 LFR2503 LFR2505 LFR2506

Little Caesars did kids promotions over the years, but didn't settle into a regular program system-wide until 1992 when it instituted the Crazy Kids Meal. These promotions offered Surprise Prize packets, which were originally paper packets with two pockets. The larger pocket contained the premium; while the smaller pocket held a numbered trading card. Later Nerf packets were single-pocket pouches made of plastic, which included a rub-off game card instead of a trading card. After the Nerf program ended, the single prize concept continued in yellow plastic containers, and cards were dropped altogether.

Little Caesars can be found in a growing number of K mart stores.

MEATSA MEATSA MAN DOLL, 1990

The Little Caesars mascot in a 5" soft sculpture toga-wearing Roman figure came complete with a slice of pizza stitched to his right hand. A "pocket" in the back of his head allowed this premium to become a mini finger puppet.

LI5501	Meatsa Meatsa Man	5 - 8

MY SCHOOL STUFF, 1988

Premiums offered during this late summer promotion have a back-to-school theme. A pencil box could be made from a Little Caesars Pizza box. It came with stickers of pizza pies for use in decorating it. A Pizza Box for "My School Stuff" came with a cardboard protractor and 6" ruler.

LI5901	Pizza Box w/Pizza Stickers, protractor, & ruler	8 - 15

SURPRISE PRIZE 1992-94

The first three surprise prize promotions were done in waves of eight themed premiums, each with a numbered trading card. The various promotions are broken into sub-categories below. Each phase includes eight premiums, but only known items are listed.

Sports! Sports!, 1992

LI7301	Ball w/Basketball! Basketball! card	3 - 6
LI7302	Throwing Spinner w/Tumble! Tumble! card	3 - 6
LI7303	Water Squirter w/Swim! Swim! card	3 - 6
LI7304	Pizza! Pizza! Jumper Game w/Jump! Jump! card	4 - 8
LI7305	Punch-out Soccer Game w/Soccer! Soccer! card	4 - 8
LI7308	Maze Game w/Hockey! Hockey! card	3 - 6

Music! Music!, 1992

LI7309	Song Song punch-out book w/Bass! Bass! card	3 - 6
LI7310	Fold 'N' Solve Puzzle w/Tuba! Tuba! card	3 - 6

LI5501 LI5901

LI7301 LI7302 LI7303 LI7304

LI7308 LI7309 LI7310

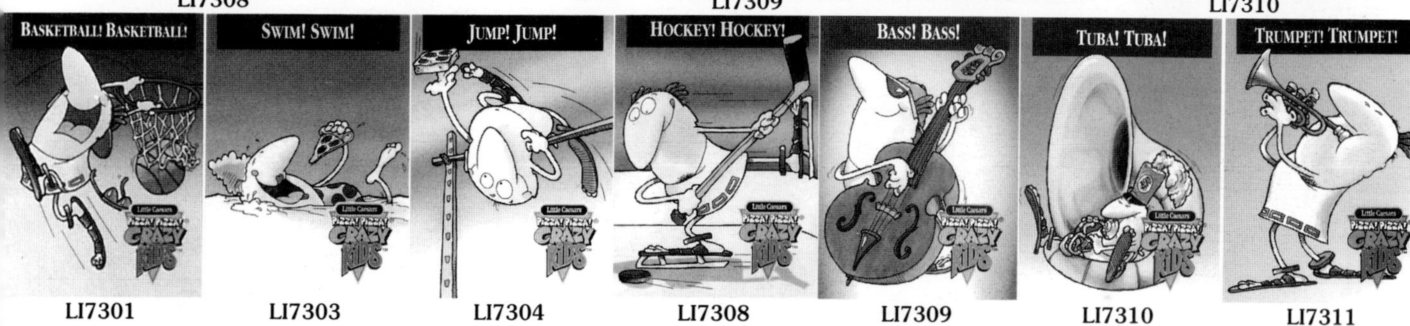

LI7301 LI7303 LI7304 LI7308 LI7309 LI7310 LI7311

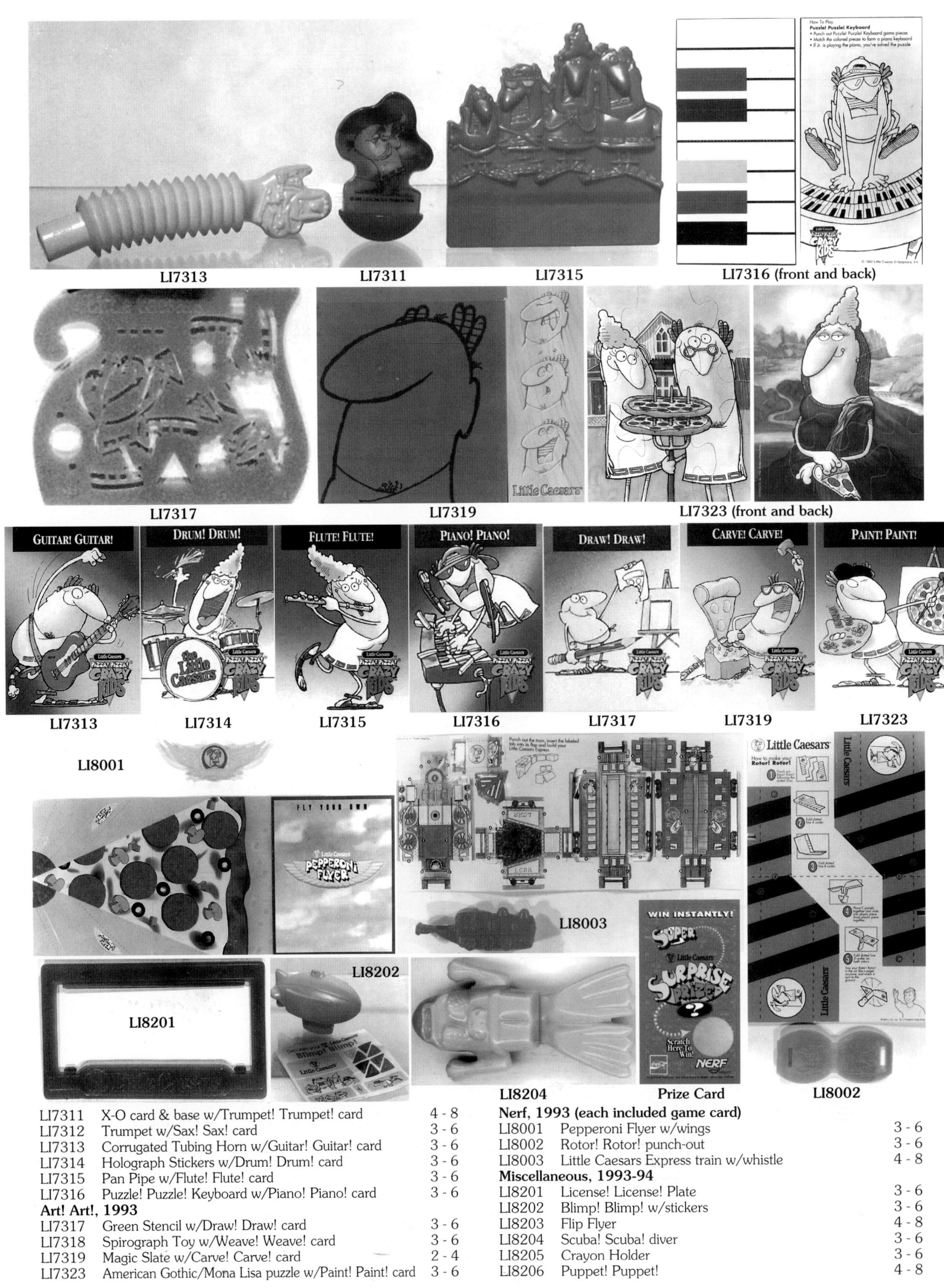

LI7311	X-O card & base w/Trumpet! Trumpet! card	4 - 8
LI7312	Trumpet w/Sax! Sax! card	3 - 6
LI7313	Corrugated Tubing Horn w/Guitar! Guitar! card	3 - 6
LI7314	Holograph Stickers w/Drum! Drum! card	3 - 6
LI7315	Pan Pipe w/Flute! Flute! card	3 - 6
LI7316	Puzzle! Puzzle! Keyboard w/Piano! Piano! card	3 - 6
Art! Art!, 1993		
LI7317	Green Stencil w/Draw! Draw! card	3 - 6
LI7318	Spirograph Toy w/Weave! Weave! card	3 - 6
LI7319	Magic Slate w/Carve! Carve! card	2 - 4
LI7323	American Gothic/Mona Lisa puzzle w/Paint! Paint! card	3 - 6
Nerf, 1993 (each included game card)		
LI8001	Pepperoni Flyer w/wings	3 - 6
LI8002	Rotor! Rotor! punch-out	3 - 6
LI8003	Little Caesars Express train w/whistle	4 - 8
Miscellaneous, 1993-94		
LI8201	License! License! Plate	3 - 6
LI8202	Blimp! Blimp! w/stickers	3 - 6
LI8203	Flip Flyer	4 - 8
LI8204	Scuba! Scuba! diver	3 - 6
LI8205	Crayon Holder	3 - 6
LI8206	Puppet! Puppet!	4 - 8

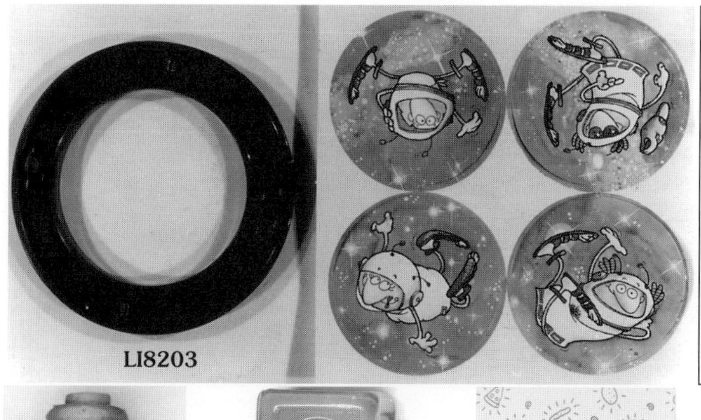

LI8203

LI8206

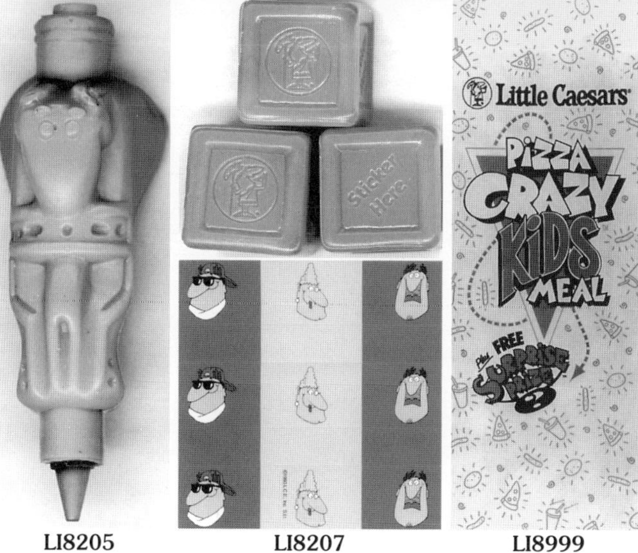

LI8205 LI8207 LI8999

LI8207	Three-in-a-Row game	2 - 4
LI8208	Piece O' Pizza Maze	3 - 6

Sack

LI8999	Surprise Prize Sack (used will all promotions)	.50 - 1

LONG JOHN SILVER'S

Long John Silver's is a national franchised seafood chain operated in most states. Several kid's meals going back into the 1980s are known. Back then a standard treasure chest box was used. Tomart has acquired two versions: a regular treasure chest box and a second which is identical to the first on the outside, but with a "secret panel" on the inside which opened to reveal the hidden treasure. The box found had Walt Disney's *Peter Pan* stickers in the false bottom, but these could not be verified as a Long John Silver's premium. A variety of other items listed under Miscellaneous Premiums might have been used in this way.

In 1990, the program changed to a more traditional kid's meal concept, and a wider variety of premiums have since been included.

AQUATIC SERIES TRADING CARDS, 1993

Sets of trading cards depicting aquatic animals. Each shrink-wrapped set included three cards; the last set included a checklist as well.

LO0501	Set #1 (cards 1, 2, & 3)	1 - 2
LO0502	Set #2 (cards 4, 5, & 6)	1 - 2
LO0503	Set #3 (cards 7, 8, & 9)	1 - 2
LO0504	Set #4 (cards 10, 11, & 12)	1 - 2
LO0505	Set #5 (cards 13, 4, & 15)	1 - 2
LO0506	Set #6 (cards 16, 17, & 18)	1 - 2
LO0507	Set #7 (cards 19, 20, & 21)	1 - 2
LO0508	Set #8 (cards 22, 23, 24, & Checklist)	1 2

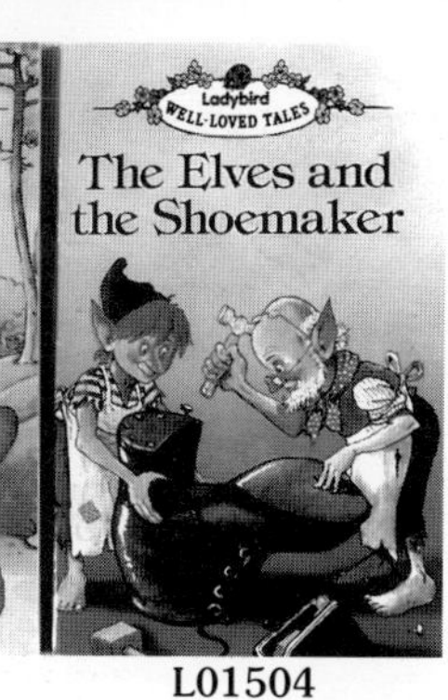

L01501 L01502 L01504

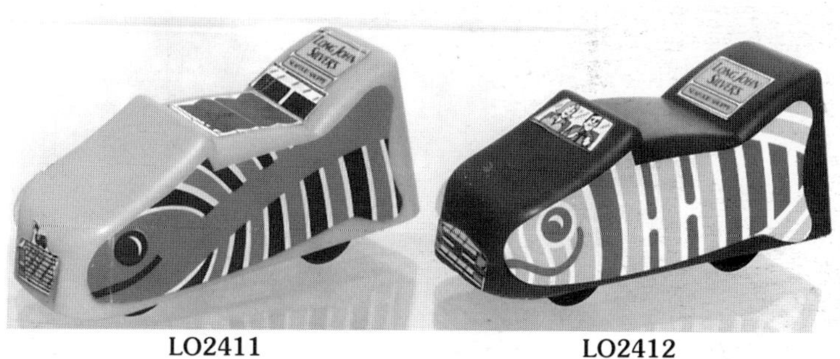

LO2411 LO2412

CLASSIC TALES, 1991, 1993

Ladybird Books Inc. published the "Ladybird Well-Loved Tales" for Long John Silver's. Fully-illustrated paper storybooks 3" x 4½ in size.

LO1501	Thumbelina	2 - 4
LO1502	The Gingerbread Man	2 - 4
LO1503	Jack and the Beanstalk	2 - 4
LO1504	The Elves and the Shoemaker	2 - 4

FISH CARS, 1986

Plastic cars shaped like fish. Each came with decals to decorate the car.

LO2411	Yellow Car	2 - 4
LO2412	Blue Car	2 - 4

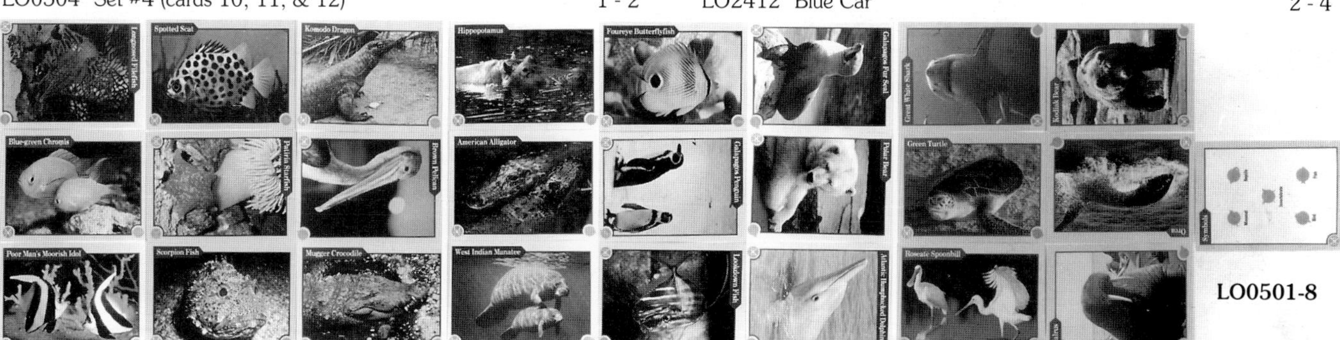

LO0501-8

LO3501 LO3502

LO3503 LO3504

I ♥ DINOSAURS, 1993

Softcover Golden Look Look Books written and illustrated by Michael Berenstain were used.

LO3501	King of the Dinosaurs — Tyrannosaurus Rex	1 - 4
LO3502	The Horned Dinosaur — Triceratops	1 - 4
LO3503	The Spike-Tailed Dinosaur — Stegosaurus	1 - 4
LO3504	The Biggest Dinosaurs	1 - 4

LO4651

LO4652

MAP ACTIVITIES, 1991, 1993

Coated paper maps featuring 3 diverse locales came with individual sheets of whimsical stickers featuring the Long John Silver's characters. On the back was a fill-in game of questions regarding items found on the reverse side of the map.

LO4653

LO6507

LO4651	Solar System	2 - 4
LO4652	U.S.A.	2 - 4
LO4653	The World	2 - 4

ONCE UPON A FOREST, 1993

Premiums of this kid's meal promotion tied in with the Twentieth Century Fox movie, *Once Upon a Forest*. Each of these five animal characters were featured as a 2" hard plastic straw hugger. One variation is known to exist for this set. Russell was issued with two different basic body colors —flesh and rust.

LO6501	Michelle, pink dress	2 - 4
LO6502	Abigail, blue overalls	2 - 4
LO6503	Edgar, yellow coat & scarf	2 - 4
LO6504	Cornelius, khaki coat	2 - 4
LO6505	Russell, flesh color w/green pants & shirt	2 - 4
LO6506	Russell, rust color w/green pants & shirt	2 - 4

LO7321 LO7322 LO7323

LO7324 LO7325

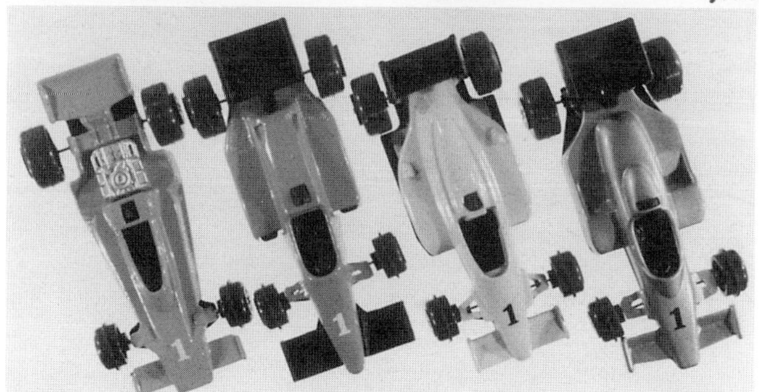

LO6751 LO6752 LO6753 LO6754

Sacks

LO6506 Coming June 18 1 - 2
LO6507 Now Playing 1 - 2

RACING CHAMPIONS, 1989

Metal Indy-style racers made by Racing Champions were given.

LO6751 Blue car 3 - 6
LO6752 Green car 3 - 6
LO6753 Yellow car 3 - 6
LO6754 Gold car 3 - 6

SEAWALKERS, 1990

Ramp Walkers in 3" plastic sea creatures each figure had a white thread attached to a round 1⅜" plastic disk.

LO7321 Sylvia, sea monster, lt purple/pink 2 - 5
LO7322 Sydney, sea monster, yellow/dk purple 2 - 5
LO7323 Flash, turtle, green/yellow 2 - 5
LO7324 Quinn, penguin, black/white 2 - 5
LO7325 Captain Flint, parrot, green/yellow/red 2 - 5

Box

LO7326 Seawalkers 3 - 6

LO7341 LO7342 LO7343

SEA WATCHERS, 1990

Telescopes with a paper scenes around the base were given away with this kids meal. Each was molded in two parts so that characters or ships in the scenes could be mixed or matched for humorous effects.

LO7341 Orange Sea Watcher 2 - 5
LO7342 Pink Sea Watcher 2 - 5
LO7343 Yellow Sea Watcher 2 - 5

SUPERSTAR BASEBALL CARDS, 1990

Eight different sets of trading cards were issued. Each set included 5 cards featuring different baseball superstars, plus a cover card.

LO7651 LO7652 LO7653 LO7654

LO7655 LO7656 LO7657 LO7658

LO7651 Set #1, Don Mattingly Set 6 - 10
LO7652 Set #2, Wade Boggs Set 6 - 10
LO7653 Set #3, Mark McGwire Set 6 - 10
LO7654 Set #4, Mark Grace Set 6 - 10
LO7655 Set #5, Darryl Strawberry Set 6 - 10
LO7656 Set #6, Nolan Ryan Set 6 - 10
LO7657 Set #7, Bobby Bonilla Set 6 - 10
LO7658 Set #8, Bret Saberhagen Set 6 - 10

Puzzle Cards from LO7801

LO7841

TREASURE CAPS, 1994

A set of 32 cardboard trading caps and four foil caps depicting four categories of undersea curiosities: Sunken Treasures, Natural Treasures, Underwater Vehicles, and Shells. Four puzzle cards each have a checklist. The various caps are as follows:

Sunken Treasures	Natural Treasures	Underwater Vehicles	Seashells
Galleon	Black Coral	Bathysphere	Turrids
Silver Bars	Sea Fan	Bathyscaphe	Sundails
Jewels	Coral Reef	Early Sub	Top Shells
Chest	Kelp	Diving Bell	Wentletraps
Cups	Clams	Nuclear Sub	Murex Shells
Anchors	Sponges	Submersible	Volutes
Necklaces	Pearls	Diving Saucer	Cones
Crowns	Snails	Station	Augers
Gold Coins (foil)	Red Coral (foil)	Scuba Diver (foil)	Conch Shell (foil)

Caps from LO7801

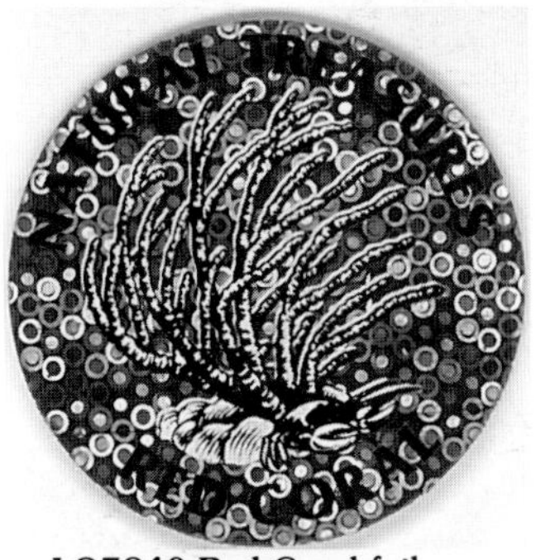

LO7840 Red Coral foil cap (actual size)

LO8021

LO7801	Set of 32 caps and 4 puzzle cards	10 - 20
LO7840	Foil Caps, each	4 - 8
Sack		
LO7841	Treasure Caps	1 - 2

TREASURE ISLAND, 1990

A Treasure Island Activity book by Bantam Doubleday Dell Publishing.

LO8021	Treasure Island Activity Book	2 - 4

TREASURE TROLLS PENCIL TOPPERS, 1993

The standard promotion used also by Hardee's, Roy Rodgers, and Wal-Mart. Only the sack was unique.

LO8201	Pink Hair	1 - 2
LO8202	Purple Hair	1 - 2
LO8203	Blue Hair	1 - 2
LO8204	Green Hair	1 - 2
LO8205	Orange Hair	1 - 2
LO8206	Yellow Hair	1 - 2

LO8201 LO8202 LO8203 LO8204 LO8205 LO8206

LO8210

LO8831 **LO8832**

LO8833 **LO8834**

LO8836

Sack		
LO8210	Treasure Trolls	1 - 2

WATER BLASTERS, 1990

Long John Silver's character heads as 2" rubber water squirters.

LO8831	Billy Bones	3 - 6
LO8832	Long John Silver	3 - 6
LO8833	Captain Flint	3 - 6
LO8834	Ophelia Octopus	3 - 6
Box		
LO8836	Water Blasters	4 - 8

YO-YOs

Standard plastic yo-yos were issued. Each had the Long John Silver's name printed on one side and a sea creature printed on the other side.

LO9611 LO9612 LO9613

LO9797

LO9798

LO9802

LO9611	Sea Horse, red	4 - 8
LO9612	Octopus, yellow	4 - 8
LO9613	Dolphin, blue	4 - 8

MISCELLANEOUS PREMIUMS

The following items are known to exist, but no further information is currently available.

LO9790	Long John Silver's Doubloon - 1754 - Mary Read	5 - 10
LO9791	Long John Silver's Doubloon - 1754 - Anne Bonney	5 - 10
LO9795	Food container in shape of a ship with a stand-up piece featuring a sailor and the Jolly Roger	2 - 4
LO9797	Adventure on Volcano Island Paint with Water Fun	4 - 6
LO9798	"Welcome to Captain Flint's Undersea Adventure."	4 - 6
Boxes		
LO9801	Treasure Chest	4 - 8
LO9802	Treasure Chest w/false bottom	5 - 10

PIZZA HUT

Pizza Hut, owned by Pepsico, is the largest national chain of pizza restaurants. Occasional kids promotions were transformed to a weekly marketing program in 1990. Pepsi ownership spotlights special attention on the drink by including special plastic cups with each promotion. Wherever possible, the cup becomes the main focus of the "Kids Pizza Pack" by use of a special top.

Self-liquidating tie-in premiums have been used on several major promotion occasions. A typical offer will include the cup, toy premium, illustrated pizza box, and placemat for dine-in customers. When none of the regular premiums are suitable for children under 3, a sticker sheet has been used. Kid Packs are available at all regular restaurants, but not delivery/carry-out only locations. Every Tuesday night at Pizza Hut kids receive a pack of gummi bears or a special tie-in premium. These are only available to children who eat-in on Tuesday.

"While supplies last" is extremely important at Pizza Hut. Premiums never seem to be available in equal numbers, and outlets seem to run out of toys more often than other fast food outlets...and never offer a fill-in or past premium. Kids are just out of luck that visit...which is very difficult to explain to a six year old.

Pizza Hut does 6-8 promotions per year, so items don't change regularly each week. Consumers never know how often they need to visit to collect all the different cups and premiums. Table signs are usually miniatures of the window signs.

PI0153 Detail

AIR GARFIELD, 1993

A12" blue vinyl inflatable spaceball, weighted at the bottom, featured a flat vinyl piece with Garfield in a space-suit suspended inside with clear vinyl strips. The effect is seeing him "walk in space." A vinyl kite featured a painting of Garfield in a hang-glider rigging. The kite had a 20" span and a yellow plastic tail. The parachute was 3" in diameter with a PVC figure of Garfield with a red parachute pack on his back in a free fall pose. A flying disk was the fourth announced premium but was not found in any Pizza Hut visited.

PI0151	Inflatable Spaceball	4 - 8
PI0152	Kite	3 - 6
PI0153	Parachute	4 - 8
PI0154	Flying Disk	4 - 8
PI0155	Garfield & Odie Free Falling, cup	1 - 4
PI0156	Garfield & Odie in Outer Space, cup	1 - 4
Box		
PI0158	Garfield	2 - 4

PI0155 PI0156

PI0158

PI0160

PI0258

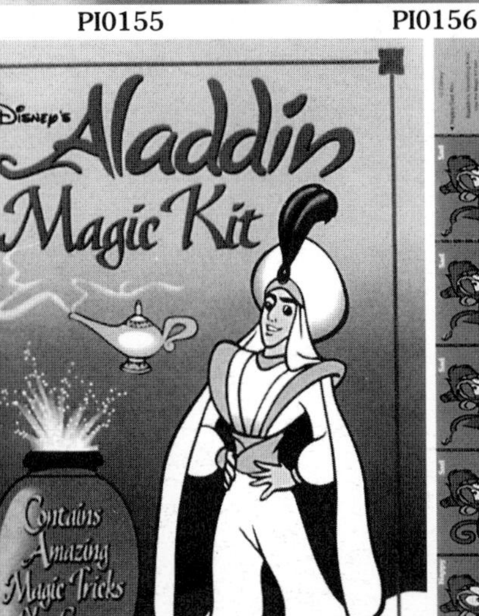

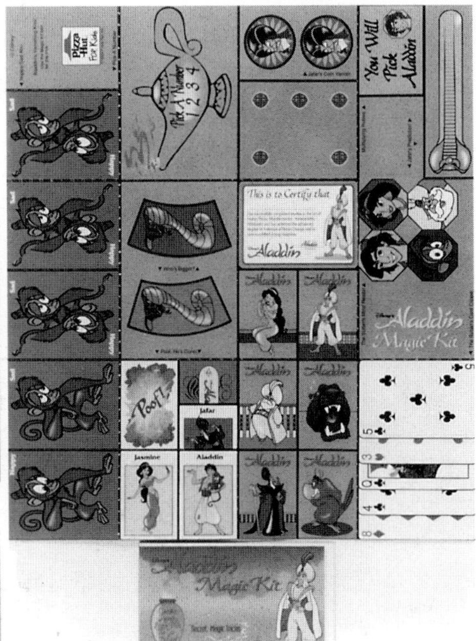

PI0250

PI0252

PI0251

Point of Purchase

PI0160	Table Card	1 - 3

ALADDIN, 1993

Three magical items were used to tie-in with the video release of this classic Walt Disney animated film. Characters did not appear on the Pepsi cup, only a star in a blue sky was shown. The Magic Kit included a variety of paper tricks, an instruction book, and a storage box.

PI0250	Magic Kit	3 - 6
PI0251	Story Book w/Magic Carpet decoder	3 - 6

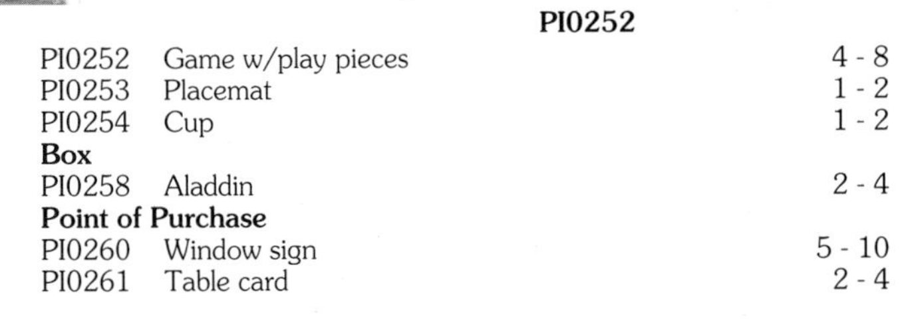

PI0252	Game w/play pieces	4 - 8
PI0253	Placemat	1 - 2
PI0254	Cup	1 - 2
Box		
PI0258	Aladdin	2 - 4
Point of Purchase		
PI0260	Window sign	5 - 10
PI0261	Table card	2 - 4

PI0272 PI0274 PI0271 PI0273

ALIENS, 1980s

Flexible 3"-4" alien figures were issued for this promotion. The Pizza Hut logo appears prominently on the back of each head. These have since been re-molded with the logo removed.

PI0271	Green/Yellow w/ray gun & hat w/#3	8 - 12
PI0272	Red/Black/White w/ray gun	8 - 12
PI0273	Yellow/Pink in polka dot bow & dress	8 - 12
PI0274	Yellow/Orange round body w/big smile	8 - 12
PI0276-9	Remolded figures w/o Pizza Hut logo, each	2 - 4

JACK IN THE BOX
THE JACK PACK CHARACTERS GO
BACK in TIME
the VIKINGS
The Vikings were people who lived about 1000 years ago in northern Europe. They were best known as excellent seafaring explorers and settlers.
The Muppet Christmas Carol
TACO BELL
ONLY IN THEATRES
HAPPY BIRTHDAY!
TACO MAN
HOME SWEET HOME
A PEEK INSIDE THE
RAIN FOREST
A&W PLAYTOWN MEAL
A Day at the Zoo
TRANSFORMERS
ROBOTS IN DISGUISE
GENERATION 2
Puppy Surprise
The Busy World of Richard Scarry
MIGHTY MOUSE
CELEBRATE EARTH DAY
APRIL 22
LONG JOHN SILVER'S
Chick-fil-A
DOG FOOD
DOG AID

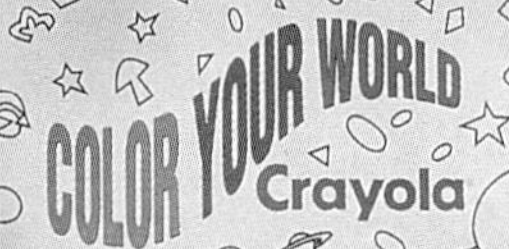

Roy Rogers
Roy Rogers
Roy Rogers
Roy Rogers
TREX
TRI-TOPS
Aquameals
Roy Rogers
Roy Rogers
DINO MEAL
PULL OFF FOR SURPRIZE
FUN FLYER
Roy Rogers
STAR SEARCHERS
SPACESHIP
Roy Rogers
Treasure Trolls
PULL OFF FOR SURPRIZE

AMAZING ANIMALS
Wendy's Kids' Meal
Wendy's Kids' Meal
DID YOU KNOW?
Wendy's Kids' Meal
Wendy's Kids' Meal
Wendy's Kids' Meal
Say What?!
NATURE NOTES JOURNAL
KIDS 4 PARKS
WILLOW
GO BOTS
MOONSTRIKE
ALF TALES
Too much traffic! It's rush hour and George is late for dinner. Help him find his way through this sky-jam maze.
Charlie and Anne Marie are visiting Flo's home for lost puppies. How many puppies can you count in this scene.
YOGI BEAR
Uh-oh! Yogi's been up to his old tricks! Can you help Ranger Smith ride the surf to rescue the stolen picnic basket?
WENDY'S KIDS' MEAL
START
Disney's Gummi Bears
FAST FOOD RACERS
Wendy's
YIKES!
A METEOR IS HEADING FOR MOUSEVILLE!
HELP MIGHTY MOUSE FLY HIS WAY AROUND THE CLOUDS TO DESTROY IT.
Play-Doh
Play-Doh
Fingles
Wendy's
CIRCUS Wendy's WAGON

FEEL THE WARMTH
NOW APPEARING WEEKLY, THURSDAY NIGHTS ON FOX
ADOPT THE SIMPSONS COLLECTIBLE TOYS
*with any purchase of New Mini Muffins or New Cholesterol-Free Fries
Only $3.49* PLUS TAX
COLLECT ALL FIVE

GO WILD WITH THE SIMPSONS CAMPING FIGURES
Collect All 5
Get a new figure and pop-up camping scene only when you buy a Kids Club Meal!

Kid Transporters
Mix 'em! Match 'em! Race 'em!
Get one with purchase of a Kids Club Meal.
COLLECT ALL 6
For a limited time. While supplies last.

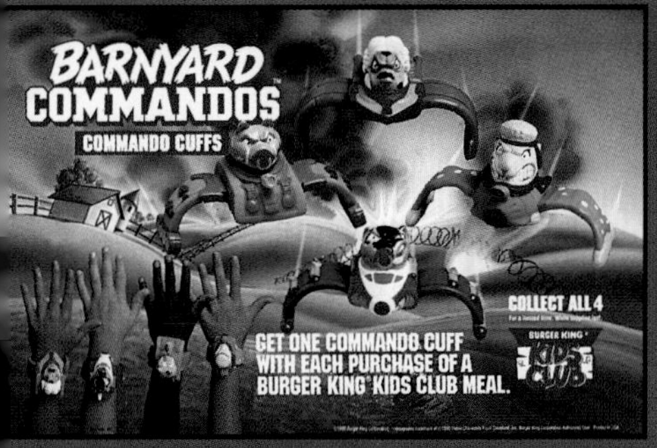
BARNYARD COMMANDOS
COMMANDO CUFFS
COLLECT ALL 4
GET ONE COMMANDO CUFF WITH EACH PURCHASE OF A BURGER KING KIDS CLUB MEAL.

BEETLEJUICE
SPOOKY 2-SIDED FIGURES
Get One Only When You Buy A Kids Club Meal!
Collect All 6– They're A Scream!

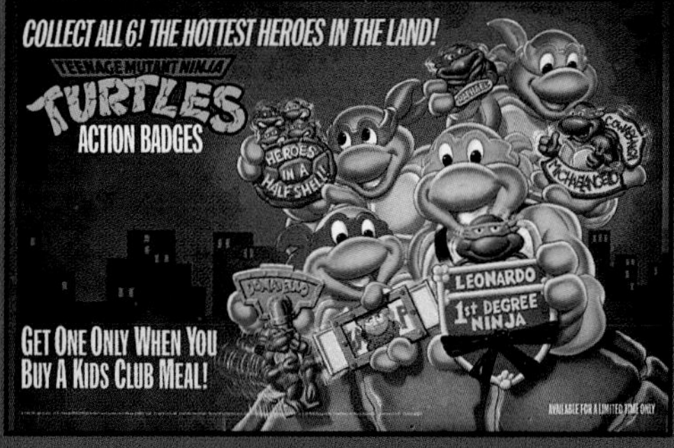
COLLECT ALL 6! THE HOTTEST HEROES IN THE LAND!
TEENAGE MUTANT NINJA TURTLES ACTION BADGES
LEONARDO 1st DEGREE NINJA
GET ONE ONLY WHEN YOU BUY A KIDS CLUB MEAL!

Bring the Magic Home!
Get a "Beauty and the Beast" Character
When You Buy a Kids Club Meal.
Collect all Four
See the movie at a theatre near you!

Life Savers Freaky Fellas!
Mix'em & Match'em.
Collect more than just Four!
Get a toy and Life Savers with each Kids Club Meal.

Make a SPLASH!
with Pinocchio and friends
Walt Disney's Pinocchio
See the movie at a theatre near you.
For More Fun, Collect Each One!
Get an inflatable toy from Walt Disney's "Pinocchio" with each Kids Club Meal purchase.

Disney's THE LITTLE MERMAID TOYS
GET ONE WITH EVERY KIDS CLUB MEAL PURCHASE
ARIEL WIND-UP
URCHIN SQUIRT TOY
SEBASTIAN WIND-UP
FLOUNDER SQUIRTER
COLLECT ALL 4! LIMITED TIME ONLY

Mickey's TOONTOWN Disneyland TOYS
Get One Wind-up Toy, Fun Pop-up & A Piece Of Mickey's TOONTOWN Map With Every Kids Club Meal Purchase.
Collect All 4
Disneyland

Happy Star Meal
Meal Includes:
• Choice of Hamburger, Cheeseburger, or Two Jr. Crisp Burritos
• Small French Fries
• Small Soft Drink
• One Beach Creatures Surf-prize!

Magic Frame
Magic Remote Control
Magic Tricks
Disappearing Food Trick
Magic Trunk

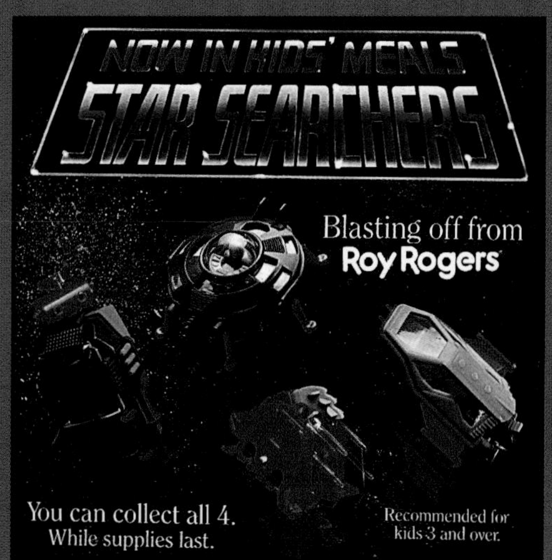
NOW IN KIDS' MEALS
STAR SEARCHERS
Blasting off from Roy Rogers
You can collect all 4.
While supplies last.
Recommended for kids 3 and over.

ACTUAL SIZE SHOWN HERE!
SAVE THE Animals
GET ONE
COLLECTOR ALBUM & 17 CARDS WITH EVERY KIDS CLUB MEAL PURCHASE
COLLECT ALL 4 SETS!
LIMITED TIME ONLY

FEATURING THE REAL GHOSTBUSTERS SURPRISE IN THE CASTLE MEAL.
Collect All 4!
There's one included in every Castle Meal.
White Castle
Castle Meal
It's Like Nothing Else. Nothing.

Join the Parade!
Collect all 4!
Get a Walt Disney World 20th Anniversary Parade Action Toy & Track when you buy a Kids Club Meal.

TootsieRoll Express
Includes a Castleburger, fries, soft drink, and Tootsie Roll Express car loaded with a ½ oz. chocolatey Tootsie Roll!
$1.59
COLLECT ALL
Castle Meal

READY TO ROLL
Hey Kids... Collect all 3!
Get A Lickety Split With Purchase Of A Kids Club Meal!

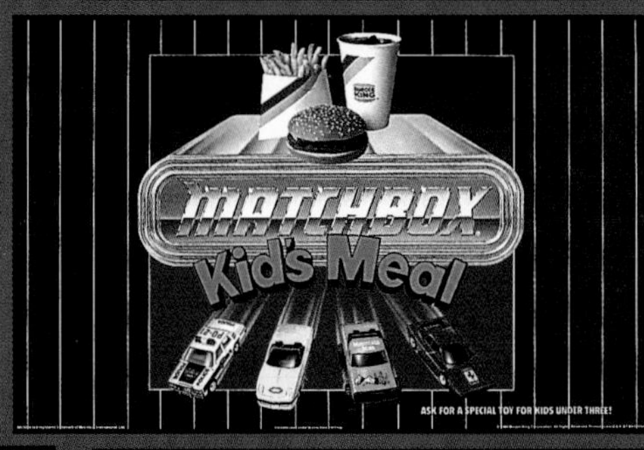
MATCHBOX
Kid's Meal
ASK FOR A SPECIAL TOY FOR KIDS UNDER THREE!

Disney's Aladdin
TOYS
GET ONE WITH EVERY KIDS CLUB MEAL PURCHASE
SEE THE MOVIE AT YOUR LOCAL THEATER!
BURGER KING KIDS CLUB
COLLECT ALL 5!

Join the Action with
WORLD TRAVEL ADVENTURE KITS
Collect Them All!
Get One When You Buy a Kids Club Meal.
BURGER KING KIDS CLUB

Crayola
Mystery Coloring Books
Get a Crayola Coloring Book and Crayons with purchase of a BURGER KING Kids Club Meal
¿QUE PASA, AMIGOS? I LINGO'S MY NAME.. ART'S MY GAME!
Collect all 6
BURGER KING KIDS CLUB

Happy Star Meal
FUN HOUSE FACES

Get Cool
KIDS CLUB SPINNING TOPS!
GET ONE TOP & LAUNCHER WITH EVERY KIDS CLUB MEAL PURCHASE!
COLLECT ALL 4
LIMITED TIME ONLY/WHILE SUPPLIES LAST

TEENAGE MUTANT NINJA TURTLES
BIKE GEAR
GET ONE RADICAL BIKE ACCESSORY WITH EVERY KIDS CLUB MEAL.
BIKE POUCH
COLLECT ALL FIVE! LIMITED TIME ONLY.
LICENSE PLATE & STICKERS
BIKE HORN
WHOA!
SQUEEZE BOTTLE
SPOKE SLIDERS
BURGER KING KIDS CLUB

DAYS OF Thunder
COLLECT ALL FOUR 32 OZ. CUPS
CAR 1
CITY CHEVROLET
CAR 2
SUPERFLO
CAR 3
HARDEE'S
CAR 4
MELLO YELLO
COLLECT ALL FOUR THUNDER RACERS
WHILE SUPPLIES LAST
THUNDER RACERS
99¢ each plus tax WITH ANY PURCHASE
32 OZ. COLLECTIBLE CUP WITH SOFT DRINK

Hardee's
MAGIC ZOO STRAWS
ONE IN EVERY FUNMEAL PACK
Collect all 4
While supplies last

Life Savers Freaky Fellas!
BURGER KING KIDS CLUB
LIFE SAVERS
Collect more than just Four!

Disney's GOOF TROOP BOWLING TOYS
GET ONE WITH EVERY KIDS CLUB M
PURCHASE!
PULL BACK...
LET IT GO!
CATCH DISNEY'S GOOF TROOP ON TV! CHECK LOCAL LISTINGS.

FENDER BENDER 500
RACERS
As seen on the Wake, Rattle & Roll TV Show
ONE RACER IN EACH FUNMEAL PACK!
While Supplies Last.

BURGER KING KIDS CLUB
ACTION FIGURES
COLLECT ALL 4!
GET ONE ACTION FIGURE WITH EACH PURCHASE OF A BURGER KING KIDS CLUB MEAL

TEENAGE MUTANT NINJA
TURTLES
ACTION CUPS!
COLLECT ALL 4
ONLY 39¢
with any drink purchase.
For a limited time.
While supplies last.

MINI FRICTION DRIVEN
Record Breakers
WORLD OF SPEED
TOTALLY AWESOME!
COLLECT ALL 6
For a limited time only
Get one with any Kids Club Meal purchase.

Join the Parade!
Collect all 4!
See details inside!

WOW KIDS! THESE TOYS ARE MADE WITH RECYCLED MATERIALS.
CAPTAIN PLANET
AND THE PLANETEERS
FLIP OVER STAR CRUISERS
COLLECT ALL 4
Get One Star Cruiser With Each Purchase Of A BURGER KING Kids Club Meal.

DAYS OF Thunder
Hardee's
32 OZ. CUP WITH SOFT DRINK $1.05 EACH PLUS TAX
COLLECT ALL FOUR WHILE SUPPLIES LAST.

THE FLINTSTONES
30TH ANNIVERSARY
FUNMEAL PACK
ONLY $2.59 each plus tax
While Supplies Last.
Includes Reg. Hamburger, Small Fries And Kid's Soft Drink.
Hardee's
THE FLINTSTONES FIGURINE & PREHISTORIC GADGET
One With Every FUNMEAL PACK Purchase

SMURFS
Funmeal Pack
COLLECT ALL SIX!
While supplies last.
Each Funmeal includes one figurine, Reg. Hamburger, Reg. Fries and Sm. Soft Drink.

SQUIRTERS
children's meal
Hardee's
ollect All Four!
ch Children's Meal Includes A Squirter.

Benny
Alotta Stile
Anita Break
Buster
NEW!
CALIFORNIA RAISINS
COLLECT ALL FOUR!
99¢
The California Raisins.

MARVEL
SUPER HEROES
Funmeal Pack
Collect All Four!
Each Funmeal includes a Super Hero, Reg. Hamburger, Reg. Fries, Sm. Soft Drink.
While Supplies Last.
Actual Size Not Shown.

Now in Kids' Meals
Take-off with Roy's
FUN FLYERS
le supplies last.
mended for kids over 3.
Collect all 4

DINO FUN
WITH EVERY ROY ROGERS KIDS' MEAL!
Roy Rogers
GET'EM BEFORE THEY'RE EXTINCT!
GLOW IN THE DARK DINOSAURS!
COLLECT ALL 8

Now in Kids' Meals
Roy Rogers presents
Gator Tales
Flora Gator
Skater Gator
Investigator
A.V. Gator
You can collect all 4.
While supplies last.
Recommended for kids 3 and over.

White Castle
Castle Meal
MARVEL Super Heroes
SPIDER-MAN
SILVER SURFER
CAPTAIN AMERICA
SHE-HULK
Wilfred
FEATURING THE REAL GHOSTBUSTERS SURPRISE IN THE CASTLE MEAL
WEEKS 1 & 2
SLIMER
Mint flavored toothpaste and toothbrush
WEEKS 3 & 4
Hairbrush
THE REAL GHOSTBUSTERS
WEEKS 5 & 6
Bubblegum flavored toothpaste and toothbrush
WEEKS 7 & 8
Soap dish and soap
Collect All 4!
There's one included in every Castle Meal.
White Castle
Castle Meal
It's Like Nothing Else. Nothing.
Tootsie Roll Express
Includes a Castleburger, fries, soft drink, and a Tootsie Roll Express car loaded with a 1/2 oz. chocolatey Tootsie Roll!
$1.59
COLLECT ALL 4!
Tootsie Roll EXPRESS
White Castle
Slugger
Ballerina
Hard Hat
Fire Chief
CAUTION:
Halloween.
White Castle
KIDS
Castle Meal
A meal fit for a kid!
Castle Meal FUN
EARTH FRIENDS
Woozy Wizard Explains Recycling!
Recycling is when you use something again and again. Or you make it into something else. It's good for the Earth because it saves natural resources and energy.
Fabulous FunShades
Collect All 4
Kid's Sunglasses
With Free FunCord!
White Castle

PI0401 PI0402

PI0403 PI0404

PI0631

PI0632

PI0638 PI0639 PI0640

PI0633

PI0642

BACK TO THE FUTURE, 1989

Sunglasses were a prominent prop in the *Back to the Future* films. Pizza Hut used this angle to offer four different exotic pairs made by Solar Shades. They were offered for sale in conjunction with *Back to the Future II* and were an introduction to regular Kids Pack promotions.

PI0401	Angles & Curves	3 - 6
PI0402	Pink Wings	3 - 6
PI0403	Black Wings	3 - 6
PI0404	Stoplights	3 - 6

BEAUTY AND THE BEAST, 1992

This promotion tied in with the release of Disney's *Beauty and the Beast* video. The regular premiums were three 32-piece puzzles. As is normal with Disney Pizza Hut promotions, no characters or Disney graphics appeared on the cups. Christmas graphics were substituted.

Beginning November 13, hand puppets could be purchased over-the-counter at Pizza Hut with any food purchase.

PI0635 PI0634

PI0637 PI0636

PI0641

PI0643

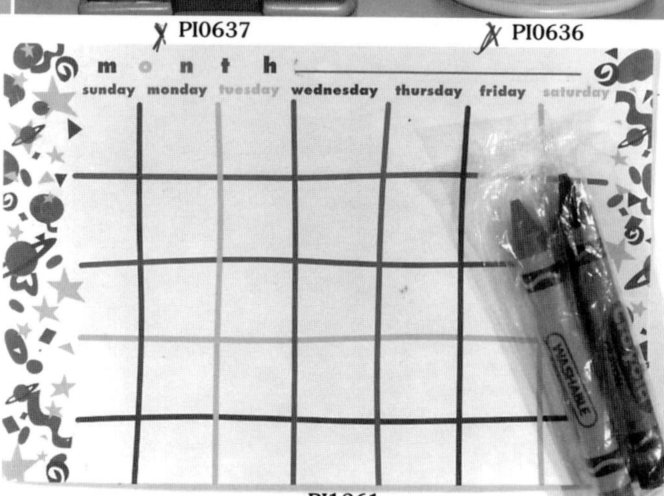

PI1261

PI0631	Beauty and the Beast puzzle (dance scene)	4 - 6
PI0632	Mrs. Potts, Lumiere, Cogsworth puzzle	4 - 6
PI0633	Lumiere puzzle (Be Our Guest dance scene)	4 - 6
PI0634	Beast, puppet	4 - 8
PI0635	Belle, puppet	4 - 8
PI0636	Chip, puppet	3 - 5
PI0637	Cogsworth, puppet	3 - 5
PI0638	Snowflake cup	1 - 2
PI0639	Christmas Stocking, Candy Can, Train cup	1 - 2
PI0640	Snowman, Sledding, Snowball cup	1 - 2
Box		
PI0641	Beauty and the Beast	2 - 4
Point of Purchase		
PI0642	Placemat	1 - 2
PI0643	Wall Poster	50 - 75

COLOR YOUR WORLD, 1993

Crayola crayons were promoted for this kid's meal with a special sixteen-ounce cup. An erasable calendar board came with a box of 4 standard-size Crayola crayons. The folded Color Your World poster measured 17" x 22" and came with two large crayons (blue and red).

PI1261	Calendar Board/Crayons	3 - 6
PI1262	Poster/Crayons	3 - 6
PI1263	Crayola Cup 16 oz (came with each meal)	2 - 4
Box		
PI1265	Color Your World	1 - 3
Point of Purchase		
PI1270	Table Card	2 - 4
PI1271	Display cup attachment w/crayons	2 - 4

PI1262

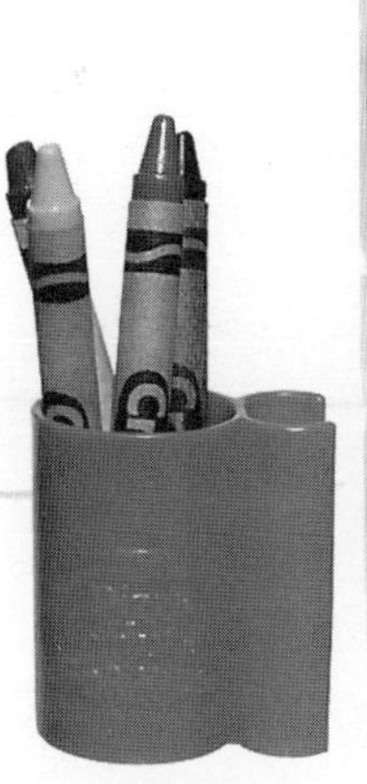

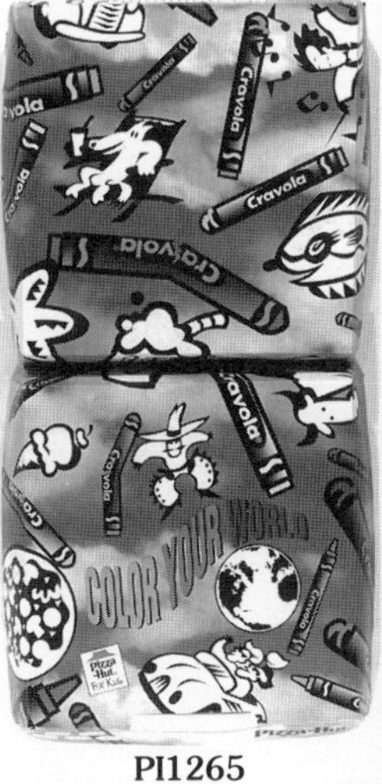

PI1263 PI1271 PI1265 PI1270 PI1509

PI1501 PI1502 PI1503 PI1504 PI1505 PI1506 PI1515

DINOSAURS!, 1993

Prehistoric Pizza Packs done with the Dinosaur Society included a 16-oz Dinosaurs! cup with a unique lid and a "Sticker-Saur" book. Each of the four white plastic cups depicted a background scene of the featured dinosaur and a brief description of it. A snap-on lid featured a vacuform head of the dinosaur. The "Sticker-Saur" book had a removable sheet of reusable embossed stickers to be applied to the cup.

PI1501	Brachiosaurus Cup & Lid	3 - 5
PI1502	Tyrannosaurus Rex Cup & Lid, 2 versions, ea.	3 - 5
PI1503	Triceratops Cup & Lid	3 - 5
PI1504	Stegosaurus Cup & Lid	3 - 5
PI1505	Brachiosaurus Sticker-Saur Book	2 - 4
PI1506	Tyrannosaurus Rex Sticker-Saur Book	2 - 4
PI1507	Triceratops Sticker-Saur Book	2 - 4
PI1508	Stegosaurus Sticker-Saur Book	2 - 4
Box		
PI1509	Dinosaurs!	2 - 4
Point of Purchase		
PI1515	Table Card	2 - 4
PI1516	Placemat	1 - 2

PI2081 PI2082 PI2083

EUREEKA'S CASTLE, 1990

Three character hand puppets (4½ x 6½ latex) from the MTV Nickelodeon series Eureeka's Castle were sold over the counter.

PI2081	Batley	2 - 5
PI2082	Eureeka	2 - 5
PI2083	Magellan	2 - 5

PI2091 PI2093

PI2091	Batley cup	1 - 3
PI2092	Eureeka cup	1 - 3
PI2093	Magellan cup	1 - 3

FERNGULLY, 1992

This animated feature called attention to ecology and the saving of the rainforest." The 16-oz drink cups with a snap-on clear plastic domed top could be used as the starter terrarium for the seeds issued as premiums. The punch-out paper illustrated stake had Colorado Blue Spruce tree seeds stuck to the glue strip inside each cardboard seed packet.

PI2230	Seed Packet	3 - 5
PI2231	Crysta and Zak cup w/seed packet	1 - 3
PI2232	Pips and the Beetle Boys cup w/seed packet	1 - 3
PI2233	Terrarium Cup 3 w/seed packet	1 - 3
PI2236	Book	3 - 5
Box		
PI2240	FernGully — The Last Rainforest	2 - 4

PI2230 (front and back)

PI2231 PI2232

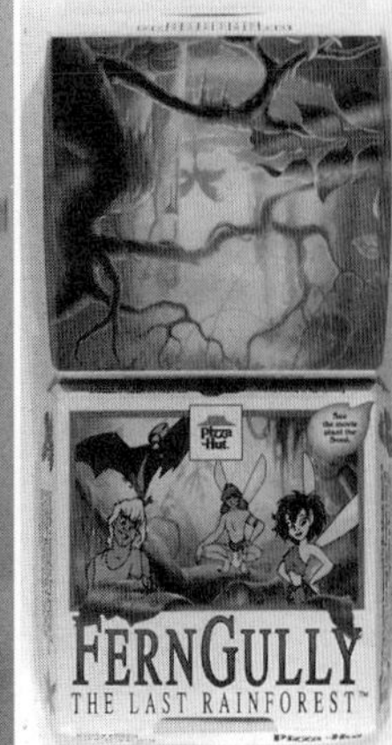

PI2240

PI2236

PI2380

PI2342 PI2341 PI2343

FIEVEL GOES WEST, 1991

Steven Spielberg's animated feature *An American Tail* promotion featured 16-oz drinking cups with a facial illustration of one of the main characters from the film." The unique snap-on lids were molded in the shape of the character's hat with a hole in the brim for the straw.

PI2341	Fievel w/gray 10-gallon hat w/orange band	3 - 5
PI2342	Cat R. Waul w/red top hat w/black band	3 - 5
PI2343	Wylie Burp w/tan tall front brim w/blue band	3 - 5

GARFIELD, 1992

Pizza Hut's first Garfield promotion.

PI2370	Cup	1 - 3
PI2371	Plastic ruler	2 - 4
PI2380	Placemat	1 - 2

GOOF TROOP, 1993

"Let's Get Goofy! Let's Get Cool!" based on Disney's *Goof Troop* TV show. A yellow and purple baseball cap came with a neck flap. On the front of the hat was a picture of Goofy and Max. White terry cloth wrist wrappers with a purple stripe around the center and embroidered head of Goofy A pair of neon green shoelaces and iron-on transfer featured Goofy and Max and the Goof Troop logo rounded out the promotion.

PI2401	Cap	5 - 10

PI2401 PI2402

PI2403 PI2404

PI2402	Wrist Wrapper	2 - 4
PI2403	Shoelaces	3 - 6
PI2404	Iron-On Transfer	1 - 3

PI2406 PI2410

PI4151 PI4152

PI4154 PI4153

Box

PI2406	Goof Troop	2 - 4
PI2410	Table Card	1 - 2

LAND BEFORE TIME, THE, 1988

From the Universal Studios movie Land Before Time 6 character 4½ x 6½ latex hand puppets were sold over the counter with any purchase. The first four were offered when the film was released. Petrie and Sharptooth were offered separately several months later with the release of the video.

PI4151	Cara	4 - 7
PI4152	Littlefoot	4 - 7
PI4153	Spike	4 - 7
PI4154	Duckie	4 - 7

PI4157 PI4158 PI4159

PI4161 PI4155 PI4156

PI4155	Petrie, purchased	6 - 10
PI4156	Sharptooth, purchased	6 - 10
PI4157	Littlefoot button	3 - 7
PI4158	Sharptooth button	3 - 7
PI4159	Petrie button	3 - 7
PI4160	Display	75 - 125
PI4161	Table Tent	4 - 8

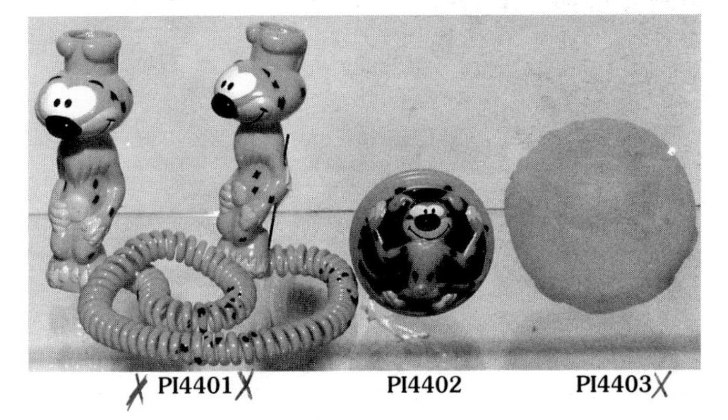

PI4401 PI4402 PI4403

MARSUPILAMI HOUBA DOUBA!, 1994

This Disney-licensed character from France was featured on three Kids Pack premiums.

PI4401	Jump rope	3 - 6
PI4402	Yo-Yo	3 - 6
PI4403	Glow Ball	1 - 4

Box

PI4408	Box	2 - 4

Point of Purchase

PI4410	Placemat	1 - 2
PI4411	Cardboard Standup	10 - 30
PI4412	Door Sign	5 - 15
PI4413	Table Card	1 - 2

NICKELODEON

Pizza Hut blew this one somehow. Local outlets never had anything but cups.

PI4801	Cup #1	1 - 3
PI4802	Cup #2	1 - 3

PI4408 PI4412 PI4413 PI4801 PI4802

PI5501 PI6961 PI6962

PI8281 PI8282 PI8283

PI6963 PI8290

PI8281 PI8283 PI8282

PIRATES OF DARK WATER (The), 1992

Two sticker sheets came with two bike wheel flappers. From the TV cartoon series, *The Pirates of Dark Water*.

PI5501	Pirates of Dark Water sticker sheets & wheel flappers	4 - 8

ROCKETEER, 1991

From the Disney movie, *The Rocketeer*. A punch-out paper Rocketeer airplane and a uniquely designed cup were the premiums.

PI6961	The Rocketeer Punch-Out Airplane	4 - 8
PI6962	The Rocketeer Cup	3 - 5
Box		
PI6963	The Rocketeer	2 - 4

UNIVERSAL MONSTERS, 1991

For Halloween a promotion for the Universal Studio monsters – The Wolfman, Frankenstein, and Dracula – were used. Each Pizza Pack included a 16-oz cup and a 2½ x 3½ trading card. The cup lid featured a 3D colored face of a Universal Monster." The snap-on lid featured a 3-D face of the character with a hole in the mouth for the straw.

PI8281	Dracula Cup w/Hologram Card	5 - 10
PI8282	Frankenstein Cup w/Hologram Card	5 - 10
PI8283	Wolfman Cup w/Hologram Card	5 - 10
Box		
PI8290	Universal Studios Monsters	2 - 4

PI8551 PI8552 PI8553

PI8554 PI8555

PI8559

WE'RE BACK! A DINOSAUR'S STORY, 1994

This promotion tied in with the video release of the animated dinosaur story. Three sets of cookie cutters which could also be used as tracing stencils were featured. Two different poses of the same character cam in each set.

PI8551	Set A	3 - 6
PI8552	Set B	3 - 6
PI8553	Set C	3 - 6
PI8554	Cup 1	1 - 3
PI8555	Cup 2	1 - 3
Box		
PI8556	We're Back	2 - 4
Point of Purchase		
PI8557	Door Sign	5 - 10
PI8558	Table Card	1 - 2
PI8559	Placemat	1 - 2

PI9001 PI9002

PI9003 PI9004

PI9011 PI9012 PI9013 PI9014

X-MEN, 1993

Marvel Comics co-sponsored this promotion which included 4 special edition X-Men comic books. Each was numbered and marked "Marvel Collector's Edition." They came with a plastic cup decorated with color X-Men cartoons.

Two VHS format video tapes were sold for $4.99 each with a Kid's Meal. Each video included a miniature comic book and trading card.

PI9001	#1-Rogue and Gambit	1 - 3
PI9002	#2-Wolverine and Jubilee	1 - 3
PI9003	#3-Beast, Storm,and Magneto	1 - 3
PI9004	#4-Bishop and Cyclops	1 - 3
PI9011	Rogue and Gambit cup	1 - 3
PI9012	Wolverine and Jubilee cup	1 - 3
PI9013	Beast, Storm,and Magneto cup	1 - 3
PI9014	Bishop and Cyclops cup	1 - 3
PI9101	#1-Night of The Sentinels w/mini-comic	10 - 15
PI9102	#2-Enter Magneto and Deadly Reunions	10 - 15
Box		
PI9105	X-Men	2 - 4
Point of Purchase		
PI9110	Placemat	1 - 2
PI9111	Table card	1 - 3

PI9110 PI9111 PI9105

PI9101 PI9102 PI9101 Mini-Comics PI9102 PI9101 Trading Cards PI9102

PI9301

PI9310

PI9307

PI9103 PI9106 PI9109

PI9304

YOUNG INDIANA JONES CHRONICLES, THE, 1993

The adventures of young Indiana Jones to Egypt, Africa and Mexico became the focus for this Pizza Hut For Kids promotion. Each week a different black plastic premium piece came with an instruction sheet/map that looked aged. For Week #1 the Egyptian Expedition was a black plastic compass with a 1¾" removable compass in a 1¾" square black plastic compass case.

Week #2 featured a black plastic spyglass for the African Adventure. Week #3 was the Mexican mission and was a magnifying glass in a black plastic case. The "Under 3" premium was a sticker sheet with 6 stickers relating to the Indiana Jones adventures.

PI9301	Compass, Adventure #1	2 - 4
PI9302	Egyptian Expedition Map	1 - 2
PI9303	Egypt 1908 cup	1 - 2
PI9304	Scope, Adventure #2	2 - 4
PI9305	African Adventure Map	1 - 2
PI9306	Africa 1909 cup	1 - 2
PI9307	Magnifying Glass, Adventure #3	2 - 4
PI9308	Mexican Mission Map	1 - 2
PI9309	Mexico 1916 cup	1 - 2
PI9310	Sticker Sheet (Under 3)	2 - 4
Box		
PI9311	The Young Indiana Jones Chronicles	2 - 4

POPEYE'S FAMOUS FRIED CHICKEN

PVC FIGURES, 1980-94

The likenesses of the main Popeye characters were made into 2⅛" hard rubber PVC figures. On the back of each figure was stamped "1980 KFS". The copyright information on the box was "1981 Popeye's Famous Fried Chicken, Inc. 1981 King Features Syndicate,

PI9302

PI9305

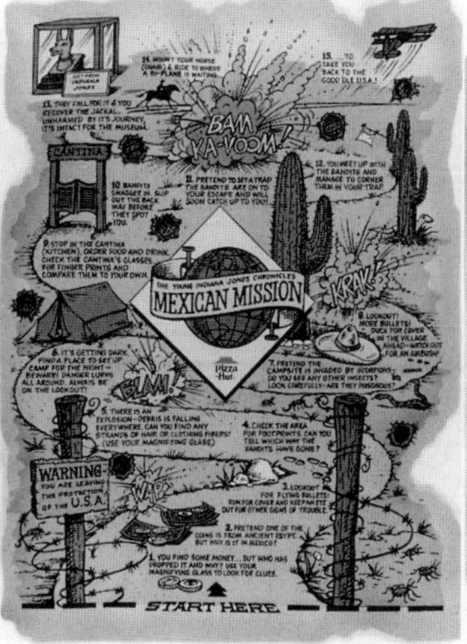

PI9308

PI9311

PO5801 PO5802 PO5803 PO5804 PO5805

PO5806

Inc." Figures were molded in red, yellow, green, orange, and purple. They have been used on a regular basis for years.

PO5801	Popeye	1 - 2
PO5802	Olive Oyl	1 - 2
PO5803	Wimpy	1 - 2
PO5804	Sweat' Pea	1 - 2
PO5805	Brutus	1 - 2
Box		
PO5806	Pal-Pack Barn	1 - 2

ROY ROGERS

When roast beef fast food restaurants were rising rapidly back in the '60s, Frisch's Big Boy of Cincinnati, Ohio started a second fast food operation. They arranged to name the chain after the famous singing cowboy of the '40s and '50s who achieved fame in films, radio, and TV...because this western star was born in Cincinnati.

The chain was sold to Marriott Corporation, which acquired all the Frisch's fast food operations, and was later sold to Hardee's. As this

RO0201-RO0216

book was going to press, many Roy Rogers restaurants in the Philadelphia area were once again sold. Roy Rogers kid's meals were quite unique in the late '80s and early '90s by tieing the drink cup in graphically, and frequently delivering the premium in a false bottom beneath the cup.

AQUA MEALS, 1993

Quarter-size cardboard disks showing cartoon illustrations of aquatic animals were the premiums for this promotion. 3 or 4 of these disks were contained in the plastic chamber attached to the bottom of the cup. The wax paper cup had an underwater scene showing several of the characters.

RO0201	Card Shark sticker	1 - 2
RO0202	Pilot Fish sticker	1 - 2
RO0203	King Fish sticker	1 - 2
RO0204	Sea Slug sticker	1 - 2
RO0205	Sea Lion Sticker	1 - 2
RO0206	Red Herring sticker	1 - 2
RO0207	Large Mouth Bass sticker	1 - 2
RO0208	Hammerhead Shark sticker	1 - 2
RO0209	Jelly Fish sticker	1 - 2
RO0210	Horseshoe Crab sticker	1 - 2
RO0211	Angel Fish sticker	1 - 2
RO0212	Catfish sticker	1 - 2
RO0213	Mussel sticker	1 - 2
RO0214	Ollie Octopus sticker	1 - 2
RO0215	Mackerel sticker	1 - 2
RO0216	Dover Sole sticker	1 - 2

RO0589

RO0221 RO0583 RO0581 RO0582 RO0584

Sacks

RO0220	Catfish	2 - 4
RO0221	Shark	2 - 4
RO0222	Jelly Fish	2 - 4
RO0223	Sea Lion	2 - 4

Point of Purchase

RO0230	Door decal	5 - 10
RO0231	Cup-Pictures of the sea	2 - 4

RO0581

ANIMAL MEALS, 1992

Small plastic batting helmets with the team logos were issued in various colors. Each cap came in a plastic compartment which was an extension on the bottom of a 4" tall wax paper cup.

RO0561	Set of 28 teams	28 - 56
RO0565	Cup-All Animals	1 - 2

Sacks

RO0571	Bear	1 - 2
RO0572	Lion	1 - 2
RO0573	Hippo	1 - 2
RO0574	Monkey	1 - 2

ANIMAL MEALS II, 1993

1½ crayon finger puppets in the shape of jungle animals. Each animal comes in brown, green, blue, and red for a total of 16 variations. The toys were contained in a green tinted plastic extension to the bottom of the special 4" wax cup.

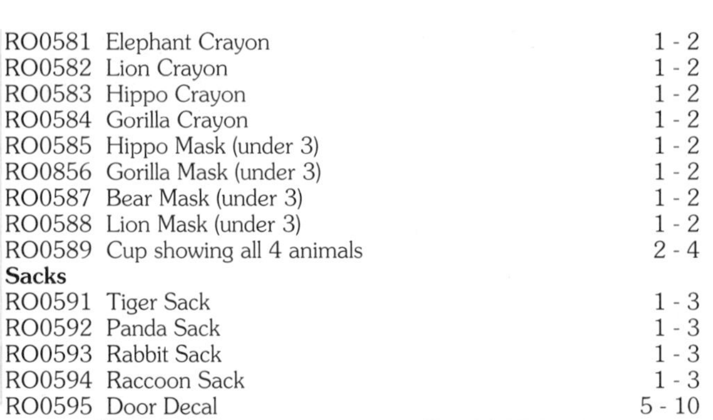

RO0581	Elephant Crayon	1 - 2
RO0582	Lion Crayon	1 - 2
RO0583	Hippo Crayon	1 - 2
RO0584	Gorilla Crayon	1 - 2
RO0585	Hippo Mask (under 3)	1 - 2
RO0856	Gorilla Mask (under 3)	1 - 2
RO0587	Bear Mask (under 3)	1 - 2
RO0588	Lion Mask (under 3)	1 - 2
RO0589	Cup showing all 4 animals	2 - 4

Sacks

RO0591	Tiger Sack	1 - 3
RO0592	Panda Sack	1 - 3
RO0593	Rabbit Sack	1 - 3
RO0594	Raccoon Sack	1 - 3
RO0595	Door Decal	5 - 10

RO0641

RO0643

RO0642

RO0644

BE A SPORT, 1989

Football, soccer, baseball and basketball were featured during this kids' meal promotion. Four punch-out cards, one for each sport, came on each of the four boxes. An additional premium was a 1½" x 2" refrigerator magnet with a picture.

RO0591 RO0592 RO0593 RO0594

RO0645 RO0646

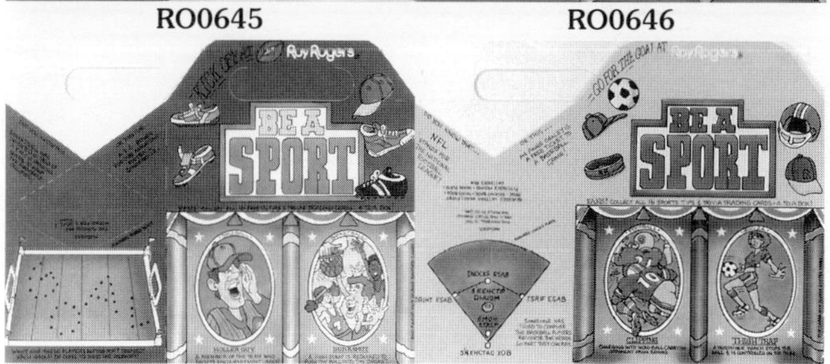

RO0647 RO0648

RO0641	Touchdown, magnet	4 - 8
RO0642	Slam Dunk, magnet	4 - 8
RO0643	Score, magnet	4 - 8
RO0644	Go For It, magnet	4 - 8
Boxes		
RO0645	Red box, Win at Roy Rogers	3 - 7
RO0647	Green box,Go For It At Roy Rogers	3 - 7
RO0648	Purple box, Kick Off At Roy Rogers	3 - 7
RO0649	Yellow box, Go For the Goal At Roy Rogers	3 - 7
Point of Purchase		
RO0650	Translite	20 - 30

RO1881 RO1885 RO1893 RO1889

CRITTERS, 1990

See-thru plastic monsters with painted eyes became the features for this Kids' Meal. The 3" tall premium came in 2 pieces; they separated at the "waist." Each came in four colors.

RO1881	Blue eyes	3 - 7
RO1885	Yellow eyes	3 - 7
RO1889	Red eyes	3 - 7
RO1893	White eyes	3 - 7
Point of Purchase		
RO1895	Translite	15 - 25

CUP CRITTERS, 1994

This stock program of 1½" plastic characters which hang on the edge of a glass or bowl have also been used by virtually every other fast food restaurant at one time or another. They are identifiable as Roy Rogers premiums only when found in the package with a paper insert. Each of these came in four different colors. The off-center Roy Rogers logo which appears on each sack in black ink suggests that it was imprinted on a previously mass-printed run.

RO1901	Lion	1 - 3
RO1902	Duck	1 - 3
RO1903	Turtle	1 - 3
RO1904	Beaver	1 - 3
RO1905	Pig	1 - 3
RO1906	Bear	1 - 3
RO1907	Frog	1 - 3
RO1908	Elephant	1 - 3
RO1909	Alligator	1 - 3
Sacks		
RO1915	Sleeping Lion	1 - 2
RO1916	Singing Bird/Alligator w/guitar	1 - 2
RO1917	Turtle and Alligator	1 - 2
RO1918	Pig	1 - 2

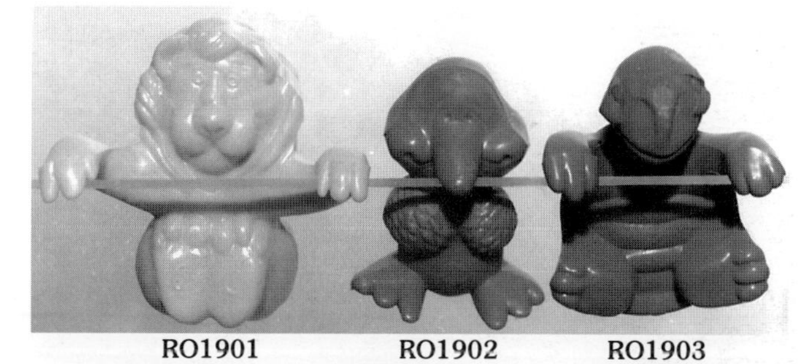

RO1901 RO1902 RO1903

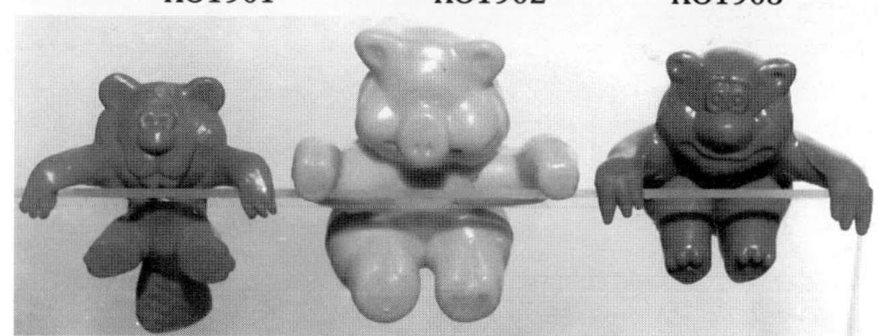

RO1904 RO1905 RO1906

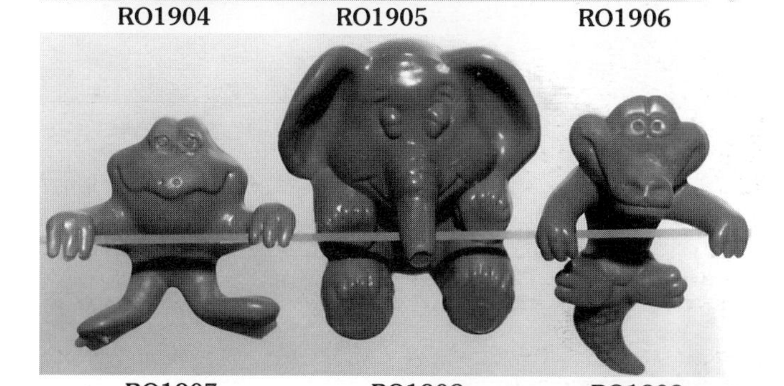

RO1907 RO1908 RO1909

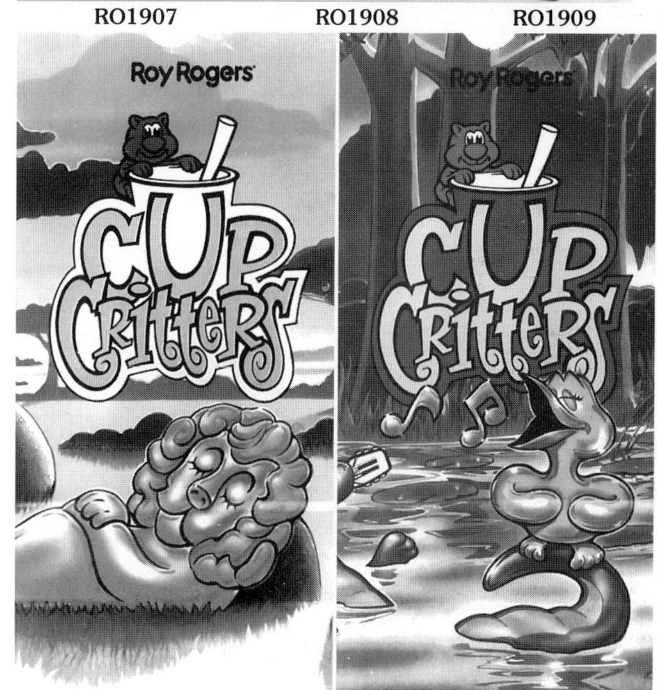

RO1915 RO1916

DINO MEALS, 1993

Eight different generic glow-in-the-dark dinosaurs were issued for Roy Rogers Kids' Meal.

RO1950	Tyrannosaurus, glow-in-the dark	1 - 2
RO1951	Triceratops, glow-in-the dark	1 - 2
RO1952	Stegosaurus, glow-in-the dark	1 - 2
RO1953	Pterodactyl, glow-in-the dark	1 - 2
RO1954	Dinosaur, glow-in-the dark	1 - 2
RO1955	Dinosaur, glow-in-the dark	1 - 2
RO1956	Dinosaur, glow-in-the dark	1 - 2

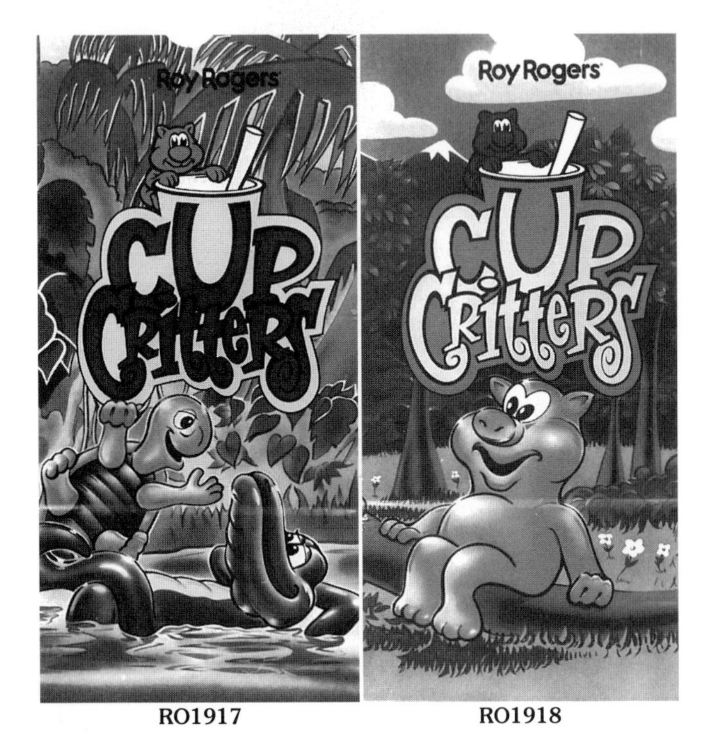

RO1917 RO1918

RO1968 RO1960 RO1961

RO1957	Dinosaur, glow-in-the dark	1 - 2
RO1958	Cup	

Sacks

RO1959	Stego	1 - 2
RO1960	Ptery	1 - 2
RO1961	Tri-Tops	1 - 2
RO1962	T. Rex	1 - 2

Point of Purchase

RO1965	Door Decal	10 - 15

ERASER RINGS, 1986

Finger rings which doubled as useable erasers with the top portion of each ring in the shape of a head. Each ring came in four colors: green, blue, yellow and red.

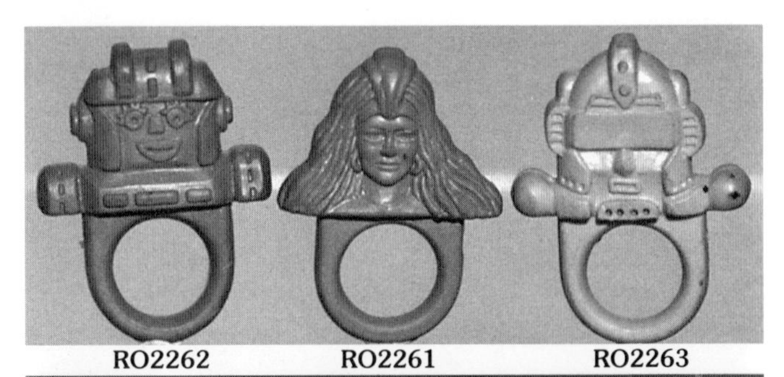

RO2262 RO2261 RO2263

RO2270

RO2261	Girl	4 - 8
RO2262	Robot	4 - 8
RO2263	Robot	4 - 8
RO2264	Man	4 - 8

Box

RO2266	Lots of eyeballs	5 - 7

Point of Purchase

RO2270	Translite	20 - 30

FANTASY MEALS, 1993

Again, the cups with the add-on compartment in the bottom were used. Each held a plastic compartment ring, and on the bag were colorful drawings from a childrens Fairy Tale.

RO2321	The Three Bears ring	3 - 6
RO2322	The Tree Little Pigs ring	3 - 6
RO2323	Jack & The Beanstalk ring	3 - 6

RO1959 RO1960 RO1961 RO1962 RO1965

RO2321 RO2324 RO2323 RO2322

RO2325 RO2321 RO2322

RO2323 RO2324 RO2334

RO2324 Hansel & Gretel ring 3 - 6
RO2325 Cup-Pictures of the four kids tales 3 - 6

Sacks

RO2331 The Three Bears 1 - 2
RO2332 The Three Little Pigs 1 - 2
RO2333 Jack & The Beanstalk 1 - 2
RO2334 Hansel & Gretel 1 - 2

Point of Purchase

RO2334 Door Decal 10 - 15

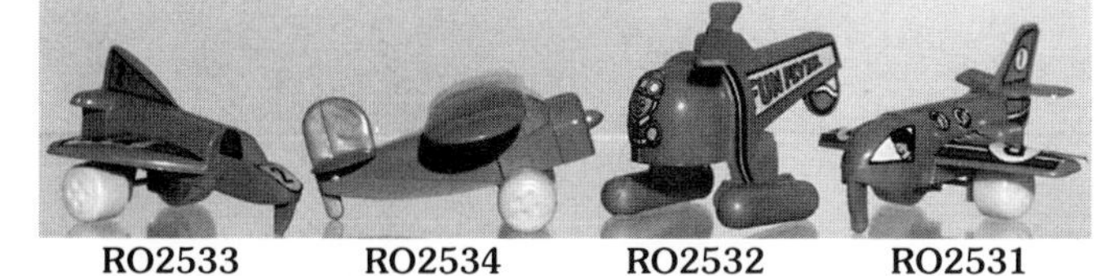

RO2533 RO2534 RO2532 RO2531

FUN FLYERS, 1989

Plastic planes were the premiums and each 3" vehicle came in 4 colors (blue, green, yellow, red) and a sheet of decals.

RO2531 Jet 1 4 - 6
RO2532 Helicopter 4 - 6

RO2560

RO2533 Jet 2 4 - 6
RO2534 Passenger Airplane 4 - 6

Boxes

RO2551 Fun Flyers Hangar 5 - 7
RO2552 Airport/Boarding Gate 5 - 7
RO2553 Airport/Marriott 5 - 7

Point of Purchase

RO2560 Translite 20 - 30

RO2660

RO255

RO255

RO255

RO2680 RO2699

RO2730 RO2950

RO2723 RO2721 RO2724 RO2722

GALAXY RANGERS, 1987

The meal container became the premium after Kids' Meal was eaten. Each vacuum-formed space ship came with a sheet of stickers to customize the craft in four colors (blue, red, green, gray).

RO2651	Interceptor	4 - 8
RO2652	Iron Falcon	4 - 8
RO2653	Beta	4 - 8
RO2654	Hyperdrive	4 - 8
Point of Purchase		
RO2660	Translite	20 - 30

GALAXY RANGERS GLOW-IN-THE-DARK LICENSE PLATES, 1987

Glow-in-the-dark white plastic plates with the name of one of the four Galaxy Rangers space craft on each plate in different colors.

RO2671	Red	3 - 5
RO2672	Blue	3 - 5
RO2673	Green	3 - 5
RO2674	Purple	3 - 5
Point of Purchase		
RO2680	Translite	20 - 30

GALAXY RANGERS SOUNDERS, 1987

Premiums for this promotion were red, green, yellow, or blue plastic whistles. Each one had the Galaxy Rangers logo printed on the front.

RO2691	Red	3 - 5
RO2692	Blue	3 - 5
RO2693	Green	3 - 5
RO2694	Yellow	3 - 5
Point of Purchase		
RO2699	Translite	20 - 30

GATOR TALES, 1989

Neverglade Alligators took to the snow in a variety of winter time activities. Each figure poseable and the headgear can be interchanged.

RO2721	Investigator	4 - 8
RO2722	A.V. Gator	4 - 8
RO2723	Skater Gator	4 - 8
RO2724	Flora Gator	4 - 8
Point of Purchase		
RO2730	Translite	20 - 30

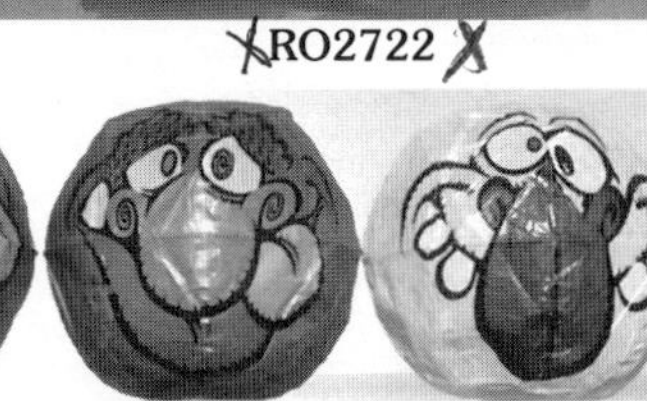

RO2811 RO2812 RO2813 RO2814

RO2821 RO2822

GOOFBALLS, Oct.-Nov. 1993

6" inflatable paper balls, each colorfully decorated with a different funny face make up this promotion.

RO2811	Blue Goofball	2 - 4
RO2812	Maroon Goofball	2 - 4
RO2813	Purple Goofball	2 - 4
RO2814	Yellow Goofball	2 - 4

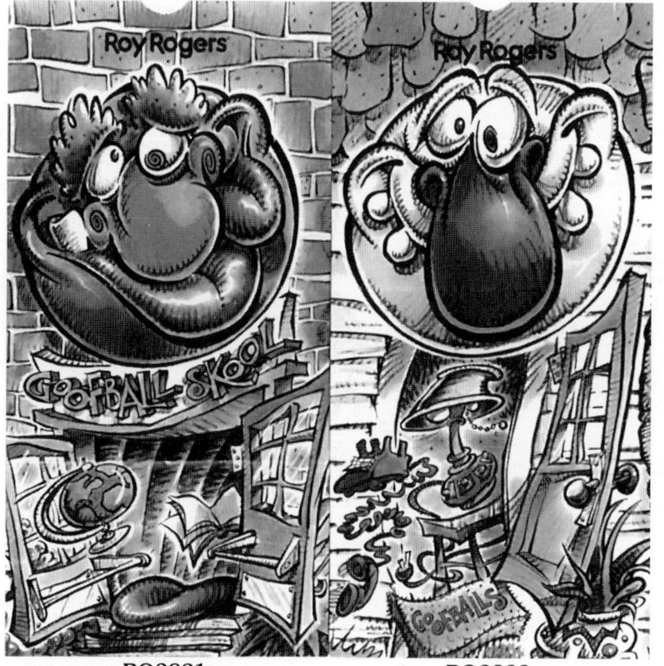

RO2821 RO2822

RO2826	Cup- Goofballs	2 - 4
Sacks		
RO2821	Blue Goofball	1 - 2
RO2822	Maroon Goofball	1 - 2
RO2823	Purple Goofball	1 - 2
RO2824	Yellow Goofball	1 - 2
Point of Purchase		
RO2825	Door Decal	8 - 15

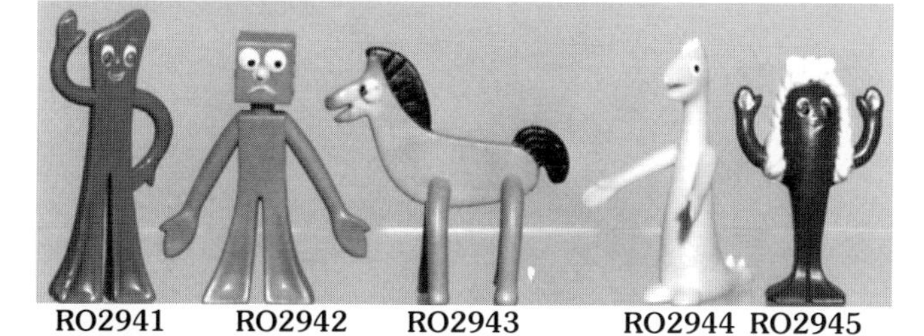

RO2941 RO2942 RO2943 RO2944 RO2945

GUMBY GANG, 1989

6" rubber figures of characters from the *Gumby* TV cartoon show were featured.

RO2941	Gumby	4 - 8
RO2942	Prickle	4 - 8
RO2943	Pokey	4 - 8
RO2944	Yellow Dinosaur	4 - 8
RO2945	Goo	4 - 8
Box		
RO2947	Gumby Beach Party	5 - 7
Point of Purchase		
RO2950	Translite	25

RO3231 RO3232 RO3233

HIDE 'N' KEEP DINOS, 1988

Caricatures of dinosaurs were issued with each Kids' Meal. Each solid-color 3" hollow plastic body had a secret hiding place in his back.

RO3231	Stegosaurus, red	4 - 5
RO3232	Brontosaurus, blue	4 - 5
RO3233	Triceratops, purple	4 - 5
RO3234	Tyrannosaurus Rex, green	4 - 5
Point of Purchase		
RO3240	Translite	20 - 30

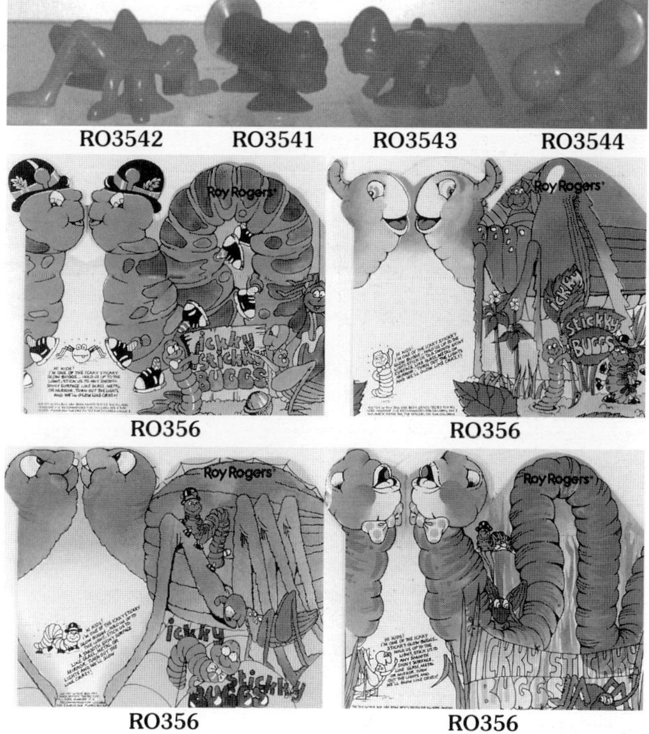

RO3542 RO3541 RO3543 RO3544

RO356 RO356

RO356 RO356

ICKKY STICKKY BUGGS, 1989

Glow-in-the-dark bugs that could be stuck on surfaces with an attached suction cups. Each 3"-4" rubber creature came in 4 colors (yellow, pink, green or blue).

RO3541	Centipede	4 - 6
RO3542	Grasshopper	4 - 6
RO3543	Spider	4 - 6
RO3544	Worm	4 - 6
Boxes		
RO3561	Centipede w/hat	5 - 7
RO3562	Grasshopper	5 - 7
RO3563	Spider	5 - 7
RO3564	Worm w/bow tie	5 - 7
Point of Purchase		
RO3570	Translite	20 - 30

MINI-CARS, 1989

From the translite we know there were 6 cars, but no idea of what they were made of or the names of the cars issued.

RO4821	Car #1	4 - 8
RO4822	Car #2	4 - 8
RO4823	Car #3	4 - 8
RO4824	Car #4	4 - 8
RO4825	Car #5	4 - 8
RO4826	Car #6	4 - 8
Point of Purchase		
RO4830	Translite	20 - 30

MINI-STUFFS, 1989

Mini cloth covered super-soft sports balls in various colors were sold over-the-counter during special offer.

RO3240 RO3570

RO4880

RO5250

RO6330

RO6760

RO6760

RO6800

RO7370

RO7420

RO4871	Football	4 - 8
RO4872	Baseball	4 - 8
RO4873	Basketball	4 - 8
RO4874	Soccer Ball	4 - 8

Point of Purchase

RO4880	Translite	20 - 30

NEAT-O NEON WRITERS, 1986

Tropical translucent plastic shape on top of the ball point pens were given away with this Kids' Meal.

RO5241	Flamingo	5 - 10
RO5242	Palm Tree	5 - 10
RO5243	Bird of Paradise	5 - 10
RO4244	Shooting Starsß	5 - 10

Point of Purchase

RO5250	Translite	20 - 30

POWER PULLERS, 1987

Muscular human figures were made of pliable rubber, enabling them to be stretched. These figures came in red, yellow, blue and green.

RO6321	Cowl-hooded male	4 - 8
RO6322	Muscle man	4 - 8
RO6323	Caped woman	4 - 8
RO6324	Caped man w/helmet	4 - 8

Point of Purchase

RO6330	Translite	20 - 30

RO6751 RO6754

RAD RIDERS - BIKE-O-MANIA, 1989

The three premiums issued for this promotion were to be used during bicycling. "Funny Bone" covers were rubber elbow pads with molded funny faces. Each came in a solid color – orange, yellow, green, purple.Noise-generating spoke snappers were 7½" clickers and in two designs,a circle and a lightning bolt.Two sheets of reflective prism stickers in various shapes and wordings were the third offering.Two sheets came in each package.

RO6741	Funny Bone Cover	3 - 7
RO6742	Spoke Snappers	2 - 5
RO6743	Stickers	2 - 4

Boxes

RO6751	1889 Olereive's Tricycle, orange box	4 - 8
RO6752	Red Box	4 - 8
RO6753	Blue Box	4 - 8
RO6754	1889 Eiffel Tower Tandem, yellow box	4 - 8

Point of Purchase

RO6760	Translite	20 - 30

RALLY RACERS, 1988

Six mini race cars were used as premiums for Kids' Meals.

RO6791	Porsche	3 - 6
RO6792	GT 1	3 - 6

Point of Purchase

RO6800	Translite	20 - 30

SAND MOLDERS, 1986

The Kids Meal food container is the toy and can later be used as a sand mold. Made of a vacuform plastic in the shape of animal heads.

RO7281	Elephant head lid/circle imprint bottom, red	3 - 6
RO7282	head lid/wavy imprint bottom, blue	3 - 6
RO7283	head lid/straight line, picket fence bottom, green	3 - 6
RO7284	Lion head lid/castle battlement bottom, yellow	3 - 6

Point of Purchase

RO7290	Translite	20 - 30

SECRET DECODER PEN, 1988

Two pens came with each premium.One pen was used to write a secret message.When the other pen wrote over the message, the invisible message appeared. The encoder pen was white; while the other pen contained ink in neon shades of green, blue, red, or purple.

RO7361	Green	4 - 8
RO7362	Purple	4 - 8
RO7363	Blue	4 - 8
RO7364	Red	4 - 8

Point of Purchase

RO7370	Translite	20 - 30

SKATEBOARD GANG KIDS, 1989

A Roy Rogers Kids' Meals offering. Each 2½"-3" PVC figures of kids came on a skateboard.

RO7411	Skateboarder standing upright	3 - 7
RO7412	Skateboarder kneeling on one knee	3 - 7

RO7411 RO7412 RO7413 RO7414

RO7413 Skateboarder doing handstand 3 - 7
RO7414 Skateboarder standing on one foot 3 - 7
Point of Purchase
RO7420 Translite 20 - 30

RO7480

RO7480

SNORKS, 1988

PVC figures of the Wallace Berrie Snorks were given away with each kids meal. There is no way to differentiate between those sold and those used as premiums.Approximately 20-30 different snork characters were available for this promotion.

RO7480 Snorks, each 2 - 4
Point of Purchase
RO7485 Translite, "Collect them all/Ask for special toy for kids under 3" 20 - 30
RO7486 Translite, "Now in Kids' Meals" 20 - 30

SPACE MEALS, December 1-31, 1992

A space theme was the basis for this end of year promotion. There were four paper premiums, four sacks and a special wax paper cup. The stickers of 6 constellations glow in the dark. The solar system model consists of punch-out pictures of the planets which can be assembled on the cardboard base to show the planets in relative size and order from the sun.

RO6221 Tattoo Sheet 3 - 7
RO6222 Sticker Scene 3 - 7
RO6223 Star Constellations 3 - 7
RO6224 Solar System Model 3 - 7
RO6225 Cup 1 - 3

Sacks
RO6581 All About Stars 1 - 3
RO6582 All About The Moon 1 - 3
RO6583 All About our Solar System 1 - 3
RO6584 All About Mars 1 - 3
Point of Purchase
RO6585 Door Decal 10 - 15

SPORTS KIDS MEAL, 1988

The Adidas name was printed repeatedly in blue on white shoelaces, wrist bands, and a shoe pocket to hold keys or change. Brake Lites and reflective adhesive stick-ons were for the heels of shoes.The box was shaped like an Adidas shoe.

RO7521 Wristband 3 - 6
RO7522 Shoelaces 3 - 6
RO7523 Brake Lites 3 - 6
RO7524 Shoe Pocket 3 - 6
Box
RO7525 Adidas Shoe 5 - 8
Point of Purchase
RO7530 Translite 20 - 30

RO7601 RO7602 RO7603 RO7604

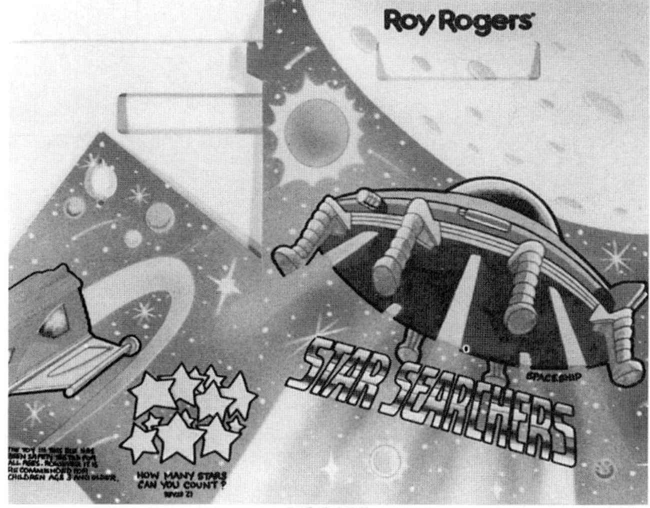

RO7605

STAR SEARCHERS, 1990

This Kids Meal gave away four different 3" space vehicles.Three colors (orange, purple and green) were used. Four designs in 6 color combinations yielded 24 possible variations.

RO7601 Robot 3 - 7
RO7602 Rover 3 - 7
RO7603 Saucer 3 - 7
RO7604 Shuttle 3 - 7
Box
RO7605 Picture of 4 toys 4 - 8

RO7481

RO7530

RO7607

RO7680

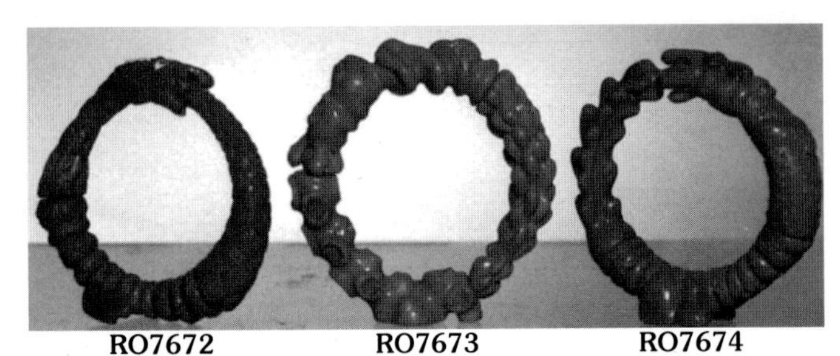

RO7672 RO7673 RO7674

Point of Purchase

RO7607 Translite 20 - 30

SWAMP PETS, 1990

Bracelets could be formed by snapping together the three pieces which came with each meal. The four different creatures could be snapped together to form one large one. All pieces were interchangeable.

RO7671	Turquoise	3 - 7
RO7672	Purple	3 - 7
RO7673	Gray	3 - 7
RO7674	Green	3 - 7

Point of Purchase

RO7680 Translite 20 - 30

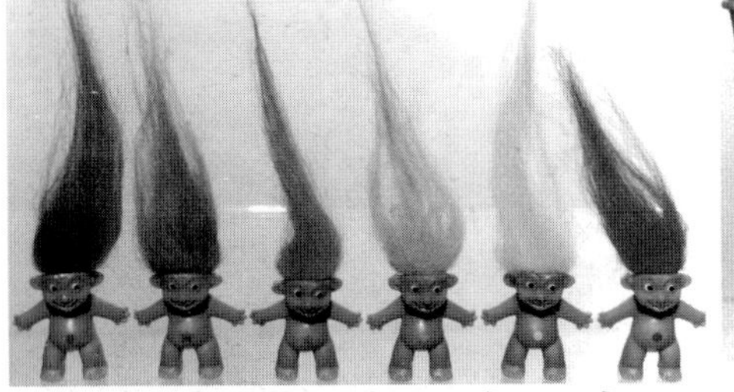

RO8831 RO8832 RO8833 RO8834 RO8835 RO8836 RO8839

TREASURE TROLLS, 1993

1½" Treasure Trolls pencil toppers were give away with each kids meal. With six different hair colors and four variations of navel markings (star, diamond, heart and circle) added to the total number of different premiums.

RO8331	Blue Hair	1 - 3
RO8332	Purple Hair	1 - 3
RO8333	Pink Hair	1 - 3
RO8334	Green Hair	1 - 3
RO8335	Yellow Hair	1 - 3
RO8336	Red Hair	1 - 3
RO8339	Cup	1 - 3

SONIC DRIVE-IN

This Texas based drive-in/drive-thru restaurant chain has traditionally been strong in Texas, Oklahoma, New Mexico, Arkansas, and Louisiana - warmer climates where car hop service is more comfortable year round. Beginning in the late 80's, Sonic embarked on an ambitious expansion program which now finds test restaurants as far East as Ohio. This chain does 6 to 8 kids' meal programs each year using a combination of imprinted stock promotions from companies like Admark and ones featuring Sonic's Brown Bag or human characters.

SO0101 SO0102 SO0103 SO0104

ADVENTURE OF THE SUPER SONIC KIDS, 1990

Three Crayons in the shape of the four Sonic Kids (Corkey, Rick, Steve, and Brin) came with a coloring book. Each character came in three different colors.

SO0101	Package 1: red, blue, tan	2 - 5
SO0102	Package 2: flesh, green, purple	2 - 5
SO0103	Package 3: pink, green, yellow	2 - 5
SO0104	Package 4: blue green, purple, orange	2 - 5

SO0181 SO0182 SO0183 SO0184

ADVENTURE OF THE SUPER SONIC KIDS, 1989

The Super Sonic Kids were featured as 3" PVC figures with "Sonic" printed on their backs. A 4¾" x 2¾" comic book accompanied each figure.

SO0181	Steve, comic title unknown	4 - 7
SO0182	Rick, comic title unknown	4 - 7
SO0183	Corkey, comic title unknown	4 - 7
SO0184	Brin w/*To Skate or Not to Skate* comic	4 - 7

SO0223 SO0221

ADVENTURE OF THE SUPER SONIC KIDS, 1989

Plastic rings with flip-top compartments featured the face and name of a different Super Sonic Kid. Each ring came with a 4¾" x 2¾" comic book.

SO0221	Steve w/comic	3 - 6
SO0222	Rick w/comic	3 - 6
SO0223	Corky w/*The SuperSonic Turbo Skateboard* comic	3 - 6
SO0224	Brin w/comic	3 - 6

SO0501 SO0502

BAG-A-WAG

A PVC male figure held bags of hamburgers in three poses. The fourth figure was posed with a large hamburger.

SO0501	Man in "hamburger" vehicle	2 - 5
SO0502	Man kneeling	2 - 5
SO0503	Man prying open a hamburger	2 - 5
SO0504	Man on roller blades	2 - 5

SO0503 SO0504

BEACH DUDE SQUIRTERS,1993

These 6" hard plastic figures have a plastic ring shaped plunger in the bottom. The figure is one color and the plunger another. The figures have a hole in the top of their heads where the water shoots out. On the back of each figure is "Sonic" in capital letters.

SO0631	Blue Dude (Orange Ring)	3 - 6
SO0632	Purple Dude (Green Ring)	3 - 6
SO0633	Orange Dude (Purple Ring)	3 - 6

SO0821 SO0822

SO0823 SO0824

BROWN BAG BOWLERS, 1994

The Brown Bag characters appeared as friction vehicles. Each came with a set of ten pins, but no way to stand them up.

SO0781	Pushing yellow ball	2 - 5
SO0782	Blue ball on head	2 - 5
SO0783	Red ball over head	2 - 5
SO0784	Orange ball in front	2 - 5

SO0821 SO0822

BROWN BAG BUDDIES, 1993

Figures of a brown paper bag with facial features, arms and legs were made into 3" PVCs. Printed in black letters across the back of each figure was "Sonic®."

SO0823 SO0824

SO0821	Brown Bag Buddy on sled	2 - 5
SO0822	Brown Bag Buddy on skis	2 - 5
SO0823	Brown Bag Buddy on sled	2 - 5
SO0824	Brown Bag Buddy on inner tube	2 - 5

SO0851 SO0852

SO0853 SO0854

Comic for SO0851

BROWN BAG JUNIORS, 1989

Each of these PVC brown paper bag figures had "Sonic" printed in raised red letters on the back. A 4¾" x 2¾" comic book accompanied each figure.

SO0851	Bookworm w/book; *Game Plans* comic	3 - 6
SO0852	Sure Shot w/basketball	3 - 6
SO0853	Too Cool w/comb	3 - 6
SO0854	Marbles on knees w/bag & shooter	3 - 6

BUMP & GO RACERS,1993

These 2" metal cars with plastic base change direction when they bump into something. Each car comes in two or more different color combinations.

SO1611	"X" on Roof	2 - 4
SO1612	Lightning Bolt on Door	2 - 4
SO1613	Super Ace	2 - 4
SO1614	Gogoback	2 - 4
SO1615	Two Stars on Door	2 - 4
SO1616	Fire Dash	2 - 4
SO1617	#4 on Door	2 - 4
SO1618	Purple Design on Door	2 - 4

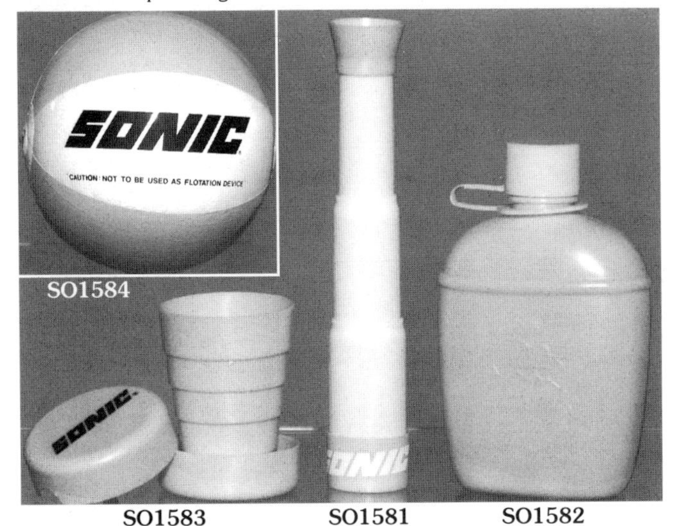

SO1584

SO1583 SO1581 SO1582

CAMP SONIC, 1992

The plastic equipment each came in several different "day-glow" colors. The Sonic name is marked on each premium.

SO1581	Telescoping Spy Glass	2 - 5
SO1582	Canteen w/screw-on cap	2 - 5
SO1583	Collapsible Cup w/removable lid	2 - 5
SO1584	Beach Ball	2 - 5

SO1751

SO1752

CLASSIC CRUISERS

The boxes were standard Admark stock promotion pieces used three different times by Sonic. The first time with license plates, then with sticker sets, and finally with the Kar Kraze meal.

SO1754

SO1731

SO1731	License Plate	4 - 8
SO1732	License Plate	4 - 8
SO1733	License Plate	4 - 8
SO1734	License Plate	4 - 8
SO1735	Sticker, Set #1	2 - 5
SO1736	Sticker, Set #2	2 - 5
SO1737	Sticker, Set #3	2 - 5
SO1738	Sticker, Set #4	2 - 5
SO1739	Key Chain	4 - 8
SO1740	Eraser	3 - 6
Boxes		
SO1751	Blue Chevy	3 - 4
SO1752	Corvette	3 - 4
SO1753	'53 Chevy Truck	3 - 4
SO1754	Pink Chevy	3 - 4

SO1781

CONEY PUP, 1986

This "sold over-the-counter" Sonic advertising aid was a 2-piece plush figure. The "carrying bag" was shaped like a hot dog in a bun with "Sonic Coney Pup" printed across the top. Inside the bag was a reclining plush dog and a coupon for free Coca Cola Classic.

Premium		
SO1781	Plush Coney Pup	15 - 20

COUNTRY CRITTERS, 1992

Four animal boxes were used in this Admark promotion.

SO1801	Cow	1 - 3
SO1802	Chicken	1 - 3
SO1803	Pig	1 - 3
SO1804	Lamb	1 - 3

SO1901 SO1902

SO1903 SO1904

CRAZY CARS

A set of four '50s cars. These were manufactured in multiple colors.

SO1901	Chevy	1 - 3
SO1902	Luxury Sedan	1 - 3
SO1903	Sportscar	1 - 3
SO1904	Pickup	1 - 3

SO1801 SO1802

SO1803 SO1804

CUSTOM CRUISERS,1993

3"-3½" Rubber bodied cars sit on a plastic chassis with rubber wheels. Each has the "Sonic" logo in the side doors.

SO2011 '57 Chevy Convertible, Blue 2 -4
SO2012 '55 Chevy Nomad Wagon, Black 2 -4
SO2013 '59 Cadillac Convertible, Pink 2 -4
SO2014 Mercury, Red 2 -4

GRAFEETIES, 1990

Popular phrases appeared on rubber stickers for application to sneaker heels were issued as premiums for this promotion.

SO2871 Get A/Life 3 - 4

SO2871-SO2875

SO2872 Chill/Out 3 - 4
SO2873 Can't Touch/This 3 - 4
SO2874 Not/!!! 3 - 4
SO2875 Awe/Some 3 - 4

HOLIDAY EXPRESS, December 1993

A train set of four cars had Dr. Pepper logos on one side and the Sonic logo on the other. They hook together. The engine and caboose are red and green, one car is red and one car is blue. This promotion was also used by White Castle and Dairy Queen.

SO3111 Engine 3 - 6
SO3112 Coal Car 3 - 6
SO3113 Box Car 3 - 6
SO3114 Caboose 3 - 6

JUMPIN' JUKEBOX BANKS, 1990

3½" plastic banks were molded in the shape of juke boxes. The back had a crease molded into it so the back "flap" could be folded down. A different decal of a Wurlitzer juke box was placed on the front of each bank. Even the boxes for this giveaway were in the shape of juke boxes.

SO2011 SO2013

SO2012 SO2014

SO3924 SO3923

SO3929 SO3928

SO3921	Red	6 - 9
SO3922	Blue	6 - 9
SO3923	Yellow	6 - 9
SO3924	Green	6 - 9
Boxes		
SO3926	Wurlitzer #1	4 - 8
SO3927	Wurlitzer #2	4 - 8
SO3928	Wurlitzer #3	4 - 8
SO3929	Wurlitzer #4	4 - 8

SO4031

KAR KRAZE, 1993

The premiums for this promotion were pullback racers.

SO4031	Red '57 Chevy Convertible	6 - 8
SO4032	Black truck	6 - 8
SO4033	Silver sports car	6 - 8
SO4034	Luxury sedan	6 - 8
Sack		
SO4039	Kar Kraze	1 - 2

SAFARI ANIMALS, 1993

3"-4" "Bendie" animals were used for this promotion. Each was two colored, plus whatever colors were used to detail the face.

SO6621	Orange Gorilla	1 - 3
SO6622	Yellow Giraffe	1 - 3
SO6623	Yellow Rhino	1 - 3
SO6624	Yellow Deer	1 - 3
SO6625	Yellow Camel	1 - 3
SO6626	Brown Hippo	1 - 3
SO6627	Yellow Tiger	1 - 3
SO6628	Brown Lion	1 - 3
SO6629	White Bear	1 - 3
SO6630	Black Leopard	1 - 3
SO6631	White Zebra	1 - 3
SO6632	Gray Elephant	1 - 3

SO7261 SO7262

SO7263 SO7264

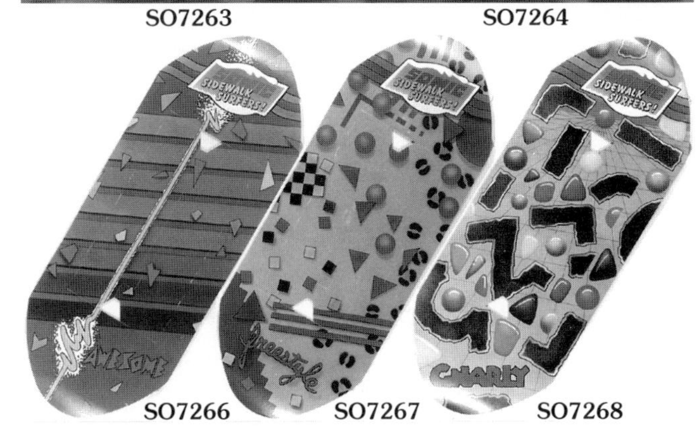

SO7266 SO7267 SO7268

SIDEWALK SURFERS, 1989

These 2½" molded soft rubber skateboards had painted facial features. On the top of the skateboard in raised letters was "Sonic®"; while imprinted was "Sidewalk Surfers!" A 4¾" x 2¾" comic book accompanied each premium.The boxes also became skateboards. A different graphic design was used on the top of each board with "Sonic Sidewalk Surfers!" and the name given to each board printed on the top.

SO7261	The Mean Sidewalk Machine, black	3 - 6
SO7262	Ms. Sidewalk Savvy, pink	3 - 6
SO7263	Mr. Big Fun, green	3 - 6
SO7264	The Sidewalk Snoot, blue	3 - 6
Boxes		
SO7266	Awesome Skateboard	3
SO7267	Freestyle Skateboard	3
SO7268	Gnarly Skateboard	3

SONIC SCHOOL DAYS, 1990

Door handle hangers and a ruler were the premiums for this school time promotion.

SO4039 SO7356

SO7357 SO7358

SO7351 Book Mark/Ruler 2 - 5
SO7352 Door Knob Sign "Do not Disturb" 2 - 5
SO7353 Door Knob Sign "Hush! Student Studying" 2 - 5
SO7354 Door Knob Sign "Keep Out" 2 - 5

Boxes

SO7356 Yellow School Bus 3
SO7357 Magenta School Bus 3
SO7358 Blue School Bus 3

SONIC VILLAGE,

Each box was a different house to make a village. The premiums for this promotion are unknown.

SQUISHERS, 1993

These were 2" tall hollow colorful soft rubber squirters that look like food items with faces, arms and feet.

SO7641 Fries 2 - 4
SO7642 Peppermint 2 - 4
SO7643 Burger 2 - 4
SO7644 Drink 2 - 4

SUPER FRICTION POWERED MONSTER TRUCKS, 1993

These 3½" multi-colored pastel friction drive trucks with monster studded wheels came in two basic models, one with a rollbar and one with a towing hook. "Sonic" appears on the windshield and tailgate.

SO7551 Purple Truck, Orange Wheels/Rollbar 2 - 4
SO7552 Pink Truck, Yellow Wheels/Rollbar 2 - 4
SO7553 Red Truck, Purple Wheels/Rollbar 2 - 4
SO7554 Orange Truck, Green Wheels/Rollbar 2 - 4
SO7555 Purple Truck, Orange Wheels/Hook 2 - 4
SO7556 Pink Truck, Yellow Wheels/Hook 2 - 4
SO7557 Red Truck, Purple Wheels/Hook 2 - 4
SO7558 Orange Truck, Green Wheels/Hook 2 - 4

SO7551 SO7634

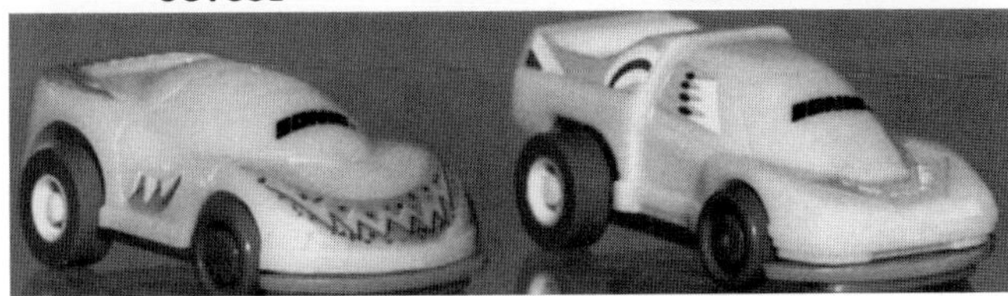
SO7632 SO7633

SUPER SONIC TURBO RACERS, 1993

1½ fluorescent-colored plastic race cars came with unique design stickers on them, blue wheels and a sticker on the bottom which read "Made in China." Pulling back on the car activated the mechanism which propelled the car forward. When the car bumped into an obstacle, it reversed direction.

SO7631 Unknown Race Car 2 - 4
SO7632 Race Car 2 - 4
SO7633 Fastback 2 - 4
SO7634 Open-back Race Car 2 - 4

TREASURE TROLLS, 1993

These standard trolls came in only four hair colors for this promotion.

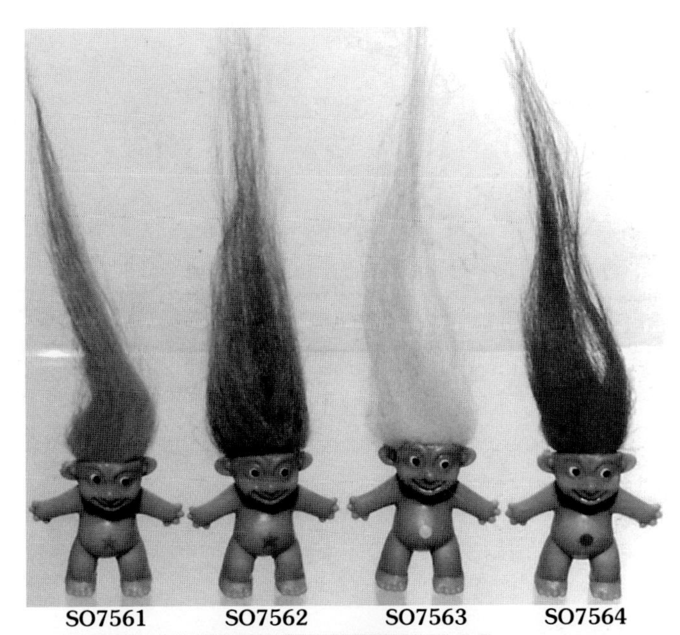
SO7561 SO7562 SO7563 SO7564

SO8701 SO8702 SO8703

SO8704 SO8705 SO8706

SO7561 Pink Hair 1 - 3
SO7562 Purple Hair 1 - 3
SO7563 Yellow Hair 1 - 3
SO7564 Blue Hair 1 - 3

WACKY SACKERS, 1994

The Sonic sacks became crazed and weird in this series of six PVCs. Each came in four different colors - blue, green, pink, and harvest yellow.

SO8701 Sunglasses 2 - 4
SO8702 Tall Guy 2 - 4
SO8703 One Tooth 2 - 4
SO8704 Wide Mouth 2 - 4
SO8705 Three Eyes 2 - 4
SO8706 Holding Eyes 2 - 4

SUBWAY

This rapidly growing sandwich operation ranks No. 2 behind Mc Donalds in total outlets. Its Kids' Meal program began in 1993and has been promoted primarily at the point-of-purchase. The start-up has not been without difficulties. Rarely has the same promotion been running at all outlets in a given area at the same time. Each franchised store seems to buy a supply of premiums and uses them until the they run out. Then they buy more for whatever promotion is running at the time the new purchase is made. One local operator was out of premiums for six weeks. The owner may have saved a little money, but lost in the long run as kids avoid his store. A common plastic bag depicting Subway's five Kids' Pak Fresh Food characters has been used for every promotion up to publication date.

SU2001

SU2102

BLOCKS 1993

8 or 9 Lego-type blocks were packaged to create a toy. Blocks were red, yellow, blue, clear and two of the sets have black wheel assembly pieces. The under 3 toy consists of 3 pink and 2 yellow oversized pieces. Each also contained a full-color 5" by 16" booklet that is folded to ¼ that size.

SU2001 Airplane
SU2002 Truck
SU2003 Helicopter
SU2004 Robot
SU2005 Large Blocks (under 3)

CAPTAIN PLANET RING, 1993

Gold plastic rings had colored stones inside a 1½ in diameter top embossed with the Captain Planet name. The package includes heavy stock paper which folds into a ring holder. Also enclosed was a poster and a folder with a cartoon strip and explanation of the five rings. Touch the center of each ring to reveal the power. When you press your finger to the stone, a signin the stone becomes visible. The sign represents one of the 5 powers.

SU2101	Earth (Globe)	1 - 3
SU2102	Water (Wave)	1 - 3
SU2103	Heart (Heart)	1 - 3
SU2104	Wind (Wavy lines)	1 - 3
SU2105	Fire (Flame)	1 - 3

SU3021

SU3022

SU3023

SU3024

CONEHEADS, 1993

As a tie-in with the release of the Paramount Pictures movie *Coneheads*, the four main characters were featured on the premiums issued with each Kids' Pak. The upper torso of each figure was made into a pencil topper. Each came with a comic book.

SU3021 Beldar
SU3022 Prymaat
SU3023 Connie
SU3024 Marlax

SU3041

DOODLETOP JR., 1994

"The top that draws" was featured in four different colors: blue, green, red, and purple. A cap covers the entire bottom of the top and reveals a color marker when removed.

SU3040	Blue top	2 - 4
SU3041	Green top	2 - 4
SU3042	Red top	2 - 4
SU3043	Purple top	2 - 4

SU3134 SU3132 SU3131 SU3133 SU3135

HACKEYSACK BALLS , 1993

2" diameter stuffed leatherette balls for this kids game feature a fluorescent colored panel and a white panel design. A picture of one of Subway's kids' pak fresh food character's is printed on the white panel.

SU3131	Pappy Pepper	1 - 3
SU3132	Lenny Lettuce	1 - 3
SU3133	Petey Pickle	1 - 3
SU3134	Pearl Onion	1 - 3
SU3135	Tilly Tomato	1 - 3

Sack

SU3140 Picture of all 5 characters.

SU6301 SU6302

LAND OF THE LOST, 1993

In conjunction with the Saturday morning TV show, *Land of the Lost*, Subway issued PVC dinosaur figures from Admark. Each came with a paper insert.

SU6301	Tyrannosaurus Rex	1 - 3
SU6302	Stegosaurus	1 - 3
SU6303	Dimetrodon	1 - 3
SU6304	Triceratops	1 - 3

SU6303 6304SU

SU3140

Insert from Land of the Lost

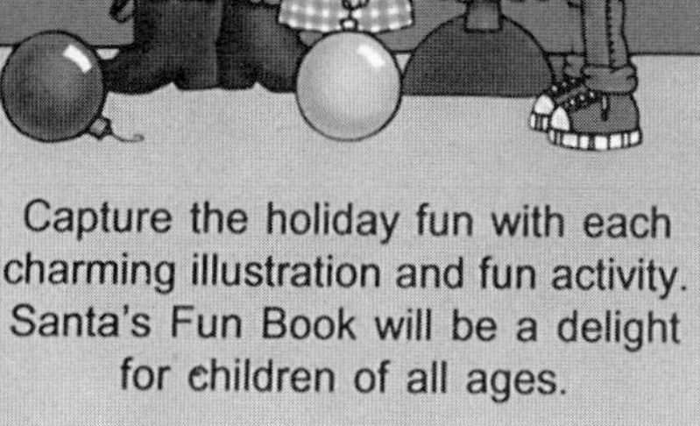

SU6101

SANTA'S FUN BOOK, 1993

A coloring/activity book was issued during the Christmas season with a box of four crayons.

SU6101 Santa's Fun Book, w/crayons.

TACO BELL

Founded in 1962 by Glenn Bell, Taco Bell now has more than 4,100 stores and an additional outlets in schools, department schools and gas stations (Taco Bell Express). Along with Pizza Hut and Kentucky Fried Chicken, Taco Bell is owned by PepsiCo. Chevy's is a subsidiary of Taco Bell. In the early '90s, Taco Bell began opening Hot & Now burger outlets, many of them on the same or adjacent property to their Taco Bell outlet.

Kid's meal promotions began about 1983 when various Hallmark properties were given away in a box. Taco Bell was primarily geared to teenagers during their earlier years, and it wasn't until the late '80s that they began to focus more on the kids. In 1988 the Hallmark tie-in was dropped in favor of imprinted stock programs, and in 1989 Taco Bell became one of the first companies to use clay-coated bags with paper premiums as their standard giveaway. A year or so later, Taco Bell introduced their own lineup of characters — Taco Man, Cheddar Fred, Hedda Lettuce and Tomato red — using these characters as the focus of a series of promotions that centered on making kids aware of a variety of social and safety issues.

TA0041 TA0042

TA0043

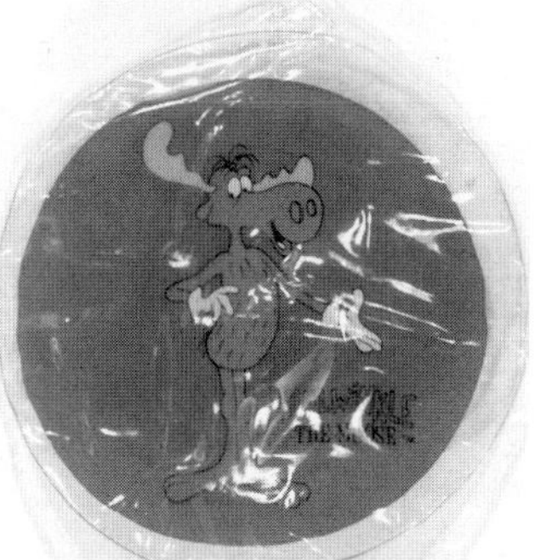

TA0044

TA0046 TA0047

ADVENTURES OF ROCKY AND BULLWINKLE, 1993

P.A.T. Ward characters, Rocket J. Squirrel and Bullwinkle The Moose, became the TV spokespersons for Taco Bell for a short period in 1993. These characters became the focus of one of the largest promotions in Taco Bell history. The stamper premiums worked, but the inflatable balls given away were difficult to blow-up.These were recalled at the same time with the Richard Scarry finger puppets (see TA0376).

TA0041	Rocket J. Squirrel Stamper	1 - 3
TA0042	Bullwinkle The Moose Stamper	1 - 3
TA0043	Rocket J. Squirrel Inflatable Ball	5 - 10
TA0044	Bullwinkle The Moose Inflatable Ball	5 - 10
TA0046	Mail-in Hat	4 - 8
TA0047	Mail-in Shirt	5 - 10
Sack		
TA0049	Sure Beats Cartoon Food!	1 - 2
Point of Purchase		
TA0055	Door decal	5 - 10
TA0059	Rocky sign	10 - 15
TA0060	Bullwinkle sign	25 - 30
TA0061	Kid's Meal sign	10 - 15
TA0065	Crunch Club sign	10 - 15

TA0049

TA0055

TA0059

TA0060

TA0061

TA0372 TA0371

ATTENTION TACO BELL. CUSTOMERS

IMPORTANT SAFETY NOTICE TO OUR CUSTOMERS

In order to ensure the safety and comfort of our customers, Taco Bell. is electing to RECALL the following promotional items that were included free with recent kids meals programs.

If you or your children are in possession of:

The Richard Scarry Finger Puppets

The Rocky & Bullwinkle Inflatable Balls

Please return them to this or any Taco Bell. location. All returned items will be exchanged for a free Original Taco. If you have any questions concerning the recall of these promotional items, please call our dedicated toll-free number 1-800-374-8220.

Recall Notice

TA0065

TA0071

TA0451

TA0621 TA0623

TA0629

AFRICAN WILD PUPPETS, 1991

Heads of African wild animals were printed on sturdy index paper stock. These punch-out pieces were then assembled into a hand puppet. The same puppets from Admark have been used by other chains with the Taco Bell name removed.

TA0071 Lion 2 - 4
TA0072 Elephant 2 - 4
Sack
TA0079 Sack 1 - 3

BUSY WORLD OF RICHARD SCARRY, 1993

Character illustrations by Richard Scarry were featured on the sacks and used to create the premiums during this promotion.The premiums included stickers sheets as well as two 2" tall hollow rubber finger puppets. These finger puppets were recalled as a safety hazard.

TA0371 Lowly Worm Finger Puppet 4 - 6
TA0372 Huckle Cat Finger Puppet 4 - 6
TA0373 Busy Town Glow In The Dark Stickers 1 - 3
TA0374 Getting Around Busy Town Glow In The Dark Stickers 1 - 3
Sack
TA0375 The Busy World of Richard Scarry 1 - 3

CASPER THE FRIENDLY GHOST, 1992

A special issue of Harvy Comics' featuring Casper the Friendly Ghost and Little Red Riding Hood was given, perhaps in a series. In addition to the classic story, games and activities were included. A special offer to subscribe to Casper comics appeared on the back cover.

TA0451 Casper/Red Riding Hood comic 5 - 15

DINOSAUR DAYS STICKERS, 1993

The first two sets were sticker sheets; the other two were sticker sheets with Make-A-Scene backgrounds

TA0621 Sticker Set #1 1 - 3
TA0622 Sticker Set #2 1 - 3
TA0623 Make-A-Scene Sticker Set #1 1 - 3
TA0624 Make-A-Scene Sticker Set #2 1 - 3
Sack
TA0629 Dinosaur Days 1 - 2

DINOSAUR DAYS POSTERS, 1994

Large Posters unfolded to reveal a dinosaur in its natural surroundings. The four combined to form a giant Tyrannosaurus poster.

TA0711 Woolly Mammoth 1 - 3
TA0712 Triceratops 1 - 3
TA0713 Velociraptor 1 - 3
TA0714 Apatosaurus 1 - 3
Sack
TA0715 Dinosaur Sack 1 - 2

DINOSAUR DAYS PUZZLES, 1993

Cardboard puzzles in a frame with a punch-out hole. The sack from Dinosaur Days Stickers was re-used for this promotion.

TA0761 Tyrannosaurus 1 - 3
TA0762 Parasaurolophus 1 - 3
TA0763 Ankylosaurus 1 - 3

TA0711 TA0712 TA0713 TA0714 TA0715

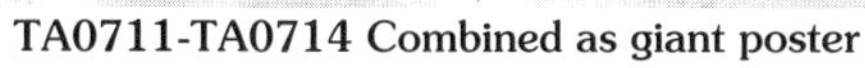

TA0711-TA0714 Combined as giant poster

TA0761 TA0762

TA0763

TA1061 TA1062 TA1063

FAIRY TALE KIDS MEAL BOOKS, 1986

Six and one half by eight inches Western Publishing Company's Golden Junior Classic books were the same as same title books previously published, but had the Taco Bell logo throughout.

TA1061	Cinderella	4 - 6
TA1062	Jack And The Beanstalk/The Princess and the Pea	4 - 6
TA1063	The Emperor's New Clothes	4 - 6

FREE WILLY, 1993

Collectible pop-up cards were given away in conjunction with the release of the film.

TA1121	Whale Jumping Over Boy	1 - 3
TA1122	Whale Jumping in Pool	1 - 3
TA1123	Boy Hugging Whale	1 - 3
Sack		
TA1129	Free Willy	1 - 2

TA1411 TA1412

TA1413 TA1414

HALLOWEEN KID'S PAILS, 1992

A pails which could be customized with different sticker faces.

TA1351	Pail with sticker sheet	2 - 4

HAPPY TALK SPRITES, 1983

Six-inch plush figures with blond faces, fuzzy bodies and rainbow colored legs each produced a different noise. A small folded index stock card was attached to each doll. A white cloth tag sewn into the seam of the doll was labeled "Made for Taco Bell."

TA1421	Spark, yellow	6 - 8
TA1422	Champ, blue	6 - 8
TA1423	Twink, white	6 - 8
TA1424	Romeo, red	6 - 8

HONEY, I BLEW UP THE KID, 1992

The 1992 Disney movie provided a variety of premiums tied-in to various scenes from the film.

TA1501	Magic Slate	2 - 4
TA1502	Flying Disk	2 - 4
TA1503	Sea Horse Stencil	2 - 4
TA1504	Growth Chart	2 - 4
TA1505	Poster	3 - 5
TA1506	Mini-puzzle	3 - 5
Sack		
TA1507	Honey I Blew Up the Kid	1 - 2

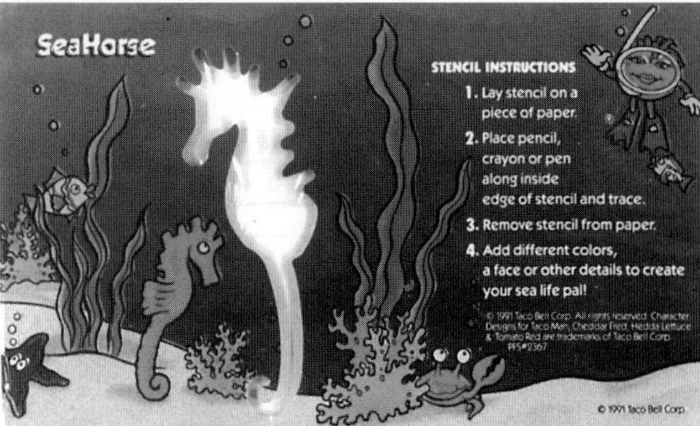

TA1503

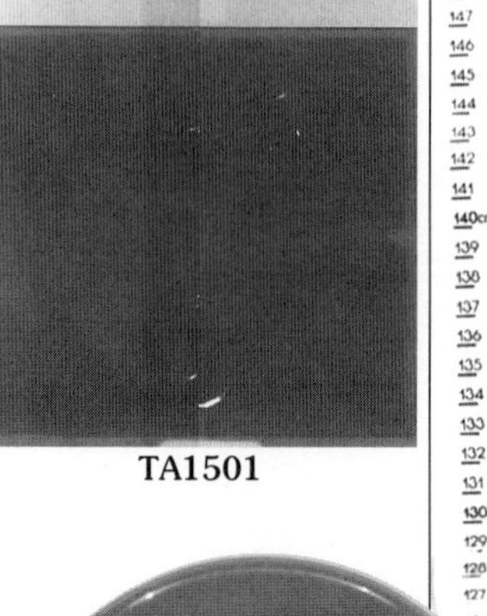

TA1501

TA1502

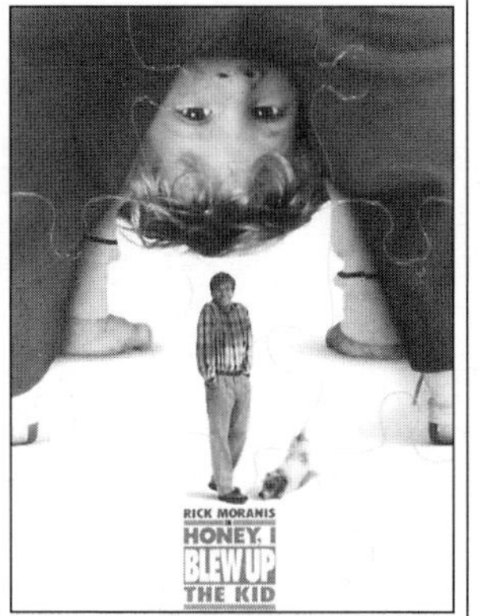

TA1506

TA1507

TA1504

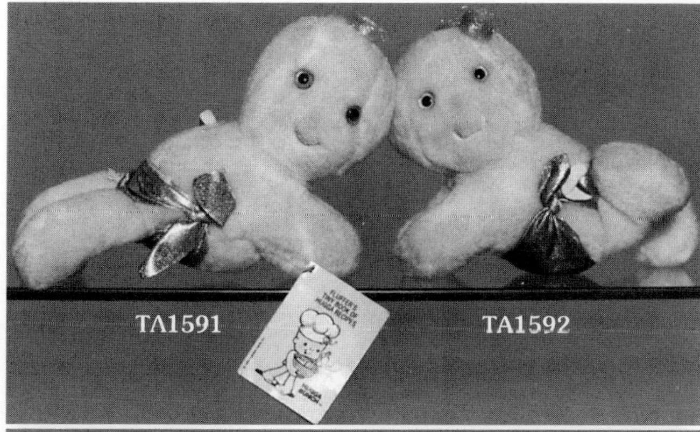
TA1591 TA1592

TA1593 TA1594

HUGGA BUNCH, 1984

Six inch plush baby figures were dressed in metallic cloth diapers. The color of the diaper matched the tint of curly lock of hair on the baby's head. Printed on the diaper back was the baby's name. Each had a clip-action mechanism in its arms which permitted it to cling.

TA1591	Fluffer, gold	8 - 10
TA1592	Hug-A-Bye, pink	8 - 10
TA1593	Gigglet, blue/green	8 - 10
TA1594	Tuggins, blue	8 - 10

TA2011

TA2012

LITTLE CRITTER'S BEDTIME STORYBOOKS, (1987)

The bedtime storybooks were written by Mercer Mayer. Logos for both Golden Books and Taco Bell appeared on the cover of the 24 page books.

TA2011	The Fussy Princess	5 - 8
TA2012	The Grumpy Old Rabbit	5 - 8
TA2013	The Bear Who Wouldn't Share	5 - 8

LOOKOUT BEAR HIDDEN PICTURE BOOKS, 1984

Zoobilee Zoo books featured Lookout Bear and were designed with a "Magic Hide 'n' See Lens" built in.

TA2311	Lookout Bear & The Who Monster	4 - 6
TA2312	Lookout Bear's Bigfoot Adventure	4 - 6
TA2313	Lookout Bear & The Phantom of the Movie	4 - 6

MERLIN'S TRUNK

The box has been found. Nothing more!

TA2380 Box		8 - 12

TA2311 TA2312 TA2313

TA2401

TA2571, TA2574

TA2579

MUPPET CHRISTMAS CAROL, THE, 1992

Jim Henson creatures were featured during this yuletide tie-in with the theatre movie release of *The Movie* . Each premium was a collectible ornament with scenes of the Muppets portraying characters from Dickens' *Christmas Carol*. A 4" x 2" white strip contained two full-color stickers which were to be used to decorate the disk.

TA2571	Kermit w/Tiny Tim, blue disk	2 - 5
TA2572	Father Christmas w/marching toys	2 - 5
TA2573	Miss Piggy w/family	2 - 5
TA2574	Fozzie w/carolers, yellow disk	2 - 5
Sack		
TA2579	The Muppet Christmas Carol	1 - 2

SAND CITY, 1993

This summer promotion featured pails and sand molds.

TA3131	Pail w/seashells	1 - 3
TA3132	Star sand mold	1 - 3

TA3131 TA3134 TA3132 TA3133

TA4411

TA4412

TA3133	Castle sand mold	1 - 3
TA3134	Pail, red	1 - 3
Sack		
TA3139	Sack	1 - 2

TACO MAN'S MYSTERY HOUSE, 1990

Three and one half inches by five and one half 20 page activity books featuring Taco Man, Hedda Lettuce, Tomato Red & Cheddar Fred in various puzzles and games. Activity book #1 shows Taco Man holding a magnifying glass, while on activity book #2 he is pictured with his dog. The Taco Bell logo is one the front cover.

TA4411	Activity Book #1	3 - 5
TA4412	Activity Book #2	3 - 5

TA4561

TA4562

TACO MAN'S WHEN YOU GROW UP 1992

Eight collectible coloring cards showing various careers.

TA4561	Teacher	2 - 4
TA4562	Policeman	2 - 4
TA4563	Dentist	2 - 4
TA4564	Judge	2 - 4

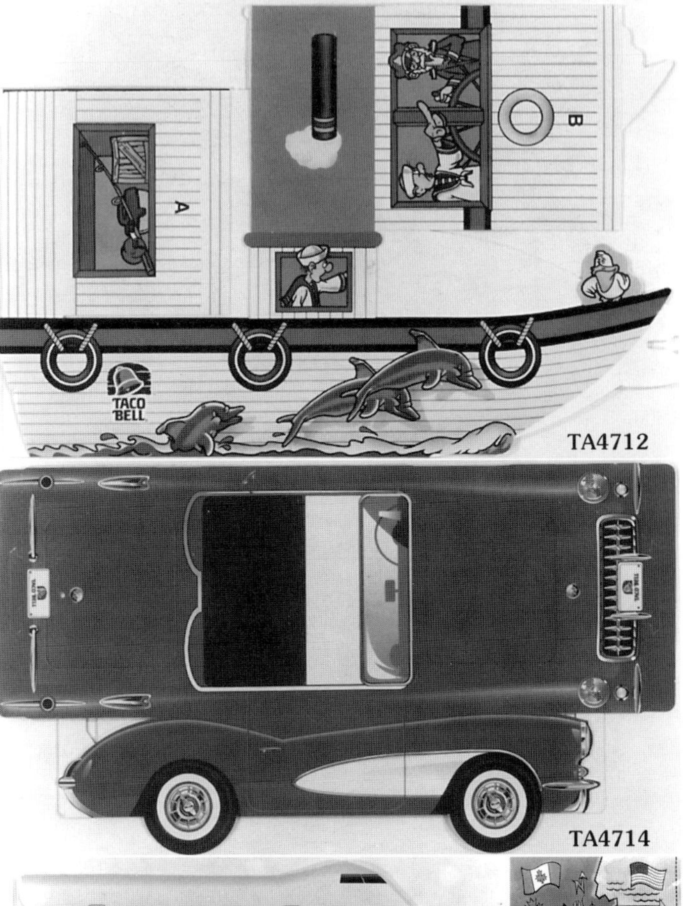

TA4712

TA4714

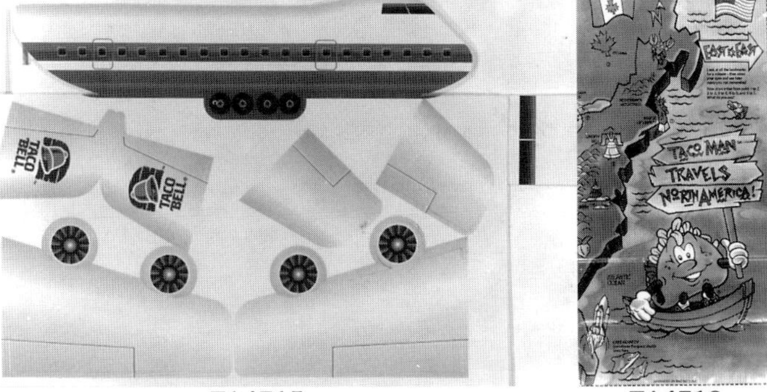

TA4715 TA4719

TA4565	Paramedic	2 - 4
TA4566	Farmer	2 - 4
TA4567	Construction Worker	2 - 4
TA4568	Reporter	2 - 4
Sack		
TA4569	Sack	1 - 2

TACO MAN TRAVELS NORTH AMERICA, 1992

Taco Bell characters Taco Man and Cheddar Fred on a paper strip to be colored came with 2 Crayola crayons with a cardboard fold-together vehicle. Larger versions of the vehicles have been used as meal containers at other restaurants.

TA4711	Scene w/crayons	1 - 3
TA4712	Boat	1 - 3
TA4713	Bus	1 - 3
TA4714	Convertible	1 - 4
TA4715	Airplane	1 - 3
Sack		
TA4719	Taco Man Travels North America!	1 - 2

ZOOBILEE ZOO COLORING STORYBOOKS, 1984

This promotion was Zoobilee Zoo coloring books which contained stories featuring Van Go Lion.

TA4851	The Mystery of the Blue Bandit	4 - 6
TA4852	My Fair Lioness	4 - 6
TA4853	Van Go and the Magic Baton	4 - 6

TA4851 TA4852 TA4853

TARGET

Target discount stores have a snack shop type food operation in most stores. These are called Food Avenues. These are found throughout the nation, except the Northeast. The company introduced the Targeteers in 1992 and has been an aggressive kids' meal promoter ever since with a steady stream of major licensed properties to attract kids.

TA5037 TA5079

3-D ADVENTURE, 1992

Three-D glasses and a 4-panel accordion-folded booklet featured an adventure story about one of the Targeteer Kids.The word "Targeteers" appeared above the nose piece of the glasses.

TA5031	Ramon Wins Gold	1 - 3
TA5032	Booklet 2	1 - 3
TA5033	Booklet 3	1 - 3
TA5034	Booklet 4	1 - 3
TA5035	3-D Targeteers Glasses	1 - 2
Sack		
TA5036	3-D Adventure	1 - 2
Point of Purchase		
TA5037	Table Card	1 - 2

ADDAMS FAMILY, THE, 1992

The release of the movie, sparked the opportunity for premium tie-ins.The multi colored cup is 3 ½" tall.

TA5071	Cup	1 - 3
Sack		
TA5079	The Addams Family	1 - 3

TA5101 TA5102 TA5103 TA5104

ADVENTURE TEAM WINDOW WALKER FIGURINES, 1994

Four plastic window/wall walkers with tacky balls of putty for hands and feet were offered briefly before spring. These would normally be incomplete out of the package.

TA5121

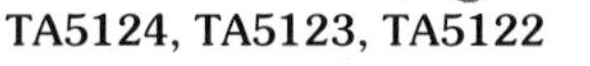

TA5124, TA5123, TA5122 TA5125

TA5101	Bungee Bob	1 - 6
TA5102	Freefallin' Freddy	1 - 6
TA5103	Rock Climbin' Rochelle	1 - 6
TA5104	Tumblin' Tommy	1 - 6

ALADDIN, 1993

This promotion featured three "pop-up" boxes in conjunction with the video release of the Disney animated film. The three different boxes were cubed shaped with a pop-up scene under the lid. When the child opened the meal, the top sprang open revealing an extra surprise. There were prizes inside, too, but distribution of these were very erratic. The third box didn't make it to most stores. Boxes and premiums didn't hit the same. The first premium was a Cave of Wonders paint with water set. Three paper finger puppets were next, followed by a color changing plastic tumbler.

TA5130

TA5121	Paint with water set, Cave of Wonders	3 - 5
TA5122	Iago paper puppet	3 - 5
TA5123	Abu paper puppet	3 - 5
TA5124	Cave of Wonders paper puppet	3 - 5
TA5125	Color changing tumbler	2 - 4
Boxes		
TA5127	Cave of Wonders	3 - 5
TA5128	Aladdin	3 - 5
TA5129	Aladdin and Jasmine on Magic Carpet	5 - 7
Point of Purchase		
TA5130	Table card	10 - 20
TA5131	Ceiling dangler	10 - 20

TA5431 TA5439

CAVEMEAL, 1993

Four 5-oz plastic cups featured a "cute" graphic of one of the "Prehistorics" with a write-up of the creature on the back of the cup.

TA5431	"Rex" the Tyrannosaurus Rex cup w/yellow straw	1 - 3
TA5432	"Tank" the Ankylosaur	1 - 3
TA5433	"Dawn" the Pteranodon	1 - 3
TA5434	"Chip" the Hadrosaur	1 - 3
Sack		
TA5439	Kids' Cavemeal	1 - 2

TA7200 TA7203 TA7207

MUPPETS ZING INTO SPRING, 1994

Kid's meal tied to a storewide promotion using the Muppets and the "Zing into Spring" theme. The three-part puzzle allowing four different Muppets to be scrambled or matched was issued in four different colors.

TA7200	Purple	2 - 4
TA7201	Pink	2 - 4
TA7202	Green	2 - 4
TA7203	Yellow	2 - 4
Sack		
TA7207	Zing Into Spring	1 - 2
Point of Purchase		
TA7209	Sign	5 - 10

PRECIOUS SPECIES ADVENTURE, 1993

Target Food Service was the founding international sponsor of this movement. The premium package consisted of a poster, sticker sheet and box of crayons. One side of the poster featured facts about endangered species, games and puzzles. The reverse side of the poster featured a large global drawing. The 5" x 7" white sticker sheet had colorful illustrations of the 11 animals to be placed on the poster. A box of four RoseArt Brand crayons came with each package.

TA8041, TA8042

TA8051

TA8459 TA8069

TA8041	Precious Species Poster/4 crayons	2 - 4
TA8042	Sticker Sheet	1 - 3

RESCUERS, THE, 1992

The video release of the Disney movie prompted a tie-in with Target. A punch-out Rescuers Glider Plane came with each kid's meal. The bag doubled as a hand puppet of Orville.

TA8062 TA8063 TA8061 TA8064, TA8065

TA8068 TA8067 TA8066

Premium
TA8051 Glider Plane 3 - 6
Sack
TA8059 The Rescuers 2 - 4

TARGETEERS FIGURES, 1992

Articulated figures of the Targeteer Kids, 3 cars and a skateboard made up this promotion. The cars were 4" plastic VW-like convertibles with larger back wheels. The cars and skateboard had pegs to fit into the figure's feet or bottom.

TA8061 Ashley 3 - 6
TA8062 Danielle 3 - 6
TA8063 Buddy 3 - 6
TA8064 Ramon 3 - 6
TA8065 Yellow skateboard 3 - 6
TA8066 Red car w/yellow trim 3 - 6
TA8067 Pink car w/blue trim 3 - 6
TA8068 Blue car w/red trim 3 - 6
Sack
TA8069 Targeteers 1 - 2

WAL-MART

The Arkansas-based Wal-Mart stores are a discount chain, the very newest of which house McDonald's restaurants. Most have just snack bar-type food outlets which offer kid's meals. There have been several major licensed deals since the company instituted its Kid's Meal in 1992. Unlike most competitors, Wal-Mart does not demand its premiums be exclusive items. Many are past or current toys. The Potato Heads Kids items were premiums previously used by McDonald's.

WA1111 WA1112 WA1113

CHRISTMAS FIGURES, 1993

Plastic figures of popular yuletide characters were issued with each kid's meal. Each colorful premium could also be used as an ornament.

WA1111 Santa Claus 2 - 4
WA1112 Snowman 2 - 4
WA1113 Toy Soldier 2 - 4
WA1114 Teddy Bear 2 - 4
WA1115 Mrs. Claus 2 - 4
WA1116 Elf 2 - 4

WA1114 WA1115 WA1116

WA1324 WA1321 WA1323

Sack
WA1118 Christmas Sack 1 - 2

DISNEY CHRISTMAS ORNAMENTS, 1992

During the 1992 Christmas season, paper ornaments featuring Disney characters were used as premiums.

WA1321 Mickey and Minnie on Sled 2 - 4
WA1322 Mickey and Pluto in Wreath 2 - 4
WA1323 Mickey in Santa Suit w/Sack of Toys 2 - 4
WA1324 Mickey on Rocking Horse 2 - 4
Sack
WA1326 Mickey and Pluto 1 - 2

WA2371

G.I. JOE/POTATO HEAD KIDS, 1993

This promotion featured different premiums for boys or girls. A micro vehicle came with each 1¼ G.I. Joe figure. The Potato Head Kids were the same as the ones given out by McDonald's restaurants in 1992, and were similar to the figures sold in stores.

WA2371 Bazooka w/Persuader 3 - 5
WA2372 Grunt w/Mobat 3 - 5
WA2373 Roadblock w/A.W.E. Striker 3 - 5
WA2374 Wet-Suit w/Warthog 3 - 5
WA2375 Slick 3 - 5
WA2376 Sabrina 3 - 5
WA2377 Spike 3 - 5
WA2378 Tulip 3 - 5
Sack
WA2379 G.I. Joe/Potato Head Kids 1 - 2

WA2373 WA2379

WA4451 WA4460

I ♥ MY EARTH ACTIVITY BOOK, 1994

An activity book with crayons.

WA4451 Activity Book w/crayons	1 - 2
WA4460 Sack	1 - 2

WA4501 WA4502 WA4503 WA4504

LISA FRANK, 1993 WA4507

Illustrator Lisa Frank created four PVC figures for this Back-to-School promotion. These figures were later sold carded at K mart.

WA4501 Hollywood Bear	2 - 3
WA4502 Penguin Surfer	2 - 3
WA4503 Markie, Unicorn	2 - 3
WA4504 Sneaker Kitties	2 - 3
Box	
WA4507 Lisa Frank	2 - 3

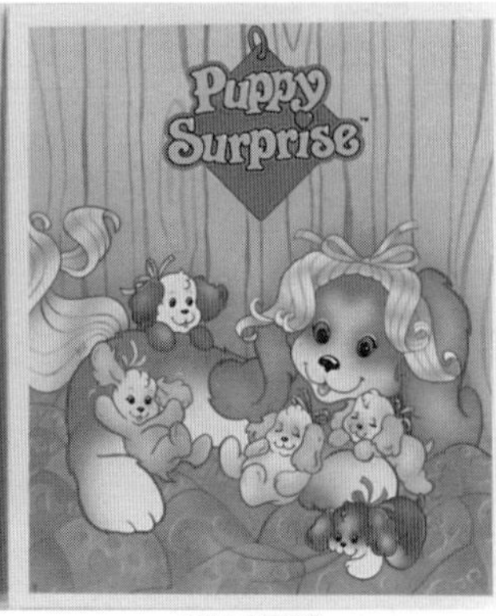

WA8751 WA8752

WA8751 (open)

WA8757 WA8807

TRANSFORMERS/PUPPY SURPRISE, 1993

There was a fold-over cover which featured a short story printed on the inner side. The related puzzle was in the "tray" back cover.

WA8751 Transformers, Generation 2	1 - 3
WA8752 Puppy Surprise	1 - 3
Sack	
WA8756 Sack with Logos	1 - 2
Point of Purchase	
WA8757 Table sign	1 - 2

TREASURE TROLLS, 1993

Trolls were the same as those used everywhere else, but attached to rings, keychains, magnets, etc. The sack was the only unique item.

WA8801 Ring	1 - 3
WA8802 Pony Tail Holder	1 - 3
WA8803 Key Chain	1 - 3
WA8804 Magnet	1 - 3
Sack	
WA8807 Treasure Trolls	1 - 2

WENDY'S

This international hamburger chain, based in Dublin (Columbus), Ohio, started kid's meals shortly after Burger King in 1982. Things never really quite jelled until the Good Stuff Gang was created in 1985. Up until then a variety of more or less off-the-shelf toys were used. The Good Stuff Gang theme was used fairly consistently through 1988, when they disappeared. Licensed promotions with special boxes were also used during this time, but the quantity of surviving boxes and premiums with no relation with any special boxes suggests a variety of Good Stuff Gang boxes were used over the course of a variety of premiums similar to the way Wendy's utilized unrelated colorful sacks in the early '90s.

Throughout the Wendy's section you will find some very specific promotion dates. In other cases there may only be a title, approximate year date, and scant listings. This is due to Wendy's policy of not retaining these types of records beyond a certain date. Unfortunately, Tomart was unsuccessful in locating any large Wendy's collectors to supplement the author's input, so some of the material presented is based strictly on odd items found over the years.

WE0151 WE0152 WE0153

WE0154 WE0155 3-D Glasses

WE0156

3-D CLASSIC COMICS, 1994

Literary classics were reproduced as 3-D comics, each packaged with a different set of prism-surface 3-D glasses. A paint with water set was also available as an under 3 premium.

WE0151	Robin Hood w/silver glasses	2 - 4
WE0152	King Arthur & the Sword in the Stone w/green glasses	2 - 4
WE0153	Call of the Wild w/purple glasses	2 - 4
WE0154	Treasure Island w/pink glasses	2 - 4
WE0155	Swiss Family Robinson w/blue glasses	2 - 4
WE0156	Black Beauty Paint with water (under 3)	3 - 5

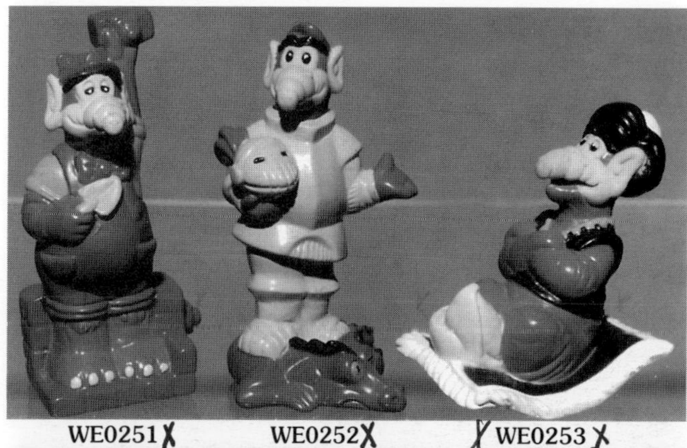

WE0251 WE0252 WE0253

WE0254 WE0255 WE0256

ALF TALES, 11/5/90-12/30/90 WE0259

Alf became a character from different storybook tales. A collector's card came with each figure as a package insert.

WE0251	The Three Little Pigs	2 - 4
WE0252	Knights of the Round Table	2 - 4
WE0253	Aladdin & His Lamp	2 - 4
WE0254	Robin Hood	2 - 4
WE0255	Little Red Riding Hood	2 - 4
WE0256	Sleeping Beauty	2 - 4
Box		
WE0259	Pictures Alf in all 6 stories	3 - 6

ALIEN MIX-UPS, 1/1/90-3/25/90

Applause produced the 2-piece PVC figures which pulled apart at the waist. The pieces were interchangeable.

WE0281	Blu-Zoid	2 - 5
WE0282	Yellow-Boid	2 - 5
WE0283	Crimson-Oid	2 - 5
WE0284	Spotta-Zoid	2 - 5

WE0281 WE0282 WE0283

WE0284 WE0285 WE0286

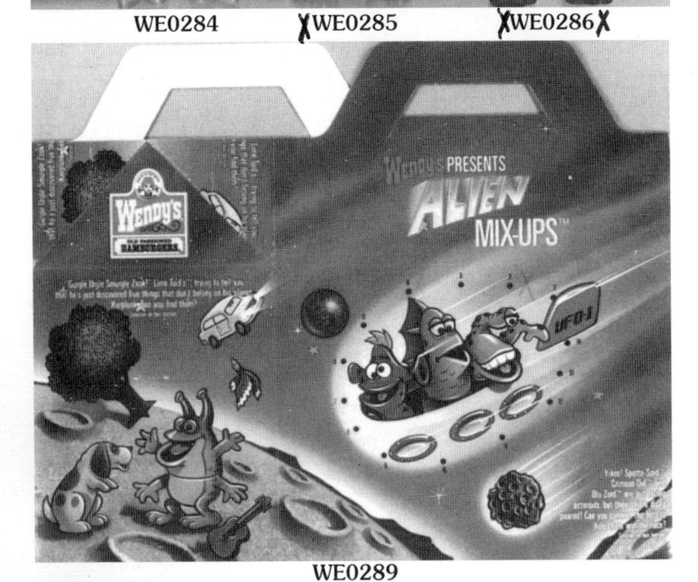

WE0289

WE0285	Purpa-Poid	2 - 5
WE0286	Lime-Toid	2 - 5

Box

WE0289	Alien Mix-Ups	3 - 6

ALL DOGS GO TO HEAVEN, 11/15/89-12/31/89

Don Bluth's Christmas-time animated movie, spawned six 3"-3¼" PVC figures of the characters

WE0351	Charlie	2 - 4
WE0352	Flo	2 - 4
WE0353	Itchy	2 - 4
WE0354	Anne Marie	2 - 4
WE0355	Carface	2 - 4
WE0356	King Gator	2 - 4

Box

WE0359	All Dogs Go to Heaven	3 - 6

ALVIN AND THE CHIPMUNKS, 1983

WE0391	Puffy Stickers	4 - 8

ARTS, 4/12/93-6/6/93

Art supplies in the shape of Wendy's food items were issued during this spring/summer promotion. Both crayon premiums came in black vacu-formed plastic holders. The finger crayons came in purple (Frosty), red (Burger) and yellow (Fries). A flat purple case in the shape of a

WE0359

WE0471 WE0472

WE0473 WE0474

WE0351 WE0352 WE0353

WE0354 WE0355 WE0356

burger opened to reveal a paint set containing six colors. Two different types of pens came as the interlocked twin Frosty. Chalk came in a replica of a fries box. Each piece of hamburger puzzle was a different-color crayon. The Under 3 premium was a red truck with yellowish cap.

WE0471	Frosty, Burger & Fries Finger Crayons	1 - 3
WE0472	Hamburger Paint Set	1 - 3
WE0473	Frosty Pen/Marker Combo	1 - 3
WE0474	French Fries Chalk	1 - 3
WE0475	Hamburger Crayon Puzzle	1 - 3
WE0476	Truck – Under 3	2 - 4

BACK TO SCHOOL, 1984

WE0541	Ruler	4 - 8
WE0542	School time Fun Stickers	4 - 8

BIKE LICENSE PLATE, 1984

WE0731	License Plate	4 - 8

WE0852 WE0856

BRISTLE BLOCKS, 1987

These uniquely-designed building pieces by Playskool could be used to create various shapes. Pieces to complete one figure came in a sealed bag printed with the Playskool logo.

WE0851	Car	4 - 8
WE0852	Cat	4 - 8
WE0853	Boat	4 - 8
WE0854	Bear	4 - 8
Box		
WE0855	Play Make Believe - Car	4 - 8
WE0856	Play Make Believe - Cat	4 - 8
WE0857	Play Make Believe - Boat	4 - 8
WE0858	Play Make Believe - Bear	4 - 8

BRUSH-TIP MARKERS, 1985

WE0871	Markers	2 - 4

BUNNY TRAIL GAME, 1984

WE0931	Game	8 - 10

CALLIGRAPHY STENCIL, 1983

WE1041	Stencil	3 - 6

CHRISTMAS PUZZLE ORNAMENTS, 1983

WE1161	Ornament #1	4 - 8
WE1162	Ornament #2	4 - 8
WE1163	Ornament #3	4 - 8
WE1164	Ornament #4	4 - 8

CREATE-A-CARD, 1986

WE1321	Premium	4 - 8

CREATE-A-CARD II, 1987

WE1351	Kit/Stickers	4 - 8

CUP HANGERS, 1987

Unpainted PVC figures with extremities extended in such a position to hold onto the lip of a glass or cup were issued. The characters exist in

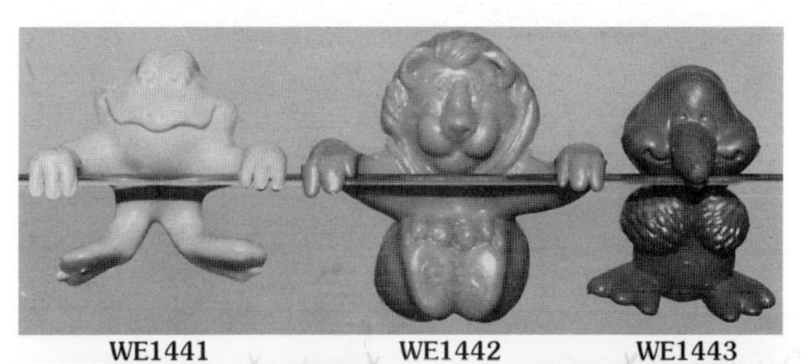

WE1441 WE1442 WE1443

WE1444 WE1445 WE1446

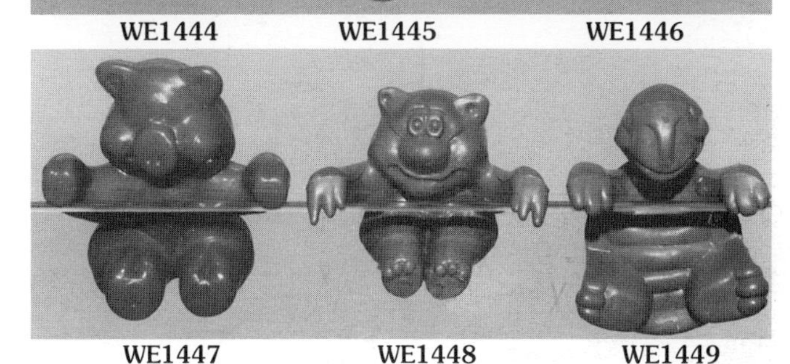

WE1447 WE1448 WE1449

10 different solid colors: two shades of yellow, two shades of blue, two shades of green, purple, aqua, pink and rose.

WE1441	Frog	2 - 5
WE1442	Lion	2 - 5
WE1443	Duck	2 - 5
WE1444	Alligator	2 - 5
WE1445	Beaver	2 - 5
WE1446	Elephant	2 - 5
WE1447	Pig	2 - 5
WE1448	Raccoon	2 - 5
WE1449	Turtle	2 - 5

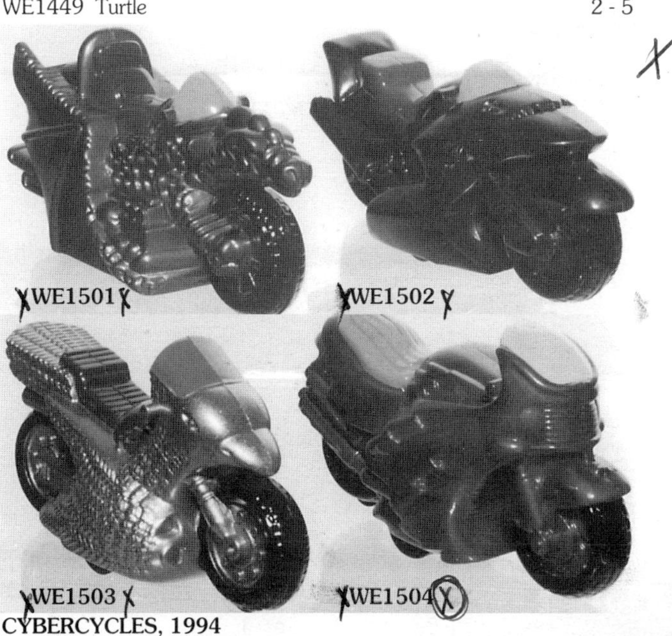

WE1501 WE1502 WE1503 WE1504

CYBERCYCLES, 1994

Three and one half-inch pull-back motorcycles painted in a bright shiny lacquer. The package also contained a paper insert showing the name of the promotion and drawing of a cycle. A second insert gives operating instructions.

WE1505 WE1506

WE1506 (detail)

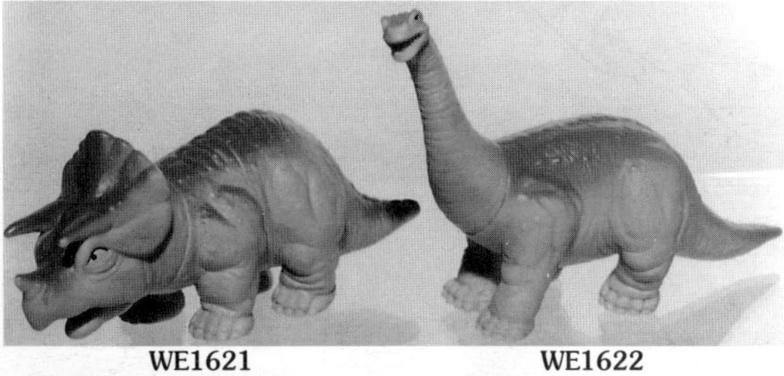

WE1621 WE1622

WE1623 WE1624

WE1501	Dragon, green	2 - 4
WE1502	Shark, blue	2 - 4
WE1503	Gryphon, or	2 - 4
WE1504	Lightning, red	2 - 4
WE1505	Techno, purple	2 - 4
WE1506	3-Wheeler (under 3)	3 - 5

DEFINITELY DINOSAURS!, 1988

Playskool hollow-hard-rubber figures of the prehistoric creatures in a 2-piece design, allowing the head or tail to move. Each figure was imprinted with the Definitely Dinosaurs! emblem, also sold in retail stores. The only determining factor these were Wendy's premiums was the sealed bag and insert.

WE1629

WE1621	Triceratops (green)	3 - 6
WE1622	Apatosaurus (blue)	3 - 6
WE1623	Tyrannosaurus	3 - 6
WE1624	Anatosaurus	3 - 6
Box		
WE1629	Definitely Dinosaurs!	2 - 4

WE1632 WE1633 WE1631

WE1634 WE1635 WE1636

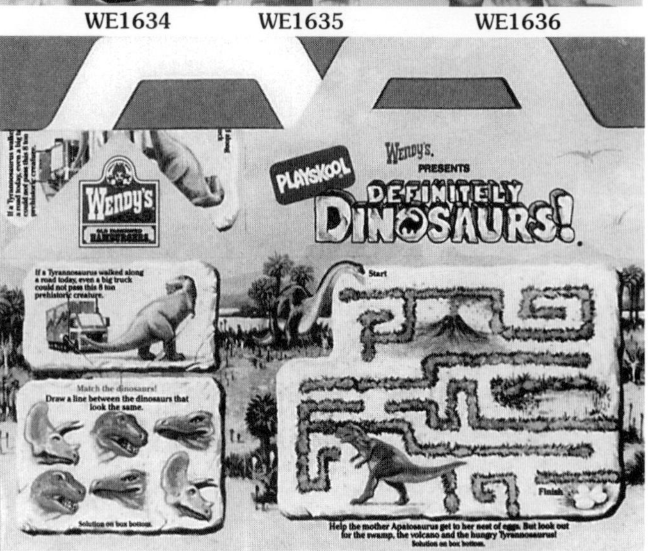

WE1639

DEFINITELY DINOSAURS II, 8/7/89-9/24/89

Wendy's repeated the Playskool dinosaur offering the following year. These figures bore the same imprint as those listed with the 1988 promotion – even the same ©1988 notation. As before, the only way to determine a premium from an over-the-counter purchase was the sealed bag and insert.

WE1631	Parasaurolophus	3 - 6
WE1632	Ceratosaurus	3 - 6
WE1633	Stegosaurus	3 - 6
WE1634	Ankylosaurus	3 - 6
WE1635	Apatosaurus (pink)	3 - 6
WE1636	Triceratops (brown)	3 - 6
Box		
WE1639	Box	2 - 4

DESIGN-A-STICKER, 1985

WE1711	Sticker Kit	4 - 8

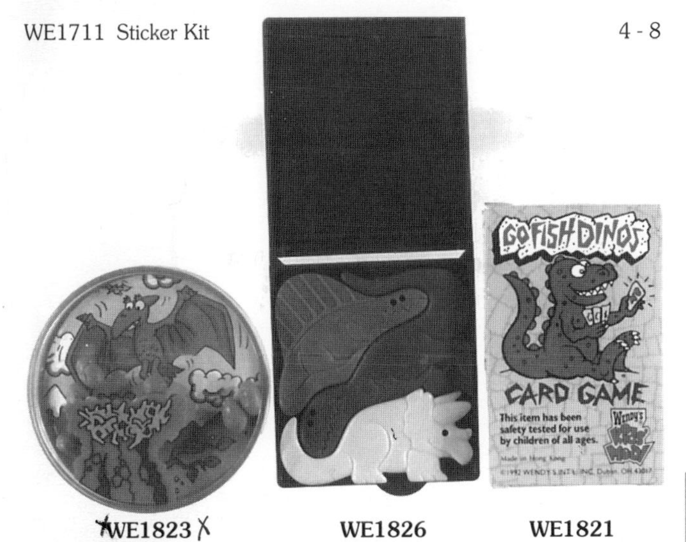

WE1823 WE1826 WE1821

WE1825 WE1824 WE1822

DINO GAMES, 11/9/92-1/3/93

Various games of skill featured dinosaur graphics or were in the shape of a dinosaur. Each game was imprinted on the back with "Wendy's Dino Games.

WE1821	Go Fish Dinos Card Deck	1 - 3
WE1822	Dinosaur Maze, blue	1 - 3
WE1823	Pterodactyl Egg Game	1 - 3
WE1824	Dino Obstacle Course	1 - 3
WE1825	Dino Jam Pinball Game	1 - 3
WE1826	Dino Puzzle – Under 3	2 - 5

DRINKING TUBES, 1993

Neon plastic drinking straws with a put-together feature were given. A card insert identified the promotion.

WE1901	Rainbow straw	1 - 3
WE1902	Trumpet straw—blue	1 - 3
WE1903	Trumpet straw—yellow	1 - 3
WE1904	Cup-wrap straw—light purple	1 - 3
WE1905	Cup-wrap straw—dark purple	1 - 3
WE1906	Color connector—all spirals	1 - 3
WE1907	Color connector—w/zig-zag part	1 - 3
WE1908	Under 3—stencils	2 - 4

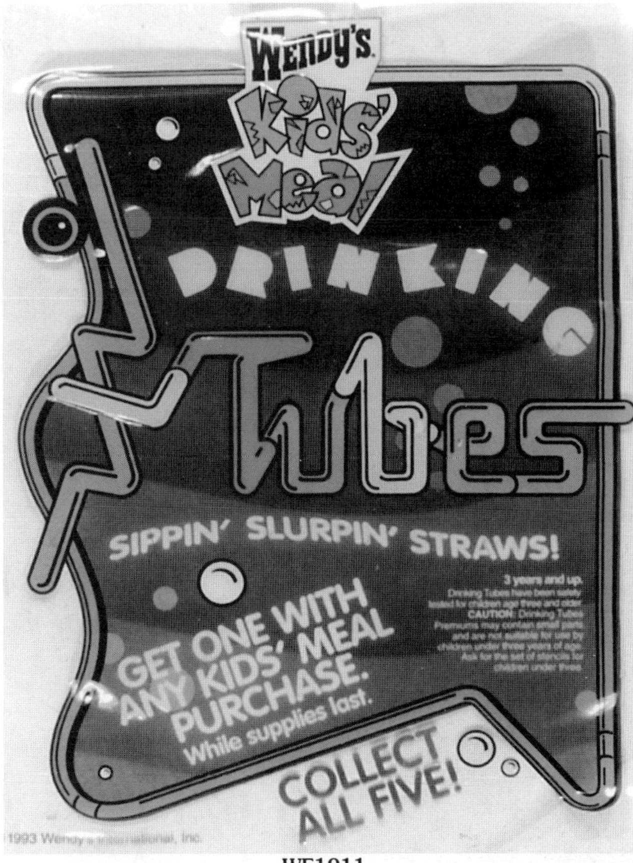

WE1911

WE1972 WE1975 WE1976

WE1974 WE1971 WE1973

ENDANGERED ANIMAL GAMES, 1993

This promotion made patrons aware of endangered animal species. Each is marked, "1993 Wendy's Int'l China." All but the jigsaw puzzle (which comes in a box) are packaged in a sealed plastic bag.

WE1971	Maze Game—Sea Turtle	1 - 3
WE1972	Catch Game—Eagle	1 - 3
WE1973	Pinball Game—Tiger	1 - 3
WE1974	Mini Puzzle	1 - 3
WE1975	Crazy Eight Card Game	1 - 3
WE1976	Elephant Puzzle (under 3)	2 - 4

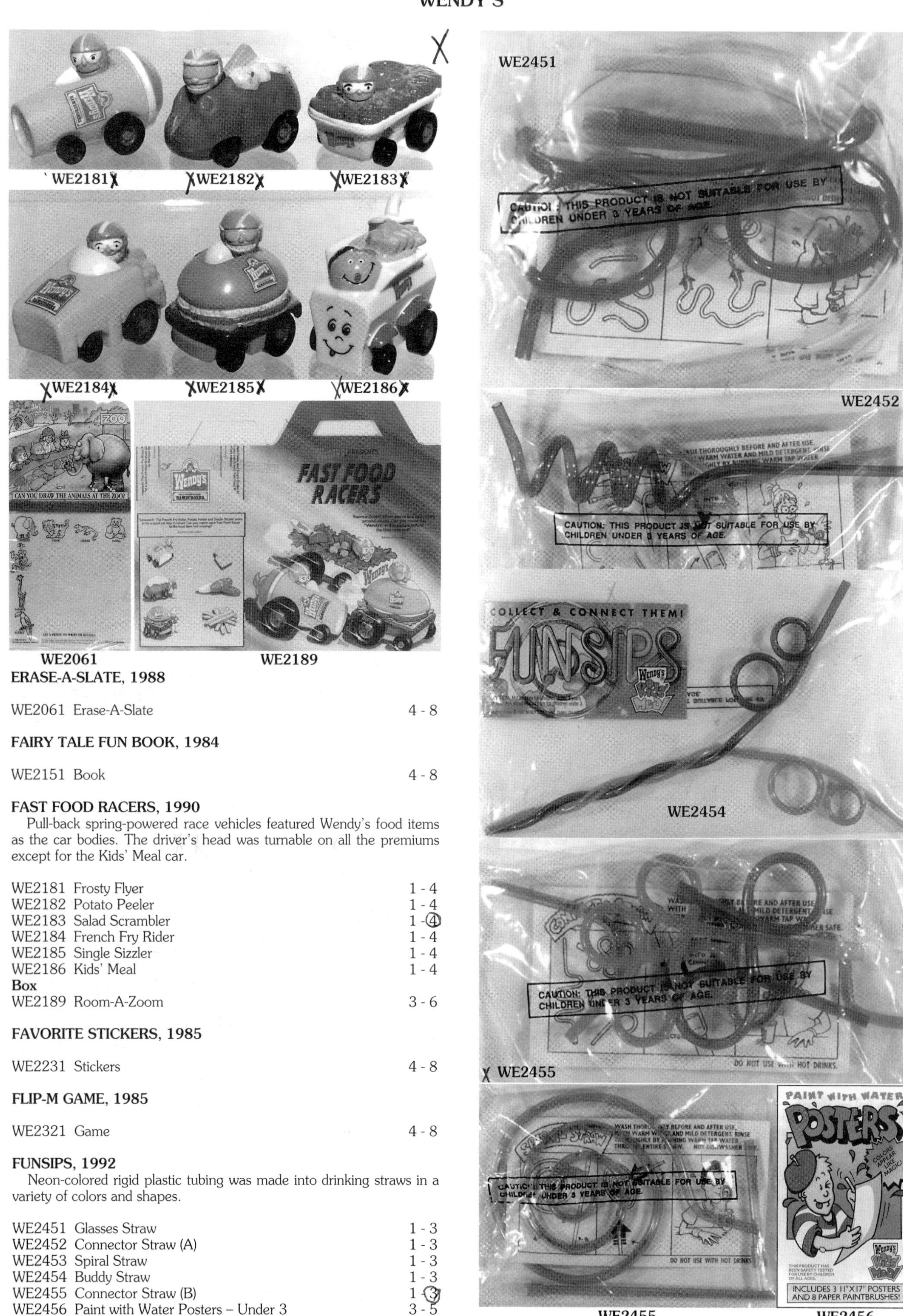

WE2181 WE2182 WE2183 WE2184 WE2185 WE2186 WE2061 WE2189 WE2451 WE2452 WE2454 WE2455 WE2455 WE2456

ERASE-A-SLATE, 1988

WE2061	Erase-A-Slate	4 - 8

FAIRY TALE FUN BOOK, 1984

WE2151	Book	4 - 8

FAST FOOD RACERS, 1990

Pull-back spring-powered race vehicles featured Wendy's food items as the car bodies. The driver's head was turnable on all the premiums except for the Kids' Meal car.

WE2181	Frosty Flyer	1 - 4
WE2182	Potato Peeler	1 - 4
WE2183	Salad Scrambler	1 - 4
WE2184	French Fry Rider	1 - 4
WE2185	Single Sizzler	1 - 4
WE2186	Kids' Meal	1 - 4
Box		
WE2189	Room-A-Zoom	3 - 6

FAVORITE STICKERS, 1985

WE2231	Stickers	4 - 8

FLIP-M GAME, 1985

WE2321	Game	4 - 8

FUNSIPS, 1992

Neon-colored rigid plastic tubing was made into drinking straws in a variety of colors and shapes.

WE2451	Glasses Straw	1 - 3
WE2452	Connector Straw (A)	1 - 3
WE2453	Spiral Straw	1 - 3
WE2454	Buddy Straw	1 - 3
WE2455	Connector Straw (B)	1 - 3
WE2456	Paint with Water Posters – Under 3	3 - 5

WE2531

WE2532

WE2532

FUN STAMP'RS, 1986

WE2481 Stamp'rs, each	4 - 8

FURSKINS, 1987

Xavier Roberts' Furskins were featured in this promotion. The 24-page storybook, *Furskins*, contained a story and art by John Lakey and had a die cut shape. "Wendy's Presents" appeared on the front cover. The board game consisted of a folded paper playing surface and punch-out pieces.

WE2531 Storybook	3 - 6
WE2532 Furskins on the Tear Britches Trail board game	3 - 6

FURSKINS BEARS, 1986

Seven-inch plush character bears were dressed in cloth outfits. A stiff paper tag was attached which had the name of the character and "Happy Holidays" with space for a name on the front.

WE2561 Dudley	6 - 8
WE2562 Boone	6 - 8
WE2563 Farrell	6 - 8
WE2564 Hattie	6 - 8

WE2561 WE2532

WE2563 WE2564

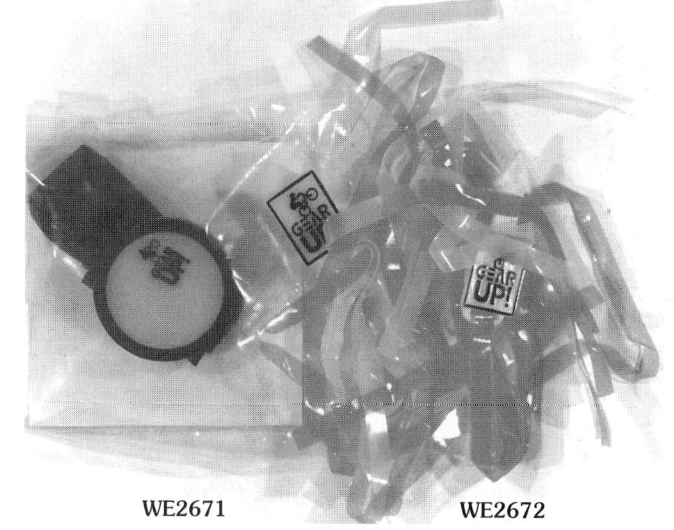

WE2671 WE2672

Box

WE2569 Moody Hollow General Store	4 - 8

Point of Purchase

WE2570 Display sign	10 - 15

GEAR UP, 1992

Various bicycle-related premiums were offered. All came in irradiant yellow and had the name of the promotion on them. Three pressure-sensitive stickers came with the license plate – "Back Off," "Smile," and "Get A Grip."

WE2671 Reflector Wrist Band, in various colors	1 - 3
WE2672 Handlebar Streamers	1 - 3
WE2673 Bike Seat Pouch	1 - 3

WE2673

WE2674

WE2675

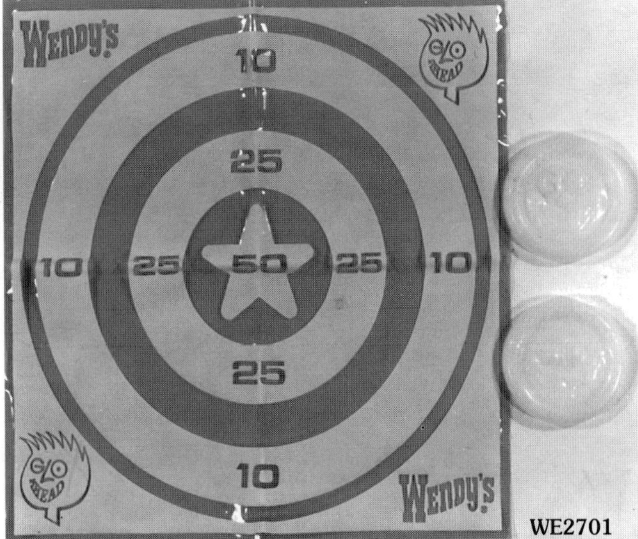

WE2701

WE2674	Water Bottle	1 - 3
WE2675	License Plate & Stickers	2 - 4

GLO-AHEAD, Fall 1993

This promotion featured a bizarre collection of glow-in-the-dark toys.

WE2701	Flicker Disks w/plastic target	2 - 5
WE2702	Gooey Glasses	1 - 3
WE2703	Pull-Back Racer	1 - 3
WE2704	Sucker Figurine	1 - 3
WE2705	Finger Puppet (under 3)	1 - 3

GLO FRIENDS, 2/20/89-4/9/89

The Playskool Glo Friends finger puppets were hollow 3" bug figures, made of a soft plastic material which glowed in the dark. There are others sold over the counter but only these were used as premiums.

WE2702 WE2703 WE2704 WE2705

WE2751 WE2752 WE2753 WE2754

WE2755 WE2756 WE2757 WE2758

WE2759 WE2760 WE2761 WE2762

WE2766

WE2751	Glo Butterfly	1 - 4
WE2752	Glo Clutterbug	1 - 4
WE2753	Glo Bashfulbug	1 - 4
WE2754	Glo Doodlebug	1 - 4
WE2755	Glo Bookbug	1 - 4
WE2756	Glo Bopbug	1 - 4
WE2757	Glo Snail	1 - 4
WE2758	Glo Snugbug	1 - 4

WE2822 WE2825 WE2821 WE2823 WE2826

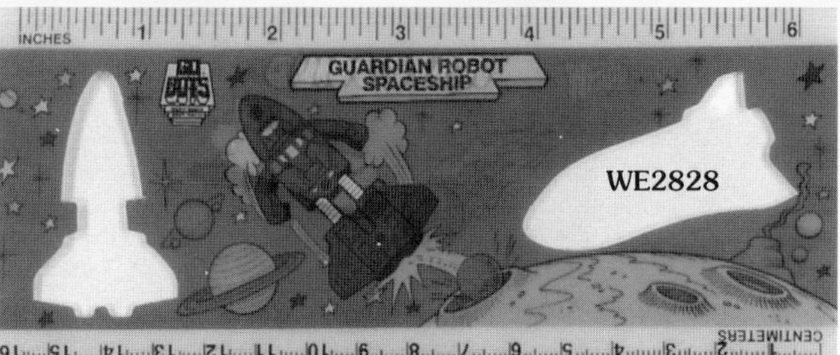

WE2828

WE2829

WE2839

WE2841

WE2842 WE2843

WE2759	Glo Cricket	1 - 4
WE2760	Glo Grannybug	1 - 4
WE2761	Glo Skunkbug	1 - 4
WE2762	Glo Bug	1 - 4
Boxes		
WE2766	Glo Friends in Glo Land	3 - 6

GLOW-IN-THE-DARK CRAZY BALL, 1983

WE2791	Ball	4 - 8

GOBOTS, 1986

Three-inch Robots which transformed into vehicles came in a blister pack. The name of the robot; the transformed vehicle; and logos for Wendy's, GoBots, and Tonka appeared on the blister pack. Other items may have been part of a separate promotion.

Premium		
WE2821	Beamer/Sports Car	8 - 12
WE2822	Sky Fly/Jet	8 - 12
WE2823	Breez/Helicopter	8 - 12
WE2824	Pow-Wow/Camper	8 - 12
WE2825	Odd Ball/Monster	8 - 12
WE2826	Guide Star (Under 3)	10 - 15
WE2827	Fun Patches	3 - 6
WE2828	Ruler/Stencil (blue)	3 - 6
WE2829	Ruler/Stencil (yellow)	3 - 6
WE2830	Color Activity Book	3 - 6
WE2831	Sticker Fun Book	3 - 6
Box		
WE2839	Moonstrike	2 - 5

GOBOTS IRON ON PATCHES, 1986

Guardian GoBots appeared in scenes printed on 5" x 4" iron-on patches. The name of the character and the resulting transformed vehicle was printed at the bottom of the scene.

WE2841	Leader-1	4 - 5
WE2842	Scooter	4 - 5
WE2843	Turbo	4 - 5

GOOD STUFF GANG, 1985

WE2871	Fun & Games Book	4 - 8
WE2872	Plastic Cup	4 - 8
WE2873	Stickers	4 - 8

GOOD STUFF GANG, 1986

Wendy and the Good Stuff Gang characters were issued as solid-color figures on a round base. Embossed on the rim of the base was the

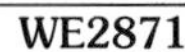

WE2871

WE2892 WE2891 WE2896

WE2894 WE2895 WE2893

WE2899

character's name. Each figure came in at least 20 different colors.

WE2891	Sweet Stuff	1 - 5
WE2892	Overstuff'd	1 - 5
WE2893	Lite Stuff	1 - 5
WE2894	Cool Stuff	1 - 5
WE2895	Hot Stuff	1 - 5
WE2896	Wendy	1 - 5
Box		
WE2899	Box	1 - 3

WE2985
(front and back)

WE2989

GOOD STUFF GANG SHRINKY DINKS, 1986

WE2911	Shrinky Dinks	3 - 6

GRABBER, 1984

WE2951	Premium	4 - 8

GUMMI BEARS, 1985

Disney characters from the TV cartoon series were featured on various premiums. A rebate-offer coupon for plush characters from Fisher Price was also included.

WE2981	Drinking Cup, Calvin & Calla	3 - 6
WE2982	Drinking Cup, the Bears	3 - 6
WE2983	Poster	3 - 6
WE2984	Straws	3 - 6
WE2985	Magical Medallion, Zummi at cauldron	3 - 6
Box		
WE2989	Disney's Gummi Bears	5 - 7

HALLOWEEN, 1983

WE3031	Witch Rocket	4 - 8
WE3032	Ghostly Glo Stickers	4 - 8
WE3033	Ghostly Pencil Top Eraser	4 - 8

HEART PENCIL, 1984

WE3121	Pencil	4 - 8

HUDDLES, 1984

WE3411	Stickers	4 - 8

HUNGRY HOUND, 1985

WE3571	Card Game	4 - 8

I WONDER NATURE BOOKS, 1993

Two soft-cover Golden Books used as fill-in premiums during the summer of 1993.

WE3601 WE3602

WE3601	I Wonder What a Rainforest Is	2 - 6
WE3602	I Wonder Where Butterflies Go In Winter	2 - 6

INVISIBLE INK PEN, 1983

WE3631	Color	4 - 8
WE3632	Color	4 - 8
WE3633	Color	4 - 8
WE3634	Color	4 - 8

WE3771 WE3772 WE3773

WE3774 WE3776 WE3777

JETSONS SPACE VEHICLES, 1989 WE3785

Characters from the TV cartoon series were the pilots of uniquely shaped space vehicles. Each plastic ship had "The Jetsons" embossed on one side and were imprinted "Available Only at Wendy's."

WE3771	George	2 - 5
WE3772	Jane	2 - 5
WE3773	Elroy	2 - 5
WE3774	Judy w/black bow in hair	2 - 5
WE3775	Judy w/pink bow in hair	2 - 5
WE3776	Mister Spacely	2 - 5
WE3777	Astro	2 - 5
WE3781	Late for Dinner Box	1 - 3
WE3785	Mat	1 - 2

WE3831 WE3832 WE3833

WE3834 WE3835 WE3836

JETSONS: THE MOVIE, 7/2/90-8/12/90 WE3839

The Jetsons family members and their space-age pets and friends were featured as PVC figures mounted on a plastic flying platform.

WE3831	Astro, fuchsia base	2 - 4
WE3832	Elroy, blue base	2 - 4
WE3833	Fergie Furbelow, pink base	2 - 4
WE3834	Little Grunchee, lime green base	2 - 4
WE3835	Judy, yellow base	2 - 4
WE3836	George, red base	2 - 4
Box		
WE3839	Jetsons: The Movie	1 - 3

KALEIDOSCOPE, 1984

WE4021	Kaleidoscope	4 - 8

KID-SIZE FLYING SAUCER, 1984

WE4041	Flying Saucer	4 - 8

KIDS 4 PARKS, 1993

Premiums were related to exploring national parks.

WE4051	Nature Notes Journal	1 - 3
WE4052	Compass	1 - 3
WE4053	Magnifying Glass	1 - 3

WE4052

WE4051

WE4053 WE4055

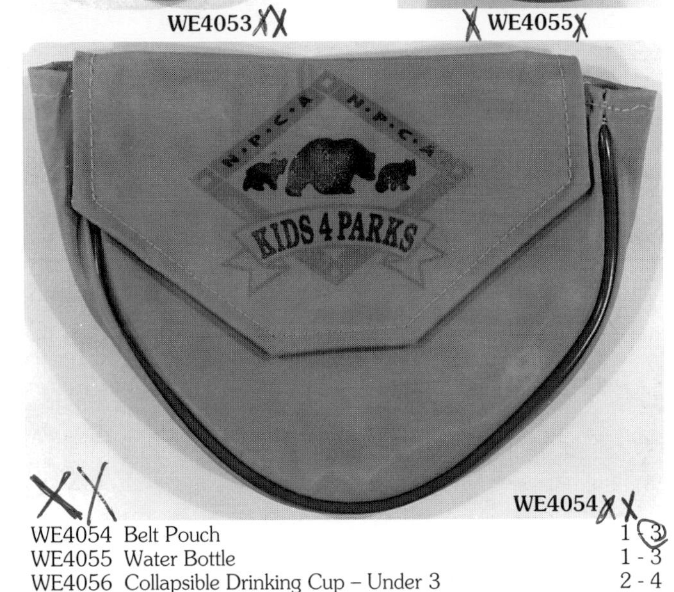

WE4054

WE4054	Belt Pouch	1 - 3
WE4055	Water Bottle	1 - 3
WE4056	Collapsible Drinking Cup – Under 3	2 - 4

KRAZY STRAW, 1984

WE4081	Straw	4 - 8

LAND OF GRUNDO, 1987

WE4131	Plastic Snack Bowls	4 - 6

LASER SLATES, 1989

"Magic" slates came with printed activities to be completed on the cover sheet. The writing surface had a glo-pink plastic cover. Lifting the plastic cover sheet, erased the slate and readied it for reuse.

WE4151	Hidden Words	4 - 6
WE4152	Draw a Face	4 - 6
WE4153	Tic-Tac-Toe	4 - 6
WE4154	Beings from Another Planet	4 - 6
WE4155	Animals At the Zoo	4 - 6
WE4156	Make a Word	4 - 6
WE4157	Let's Pretend	4 - 6
WE4158	The Maze	4 - 6

LEARN OUR LAND, 1986

WE4241	Sticker Maps	3 - 6
Boxes		
WE4242	Train	4 - 7
WE4243	Truck	4 - 7

MAGIC MOTION NOSE CARDS, 1985

WE4631	Cards	4 - 8

WE4701-WE4706 assembled as the Super Sky Carrier

MICRO MACHINES, 1990 **WE4709**

Collecting all 6 of the plastic space vehicle toys resulted in the ability to create a single snap-together Super Sky Carrier. Four of the units were in themselves airplanes; while the other two units were extensions to be placed on two of the plane assemblies. Each had peel-off stickers for detailing that particular aircraft/part.

WE4701	#1, Shuttle plane	3 - 6
WE4702	#2, Back extension for #1	2 - 4
WE4703	#3, Jet plane	2 - 4
WE4704	#4, Back extension for #3	2 - 4
WE4705	#5, Needle-nose jet	2 - 4
WE4706	#6, Round-nose transport plane	2 - 4
Box		
WE4709	Super Sky Carrier	3 - 6

MIGHTY MOUSE, 1989

Each 2½" PVC figure had a suction-cup base. A trading card came with each premium as a bag insert.

WE4821	Scrappy	3 - 6
WE4822	The Cow	3 - 6
WE4823	Pearl Pureheart	2 - 4
WE4824	Mighty Mouse	2 - 4

WE4821 WE4823 WE4826

WE4822 WE4825 WE4824

WE4831 WE4832

WE4825 Bat-Bat 2 - 4
WE4826 Petey-Pate 2 - 4

Boxes

WE4831 Gasp! 3 - 6
WE4832 Yikes! 3 - 6

WE4911 WE4912 WE4913

MOODIES, 1984

Although many different Moodies were pictured on the box for this promotion, only Happy Moody has been found. This 2½" PVC figure molded on a round base came in a variety of solid colors with yellow being the most commonly found. The name "Happy Moodie™" was embossed around the side of the base.

Premium

WE4911 Happy Yellow 2 - 4
WE4912 Happy Blue 3 - 5
WE4913 Happy Green 3 - 5

Box

WE4919 Meet the Moodies 4 - 8

WE4919 WE4970

MY FIRST BOOK, 1993

Used during clean-up weeks as needed by individual stores. The 8" x 8" book had the Wendy's Kid's Meal logo on the back cover.

Premium

WE4970 My First Book About Space 2 - 3

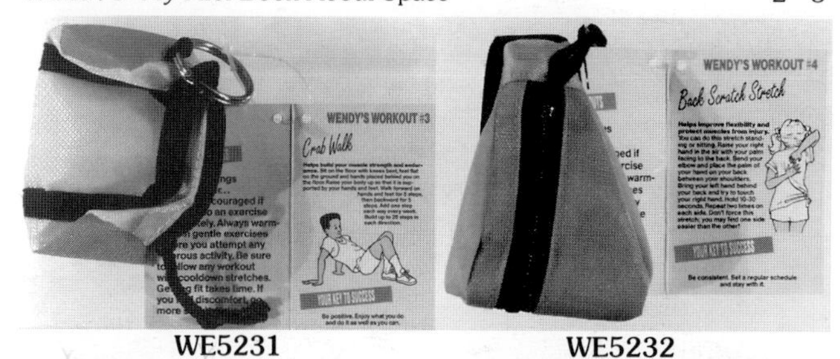

WE5231 WE5232

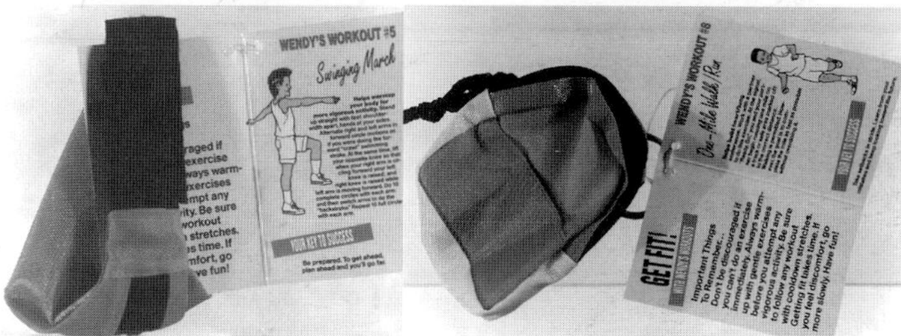

WE5232 WE5233

NEON POCKET PAKS, 4/15/91-6/2/91

"Hot tips for fitness fun" were printed on the 8 different inserts which were used with the 4 different types of pocket paks during this Kids' Meal deal. The zippered cloth mini pouches came in a variety of fluorescent colors. The Under 3 premium was identical to the wrist pak, but its paper insert showed the product had been safety tested for children of all ages and it did not have the tag attached.

WE5231 Duffel Bag 1 - 3
WE5232 Wrist Pak 1 - 3
WE5233 Back Pak 1 - 3
WE5234 Sports Bag 1 - 3
WE5239 Wrist Pak (Under 3) 2 - 5

NEW STICKER GAMES, 1985

WE5301 Sticker game 4 - 8

PICK-A-PET, 1987

WE6181 Gallery Posters 4 - 8

Box

WE6186 Help Wendy Pick-A-Pet 4 - 8

PLAY-DOH FINGLES, 9/24/90-11/4/90

A 2-oz can of glow-in-the-dark Play-Doh modeling compound came boxed with a press-together mold for making a finger puppet. The mold and the lid to the container were imprinted with the Kenner name.

WE6221 Cat, blue 2 - 4
WE6222 Pumpkin, orange 2 - 4
WE6223 Monster, green 2 - 4
WE6224 Ghost, yellow 2 - 4

WE6221 WE6223

WE6224 WE6225

WE6226

WE6227

WE6225 Bat, blue 2 - 4
WE6226 Witch, green 2 - 4
Box
WE6227 Halloween Haunted House 1 - 3

POP-UP PAINT SET, 1984

WE6261 Paint Set 4 - 8

POP-UP PIPE, 1983

WE6301 Pipe 4 - 8

WE6341 WE6342 WE6343

POTATO HEAD KIDS, 1987

Once the Potato Head figure was removed from the sealed clear bag, it was impossible to distinguish the rubber heads, plastic feet and hats from those sold in retail stores.

WE6341 Big Horn Ram 1 - 6
WE6342 Sir Scallop 1 - 6
WE6343 Cavalier 1 - 6
WE6344 Sabreena the Witch 1 - 6
WE6345 Blue Mouse 1 - 6

WE6344 WE6345 WE6346

WE6351

WE6381 WE6382 WE6383

WE6384 WE6385 WE6386

WE6346 Rabbit Nubbins 1 - 6
Boxes
WE6351 Shoe Clubhouse 2 - 4

POTATO HEAD II, 8/29/88-11/6/88

The popular Playskool toys were once again issued. There is no distinction between the premium and a retail-store figure once opened.

WE6381 Cap'n Kid 1 - 6
WE6382 Policeman Duke 1 - 6
WE6383 Fireman Sparky 1 - 6
WE6384 Slugger 1 - 6
WE6385 Nurse Sophie 1 - 6
WE6386 Krispy 1 - 6
Boxes
WE6391 Policeman Duke directing traffic 4 - 6
WE6392 Spud Memorial 4 - 6

WE6391 WE6392

PRESS 'N POP TOY, 1984

WE6421 Press 'N Pop toy 4 - 8

PRISMATIC STICKERS, 1983

WE6451 Stickers 4 - 8

PUMPKIN GAMES, 1983

WE6481 Games 4 - 8

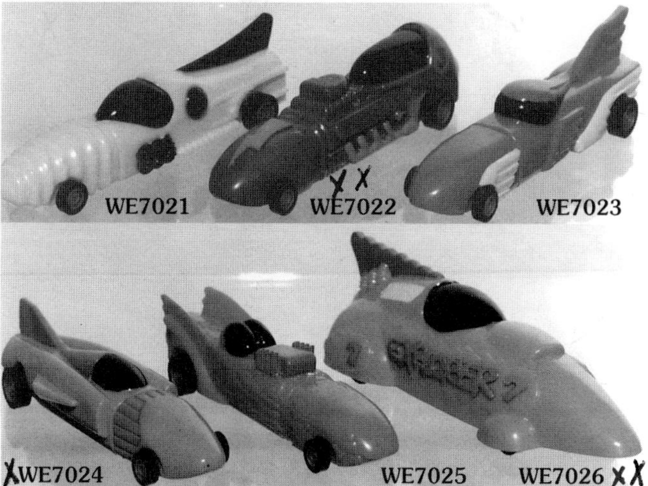

WE7021 WE7022 WE7023 WE7024 WE7025 WE7026

ROCKET WRITERS, 1992

Sleek and slender plastic pull-back rocket cars became a ballpoint pen when the front-wheeled section was removed. The color of ink was the same as one of the colors on the car. The Under 3 premium was a Rocket Car which did not convert to a pen.

WE7021 Yellow/Black, black ink 2 - 5
WE7022 Purple/Orange/Green, purple ink 2 - 5
WE7023 Green/Yellow/Black, green ink 2 - 5
WE7024 Turquoise/Pink/Black, blue ink 2 - 5
WE7025 Fushia/Green/Black, red ink 2 - 5
WE7026 Orange Rocket Car – Under 3 3 - 7

SAURUS SPORT BALLS, 1991

Miniature rubber sports balls were embossed with a dinosaur figure clad in the appropriate sports uniform. On the opposite side of the ball was printed a definition of the character.

WE7031 Soccerasaurus 1 - 3
WE7032 Baseballasaurus 1 - 3
WE7033 Footballasaurus 1 - 3
WE7034 Basketballasaurus 1 - 3

SCOOP 'N BASKET, 1984

WE7231 Scoop 'N Basket 4 - 8

SESAME STREET, 1985

WE7301 Storybook 4 - 8
WE7302 "Follow That Bird" Plastic Cup 4 - 8
Box
WE7309 Follow That Bird 5 - 8

SILLY SIPPERS AND MASK, 1991

A plastic partial face mask came with each 12" straw. There was a hole in the mouth area to enable the mask to be placed onto the straw,

WE7031 WE7032

WE7033 WE7034

WE7309

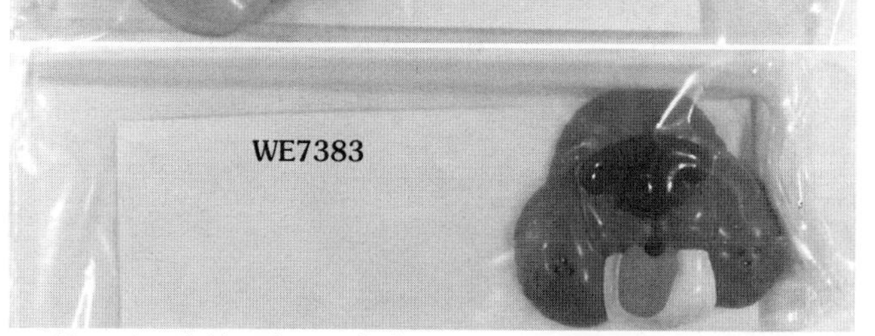

WE7381 WE7382 WE7383

enabling the child to be a silly human or animal whenever a sip was taken. The Under 3 premium was was a Silly Mask with no straw.

WE7384

WE7385

WE7386

WE7381 Funny Lips Mask & Sipper 1 - 3
WE7382 Lips w/Tongue Mask & Sipper 1 - 3
WE7383 Dog Mask & Sipper 1 - 3
WE7384 Pig Mask & Sipper 1 - 3
WE7385 Moustache Mask & Sipper 1 - 3
WE7386 Rabbit Silly Mask (Under 3) 2 - 4

SPACE SHUTTLE REPLICA, 1984

WE7431 Space Shuttle Replica 4 - 8

WE7471 WE7472 WE7473

WE7474 WE7475 WE7476

SPEED BUMPERS, 1992

Three-inch pullback spring-driven cars which reversed direction when they bumped into a solid object. The Under 3 premium was called a Speed Roller. It simply rolled in one direction on the four wheels.

WE7471 CRUSHER, yellow 2 - 5
WE7472 FLY, light blue 2 - 5
WE7473 BUMP, dark blue 2 - 5
WE7474 FUN, red 2 - 5
WE7475 WILD THING, pink 3 - 6
WE7476 Truck Speed Roller, purple (Under 3) 3 - 7

WE7511 WE7512

WE7513 WE7514

WE7515 WE7516

SPEED WRITERS, 1991 WE7517

Ballpoint pens disguised as cars were pull-back racers with elongated front sections. When these front sections were pulled off, a ballpoint pen was exposed. The Under 3 premium was a 5" x 8" Paint-with-Water book.

WE7511 Green body truck, green ink 2 - 4
WE7512 Black roadster, black ink 2 - 4
WE7513 Blue tall fins, blue ink 2 - 4
WE7514 Red convertible, red ink 2 - 4
WE7515 Purple racer, blue ink 2 - 4
WE7516 Orange sports car, red ink 2 - 4
WE7517 Paint-with-Water Book – Under 3 3 - 5

SPINNING TOP GAME, 1983

WE7551 Game 4 - 8

WE7602

WE7603

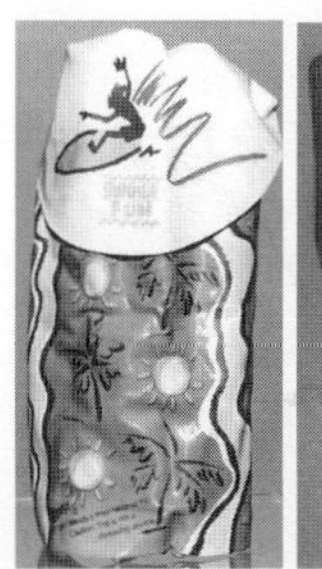
WE7601

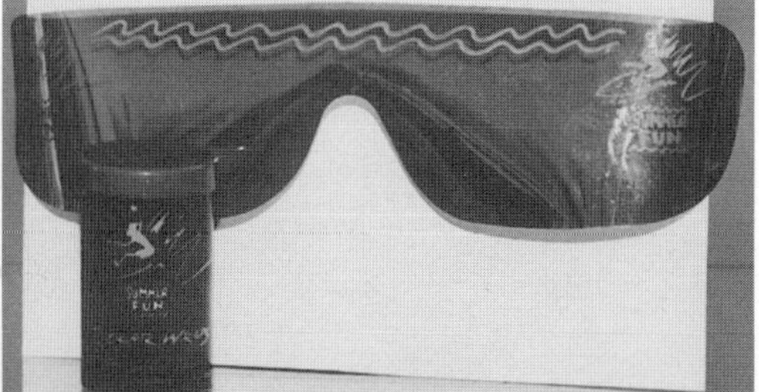
WE7605

WE7604

SUMMER FUN SUN GEAR, 6/3/91-7/28/91

Typical summer fun and inflatables promotion. The silver metallic-looking glasses came in a film can-like plastic case. These were recalled early in the promotion.

WE7601	Inflatable Pouch	2 - 4
WE7602	Beach Bag	2 - 4
WE7603	Inflatable Sky Saucer	2 - 4
WE7604	Bicycle Cap	2 - 4
WE7605	Solar Wrap, recalled	4 - 8

WE7819

TED E. BEAR, 1984

WE7811	Stickers	4 - 8
WE7812	Coloring Poster	4 - 8
Box		
WE7819	Ted. E. Bear	3 - 5

TEDDY RUXPIN, 1987

Four of these 2"-3" figures were flocked; Newton Gimmic was not flocked. All except Fob were poseable.

WE7831	Teddy Ruxpin	4 - 8
WE7832	Grubby Worm	4 - 8
WE7833	Newton Gimmic	4 - 8
WE7834	Wooly What's It	4 - 8
WE7835	Fob	4 - 8

WE7831 WE7832 WE7833

WE7834 WE7835

WE7837

WE7959 (front and back)

Box		
WE7836	Beautiful Garden	2 - 4
WE7837	The Search	2 - 4

TEDDY RUXPIN & FRIENDS, 1987

WE7851	Plastic Drinking Cups	4 - 6

TOM THUMB PLANT STARTER KITS, 1987

Vegetable, herb and flower seed packets for spring planting were included in this Good Stuff Gang Meal.

WE7951	Impatiens	4 - 6
WE7952	Tomatoes	4 - 6
WE7953	Green Peppers	4 - 6
WE7954	Daisies	4 - 6
WE7955	Marigolds	4 - 6
WE7956	Zinnias	4 - 6
WE7957	Thyme	4 - 6
WE7958	Lettuce	4 - 6
Box		
WE7959	Wendy/Good Stuff Gang Watch Their Garden Grow	2 - 4

TOO COOL! FOR SCHOOL, 9/21/92-11/8/92

Wendy's offered an assortment of items disguised as food which could be used during the school year. This is one of the best back-to-school promotions found. The Under 3 premium was a 4-piece plastic stencil set in the shape of a hamburger, fry pack, Frosty, and Kids' Meal sack. Various shapes and numbers were die-cut in each stencil.

WE7992

WE7991 WE7996

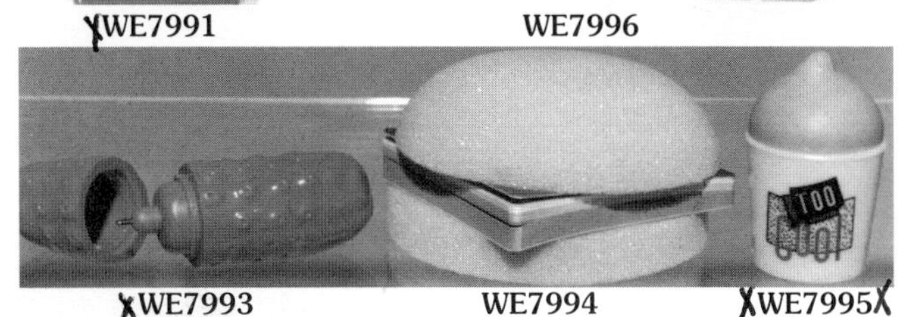

WE7993 WE7994 WE7995

WE7991	Hot Numbers Notebook	1 - 4
WE7992	Pencil Pouch w/ruler	1 - 4
WE7993	Pickle Pen	1 - 4
WE7994	Hot Notes Hamburger Pad	1 - 4
WE7995	Frosty Eraser/Pencil Sharpener	1 - 4
WE7996	Stencils – Under 3	2 - 5

WE8031

WE8032 WE8033

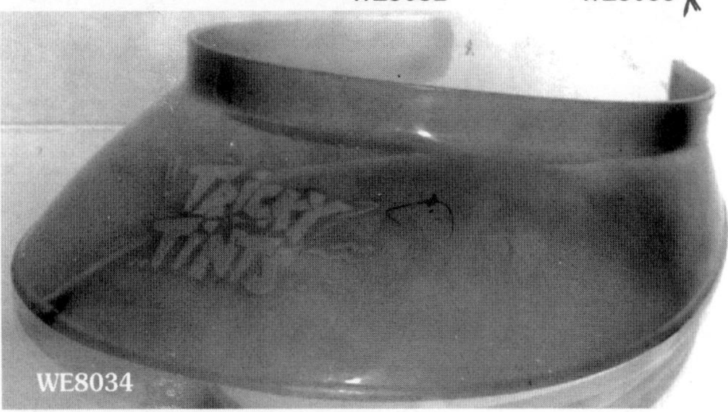

WE8034

TRICKY TINTS, 4/13/92-6/7/92

Premiums offered changed color when exposed to sunlight. The "Do It" patch doubled as the Under 3 premium.

WE8031	Shoelaces	1 - 3
WE8032	Straws, set of 3	1 - 3
WE8033	12-oz Water Bottle	1 - 3
WE8034	Sun Visor	1 - 3
WE8035	"Do It" Iron-On Patch – Under 3	2 - 4

WE8315

WE8035

WE8311 WE8312

WE8313 WE8315 WE8316

UFO (UNBELIEVABLY FUN OBJECTS), 2/22/93-4/11/93

Space-related balls came with a folded-color insert which contained the name, various facts, a game, and a riddle regarding the particular space object.

WE8311	Comet Ball w/foil streamers	1 - 3
WE8312	Satellite Sucker Ball	1 - 3
WE8313	Glow-in-the-Dark Moon Ball	1 - 3
WE8314	Squishy Saturn Ball	1 - 3
WE8315	Glow-in-the-Dark Inflatable Globe of Solar System	1 - 3
WE8316	Bouncing Planet Ball – Under 3	2 - 4

WE8445

VACATION FUN BOOK, 1984

WE8441	Book	4 - 8
Box		
WE8445	Summer Vacation Fun	5 - 10

WE8531 WE8532 WE8533

WE8534 WE8535 WE8536

WACKY WIND-UPS, 1991

Plastic wind-up food items moved in crazy ways when released. The fries wiggled from side to side; the potato waddled as it moved forward; the top portion of the burger bun moved up and down as if chomping on the hamburger inside; the frosty rolled around in a circle; and the meal box hopped. The Under 3 premium was called a Wacky Roller and was a red Kids' Meal sack on 4 small blue wheels.

WE8531	Fries	2 - 5
WE8532	Potato	2 - 5
WE8533	Burger	2 - 5
WE8534	Frosty	2 - 5
WE8535	Meal Box	2 - 5
WE8536	Wacky Roller (Under 3)	3 - 7

WE8831 WE8832 WE8833 WE8834 WE8835 WE8836

WEIRD WRITERS, 1993

Florescent color markers were disguised as baroque plastic sculptures done in the same solid-color plastic as the marker. The Under 3 premium was called a Crazy Water Toy and was a water squirter.

WE8831	Lime Green Writer (Trans-Rex Robot)	1 - 3
WE8832	Pink Writer (Surfer)	1 - 3
WE8833	Blue Writer (Hammerhead)	1 - 3
WE8834	Orange Writer (Dizzy)	1 - 3
WE8835	Yellow Writer (Slimmer)	1 - 3
WE8846	Crazy Water Toy, purple bird (Under 3)	2 - 5

WENDY & THE GOOD STUFF GANG ENTER THE GOOD STUFF GAMES, 1988

Four sticker sets were issued during this promotion.

WE8901	Create-A-Scene Sticker Set #1	4 - 8
WE8902	Create-A-Scene Sticker Set #2	4 - 8
WE8903	Create-A-Scene Sticker Set #3	4 - 8
WE8904	Create-A-Scene Sticker Set #4	4 - 8
Box		
WE8909	The Good Stuff Games	3 - 5

WE8909 WE8989

WENDY & GOOD STUFF GANG PLANT A SPRING GARDEN, 1988

Flower and vegetable seed packets were again issued for this springtime promotion.

WE8981	Aster	5 - 6
WE8982	Peppermint	5 - 6
WE8983	Tomato	5 - 6
WE8984	Daisy	5 - 6
WE8985	Green Pepper	5 - 6
Box		
WE8989	Plant a Spring Garden	3 - 5

WENDY & GOOD STUFF GANG POSTERS, 1986

WE9021	Coloring Poster w/crayons	3 - 6

WE9041 WE9042 WE9043

WE9044 WE9045 WE9046

WHERE'S THE BEEF?, 1984

Clara Peller was the cantankerous grandmotherly figure in Wendy's TV commercials. Each 9" x 3¾" sheet contained 7 or 8 puffy stickers. Sets may be differentiated by the letter at the end of the code number which appears on the package.

WE9049 (front and back)

WE9041	Set A	5 - 7
WE9042	Set B	5 - 7
WE9043	Set C	5 - 7
WE9044	Set D	5 - 7
WE9045	Set E	5 - 7
WE9046	Set F	5 - 7

Box

WE9049	Where's the Beef?	4 - 8

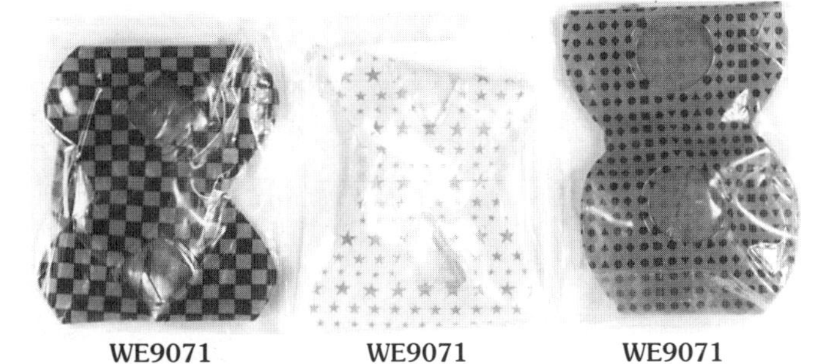

WE9071 WE9071 WE9071

WIDE EYES, 1985?

Inflatable eyeglass "masks" were shaped to fit across the eyes and over the ears. Each came with a different design in various colors.

Premium

WE9071	Inflatable Glasses, each	4 - 8

WE9111 WE9117

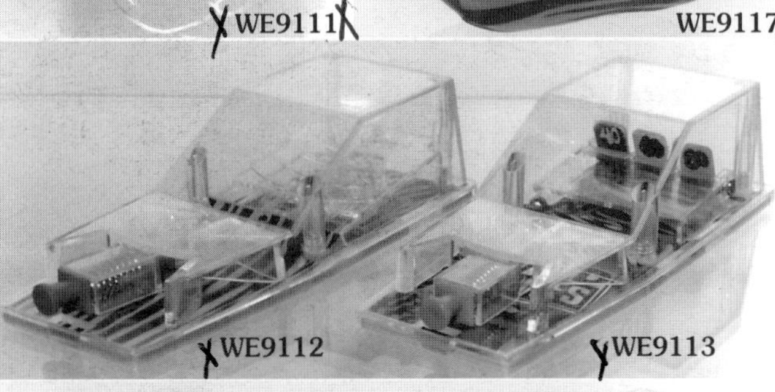

WE9112 WE9113

WE9114 WE9115

WILD GAMES, 12/30/91-2/23/92

The cloth-covered stuffed ball came in a variety of color and designs – some with spots; some with stripes. "Wendy's Wild Games" was printed on the cloth. These doubled as the Under 3 premium. A Basketball Set including a fold-down plastic hoop, net, and a soft plastic 2" basketball; two different 5" hand-held pinball games; and two different aqua-catch games were the premiums.

WE9111	Basketball w/backboard & hoop	2 - 4
WE9112	Pinball ski	2 - 4
WE9113	Pinball target	2 - 4
WE9114	Aqua Catch Game, food products	2 - 4
WE9115	Aqua Catch Game, fries	2 - 4
WE9117	Soft Ball (Under 3), various wild colors	2 - 4

WE9156 WE9157

WILLOW MAGIC CUPS, 1988

Characters from the Lucasfilm Ltd. movie were featured on cups with specially-treated stickers. When ice-cold liquid was placed into the cup, the background scene magically changed.

WE9151	Eborsisk	3 - 4
WE9152	Cherlindrea	3 - 4
WE9153	Madmartigan	3 - 4
WE9154	Raziel	3 - 4

Boxes

WE9156	Nockmaar Castle	2 - 4
WE9157	Willow Ulfgood Bids Farewell	2 - 4

WE9231 WE9233

WE9234 WE9232

WORLD WILDLIFE FUND BOOKS AND PLUSH ANIMALS, 1988

Wendy's teamed with the World Wildlife Fund to offer 14-page hardback books on endangered species.

WE9231	All About Tigers	4 - 6
WE9232	All About Giant Pandas	4 - 6
WE9233	All About Snow Leopards	4 - 6
WE9234	All About Koalas	4 - 6

WE9235 WE9236 WE9237 WE9238

Wendy's also had plush animal toys of the endangered species as an over-the-counter offering. A 2⅜" x 2½" booklet about the wild animal was attached to each plush figure.

WE9235	Tiger	6 - 8
WE9236	Giant Panda	6 - 8
WE9237	Snow Leopard	6 - 8
WE9238	Koala	6 - 8
WE9239	Wendy and The Good Stuff Gang picture to color	5 - 7

WE9691 WE9693 WE9694

WE9695 WE9696 WE9697

WE9699 WE9851

YOGI BEAR & FRIENDS, 1990

Each PVC figure was molded onto a plastic base which encased ball bearings.

WE9691	A-Yogi, green base	2 - 4
WE9692	B-Yogi, gray base	2 - 4
WE9693	Snagglepuss	2 - 4
WE9694	Ranger Smith	2 - 4
WE9695	Boo Boo	2 - 4
WE9696	Cindy Bear	2 - 4

WE9851 WE9853 WE9855

WE9697	A-Huckleberry Hound, white base	2 - 4
WE9698	B-Huckleberry Hound, blue base	2 - 4
Box		
WE9699	Yogi Bear & Friends	2 - 4

MISCELLANEOUS BOXES AND SACKS

Wendy's began packaging Kid's Meals in generic multi-use sacks in the early '90s. The Good Stuff Gang Fun & Games box may also have been used for more than one promotion.

WE9851	Fun & Games with Wendy & the Good Stuff Gang	1 - 3
WE9852	Awesome Astronomy	1 - 2
WE9853	Just for Kids	1 - 2
WE9854	The Big Bag	1 - 2
WE9855	Weather Watch	1 - 2

WHATABURGER

This predominately Texas hamburger chain is still large enough to do some nice custom premiums, but relies heavily on Admark and other stock promotion companies for its kid's-meal premiums which it has been using since at least the mid-1980s. This is one of the most incomplete sections in the book, but there were enough known premiums to give readers an idea of what they might expect upon visiting Whataburger.

WH1000

BEAR IRON-ONS, 1985

The backing paper for these iron-ons could be presented at Whataburger for a free small french fries when ordering a sandwich.

WH1000	B.B.O.C. Bear (Big Bear On Campus)	2 - 4
WH1001	Barn E. Bear	2 - 4

WH1801 WH1803

WH1802 WH1804

DINO BLOCKS, 1992

Three-piece slotted-plastic dino-blocks were issued for this prehistoric promotion. The main body piece of each creature was imprinted with "Dino Blocks."

WH1801	Stegosaurus	2 - 4
WH1802	Pteranodon	2 - 4
WH1803	Brontosaurus	2 - 4
WH1804	Triceratops	2 - 4

DINOSAUR SAFARI, 1992

Stock Admark dinosaur figures came in a variety of colors and were

WH1831/1841 WH1832/1842 WH1833/1843

WH1834/1844 WH1835/1845 WH1836/1846

WH1848 (front and back)

WH1860

WH1851 WH1852 WH1853 WH1854

made of material which either changed color when warmed or glowed in the dark.

WH1831 Color change	2 - 4
WH1832 Color change Dimetrodon	2 - 4
WH1833 Color change Tyrannosaurus	2 - 4
WH1834 Color change Triceratops	2 - 4
WH1835 Color change Stegosaurus	2 - 4
WH1836 Color change Ankylosaurus	2 - 4
WH1841 Glow-in-the-dark	2 - 4
WH1842 Glow-in-the-dark Dimetrodon	2 - 4
WH1843 Glow-in-the-dark Tyrannosaurus	2 - 4
WH1844 Glow-in-the-dark Triceratops	2 - 4
WH1845 Glow-in-the-dark Stegosaurus	2 - 4
WH1846 Glow-in-the-dark Ankylosaurus	2 - 4
WH1848 Cup	3 - 6
Point of Purchase	
WH1860 Counter Card	8 - 15

GREEN GARDNER, 1992

Kidseeds seed packets were part of this premium offer. A Whataburger sticker was attached to the seed packet which came with a sheet of stickers and an activity book.

WH2201 Lollipop Zinnias	2 - 4
WH2202 Zappin' Zinnias	2 - 4

HALLOWEEN NOSES, 1990

Nose masks were offered for this Halloween-treat kid's meal.

WH2201 WH2202

Back

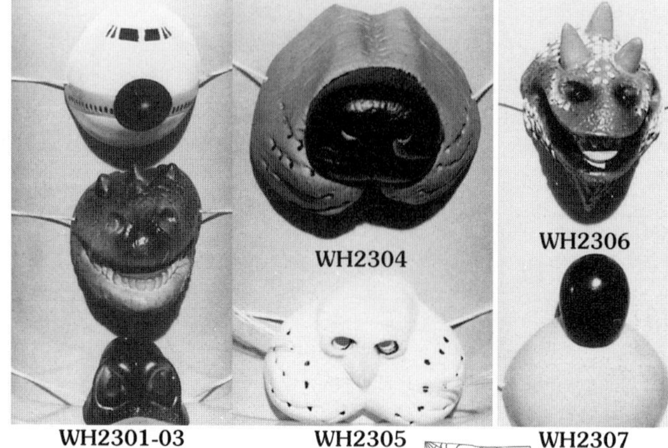

WH2301-03 WH2304 WH2305 WH2306 WH2307

WH2301 Plane	2 - 4
WH2302 Lizard	2 - 4
WH2303 Dog	2 - 4
WH2304 Bear	2 - 4
WH2305 Cat	2 - 4
WH2306 Dinosaur	2 - 4
WH2307 Mouse	2 - 4
Sack	
WH2310 Sack	1 - 2

WH2310

POSABLE ANIMALS, 1990

Small bendie figures were featured for this kid's meal offering.

WH2601 Camel	2 - 4
WH2602 Giraffe	2 - 4
WH2603 Dog	2 - 4
WH2604 Cat	2 - 4
WH2605 Monkey	2 - 4
WH2606 Rabbit	2 - 4
WH2607 Horse	2 - 4

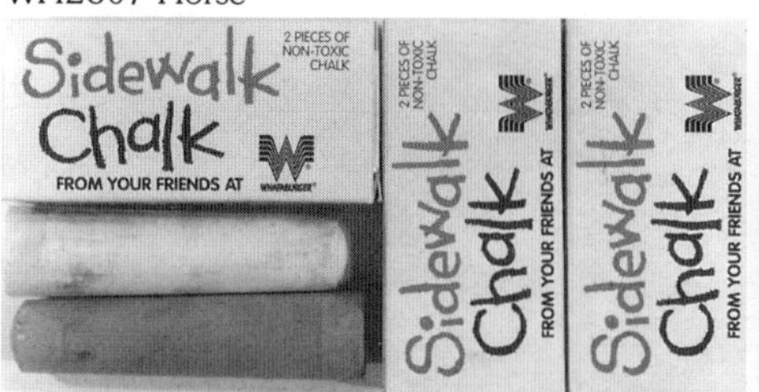

WH3001 WH3005

SIDEWALK CHALK, 1992

Boxes containing two 4" long pieces of 1" diameter chalk came with each Kid's Meal. The chalk came in eight different colors.

WH3001 Sidewalk Chalk, 4 different boxes of 2 colors, each	3 - 6
Point of Purchase	
WH3005 Counter Card	1 - 2

WHATABEAR...G-R-R-R

Plush teddy bears. The first 4 have shirts, the farmer has overalls and "Shapin' Up" bear has a leotard. Each has a cloth sticker on the front.

WH3901 Go Team Go	8 - 10
WH3902 Coca Cola	8 - 10
WH3903 O	8 - 10
WH3904 P.E. Panda	8 - 10
WH3905 Farmer	8 - 10
WH3906 Shapin' Up	8 - 10

WHITE CASTLE

This regional hamburger chain based in Columbus, Ohio, operates in 11 states. They are unique in all they do. The hamburgers are steamed on the bun with lots of onions. They are frozen and shipped to fans west of the Mississippi where no White Castles are found. The Kid's Castle meal promotion was launched in 1986 with a special crown for each child and a year-long Color Disc and Sticker promotion. There were three castle boxes used in the early years: the original, plus a summer and winter castle used for the Castle Friends promotion. The original characters are used from time to time, but the Castle Dudes, four characters based on food products, were used more frequently in the 1990s. The chain usually does six to eight kid's-meal promotions per year and has used all or parts of promotions done by Carl's Jr. or other western `regional chains. Most items are marked "© White Castle Systems."

ALL STAR STUFFS BY WILSON, 1989

A set of sports balls with the Wilson name was used. The baseball premium came as a stuffed polyester and nylon white with red trim printed on it.

WH4001 Baseball	2 - 5
WH4002 Basketball	2 - 5
WH4003 Soccer ball	2 - 5
WH4004 Football	2 - 5

WH4021 WH4023 WH4024 WH4022

ALL STAR STUFFS BY WILSON, 1991

Wilson sports balls were used once again, but each ball came in six or more color combinations and was marked "White Castle Castle Meal Wilson Stuffs."

WH4021 Baseball	3 - 4
WH4022 Basketball	3 - 4
WH4023 Soccer Ball	3 - 4
WH4024 Football	3 - 4
Sack	
WH4030 Sack	1 - 2
Point of Purchase	
WH4035 Sign	8 - 15

WH4302

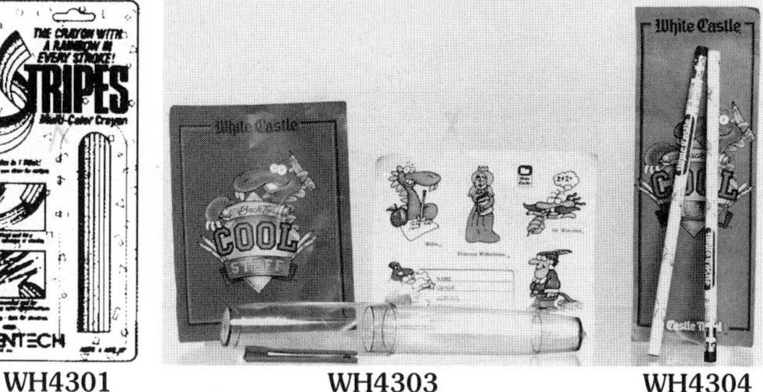

WH4301 WH4303 WH4304

BACK TO COOL STUFF, 1988

Various school supplies were featured, including a strypewriter with a coloring pamphlet, six dinosaur erasers, a 7"-8" clear blue-tinged plastic TubeTote with a sticker sheet, and two White Castle pencils.

WH4301 Strypewriter	4 - 5
WH4302 Erasersaurus, 6 different, each	2 - 4
WH4303 Tubetote	4 - 5
WH4304 Pencil Pals	4 - 5

BEACH BUDDY BUCKETS, 1988

Two different buckets were issued. Each had a beach scene featuring the White Castle Friends.

WH4391 WH4392

WH4404 WH4401 WH4403 WH4402 WH4405

WH4410

WH4406

WH4391 Bucket #1	3 - 4
WH4392 Bucket #2	3 - 4

BENDIE PENS, 1993

Flexible ball point pens were encased in a foam tube and could be bent into any shape. On the top of the pen was a full-color flat-foam head cut-out of a Castle Land character.

WH4401 Woofles	1 - 3
WH4402 Woozy Wizard	1 - 3
WH4403 Willis	1 - 3
WH4404 Wobbles	1 - 3
WH4405 Wilfred	1 - 3
WH4406 Kid's Castle Meal sack	1 - 2
WH4410 Door Decal	15 - 25

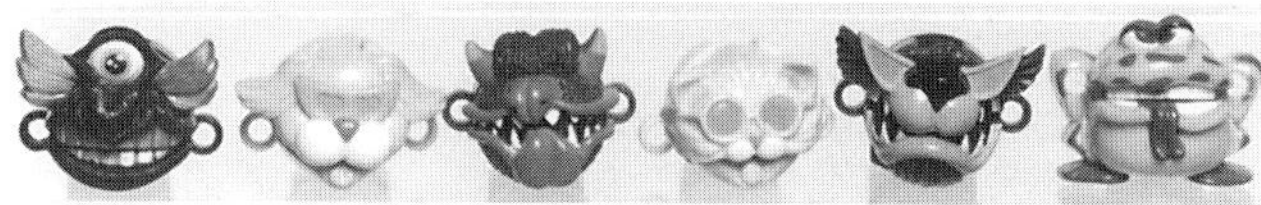

WH4451 WH4452 WH4453 WH4454 WH4455 WH4456

BOW BITERS, 10/6/89-10/31/89

One inch plastic creature heads could be "attached" to the shoe by stringing each one of the laces through the holes on either side of the face.The bow could then be placed into the hinged mouth of the figure.

WH4451 Masher	4 - 5
WH4452 Cat Zooks	4 - 5
WH4453 Blue Meany	4 - 5
WH4454 Shades	4 - 5
WH4455 Purple Heart	4 - 5
WH4456 Green Machine	4 - 5

CAMP WHITE CASTLE, 5/90-7/90

Camping utensils essentially the same as Camp Carl's Jr. were used for this summer-time promotion.

WH4801 Plate/Bowl	2 - 4
WH4802 Valuables Holder	2 - 4
WH4803 Water Bottle	2 - 4

WH4801 WH4802 WH4803 WH4804 WH4805

WH4851 WH4852 WH4853

WH4804 Fork/Spoon 2 - 4
WH4805 Toothbrush w/Case 2 - 4

CASTLE CREATURE CUPS, 1992

Three different fun in the sun scene cups featured eight of the White Castle characters. Each 4" cup came with a different molded snap-on lid which had a 3-D depiction of a character's face.

WH4851 Woofles, green lid 3 - 4
WH4852 Wilfred, orange lid 3 - 4
WH4853 Willis, tan lid 3 - 4

WH4861 WH4862 WH4863 WH4864

CASTLE CUPS, 1988

Five-ounce children's cups featuring a different White Castle character in three different poses around the cup were used.

WH4861 Wilfred & Sir Wincelot 3 - 4
WH4862 Woofles 3 - 4
WH4863 Woozy Wizard 3 - 4
WH4864 Willis 3 - 4

WH4871 WH4872 WH4873 WH4874

CASTLE FRIEND BUBBLE MAKERS, 1992

Four of the White Castle characters were featured as 4"-5" plastic figures which contained bubble soap. The heads unscrewed to open the container.

WH4871 Princess Wilhelmina 4 - 5
WH4872 Woozy Wizard 4 - 5
WH4873 Wendell 4 - 5
WH4874 Sir Wincelot 4 - 5

WH4881 WH4882 WH4883 WH4884 WH4885 WH4886

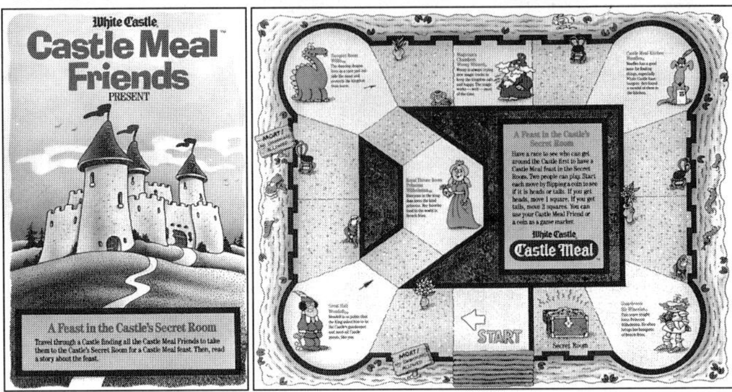

WH4887 (cover and inside)

WH4889 WH4890

CASTLE MEAL FRIENDS, 12/89-2/90

Colorful 2"-3" PVC figures depicted the first six White Castle characters. The promotion also included a game board.

WH4881 Wendell 2 - 5
WH4882 Sir Wincelot 2 - 5
WH4883 Woofles 2 - 5
WH4884 Princess Wilhelmina 2 - 5
WH4885 Willis 2 - 5
WH4886 Woozy Wizard 2 - 5
WH4887 Paper game: Feast in the Castle's Secret Room 1 - 3
WH4888 Game board 4 - 8
WH4889 Summer Box 5 - 10
WH4890 Winter Box 5 - 10

WH4891 WH4892 WH4893 WH4894 WH4895

CASTLE MEAL FRIENDS, 5/1/92-1/31/93

The remaining White Castle characters were issued to be used as fill-in premiums. Distribution was very uneven.

WH4891 Friar Wack 4 - 8
WH4892 Wally 4 - 8
WH4893 Wilfred 4 - 8
WH4894 King Wooly & Queen Winnevere 4 - 8
WH4895 Wobbles & Woody 4 - 8

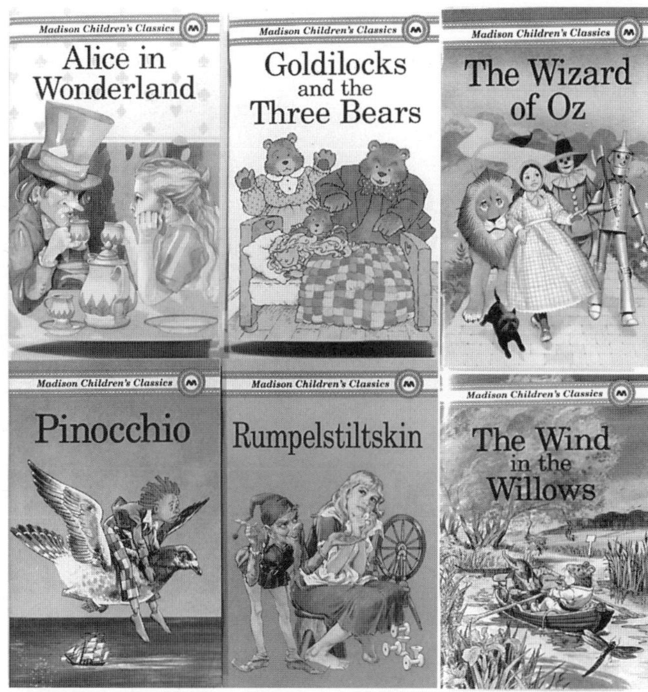

WH4901/WH4904 WH4906/WH4902 WH4903/WH4905

CASTLE TALES, 2/7/93-3/20/93

Storybooks published by Madison Children's Classics were offered.

WH4901 Alice in Wonderland	2 - 3
WH4902 Rumpelstiltskin	2 - 3
WH4903 The Wizard of Oz	2 - 3
WH4904 Pinocchio	2 - 3
WH4905 The Wind in the Willows	2 - 3
WH4906 Goldilocks and the Three Bears	2 - 3

CASTLEBURGER DUDES, 9/91-11/91

Food item PVC figures with blue gloves and shoes.

WH4921 Castle Cheeseburger Dude	3 - 4
WH4922 Castle Fry Dudette	3 - 4
WH4923 Castle Drink Dude	3 - 4
WH4924 Castleburger Dude	3 - 4

WH2112 WH2111 WH2114 WH2113

CASTLEBURGER DUDES SPORTS BALLS, 1993

Hollow rubber balls with a Castleburger Dude embossed in color on the ball, along with the name of the character and a couple of lines of print about the sport and food item involved were offered.

WH2111 Blue Soccer Ball (Fries)	1 - 3
WH2112 Pink Baseball (Hamburger)	1 - 3
WH2113 Yellow Basketball (Drink)	1 - 3
WH2114 Green Football (Cheeseburger)	1 - 3

WH5002 WH5003 WH5001

CHARACTER SIPPERS, 1989

Drink sippers were 6" plastic bottles in the shape of a Castle character with different colored snap-on lids and a built-in drinking spout.

WH5001 Woozy Wizard, blue sipper w/green top	3 - 4
WH5002 Willis, green sipper w/yellow top	3 - 4
WH5003 Woofles, tan sipper w/green top	3 - 4

WH5021 WH5022

CHRISTMAS GIVEAWAYS, 1988

Plush figures were used for this holiday promotion. Each $3\frac{1}{2}$" figure had a clip-type mechanism in the forearms.

WH5021 Woofles	3 - 5
WH5022 Willis	3 - 5
WH5023 Wilfred	3 - 5

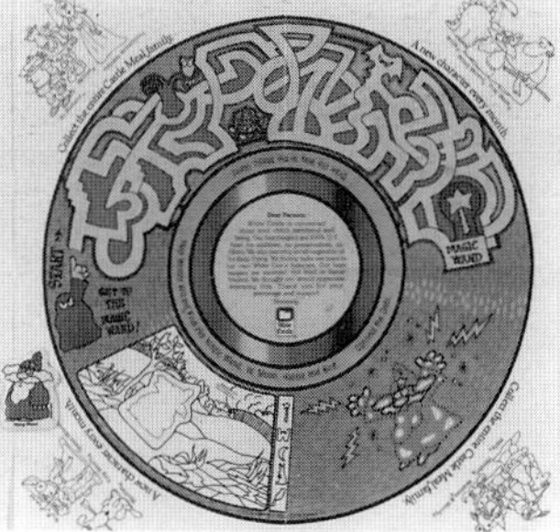

WH5122 WH5123

COLOR DISCS AND STICKERS, 1986-87

A cut-out paper disc came folded into quarter sections with kid's meal games on one side and pictures to color on the other. Each came with a different color crayon and Castle Friends puffy character stickers.

WH5121 Friar Wack	5 - 8
WH5122 Wobbles & Woody	5 - 8
WH5123 Woozy Wizard	5 - 8
WH5124 King Woolly/Queen Winnevere	5 - 8
WH5125 Princess Wilhelmina	5 - 8
WH5126 Wendell	5 - 8
WH5127 Sir Wincelot	5 - 8
WH5128 Woofles	5 - 8
WH5129 Willis	5 - 8
WH5130 Wally	5 - 8

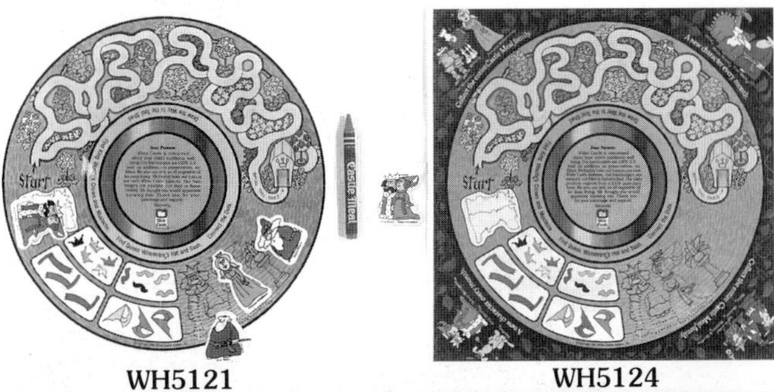

WH5121 WH5124

WH5140

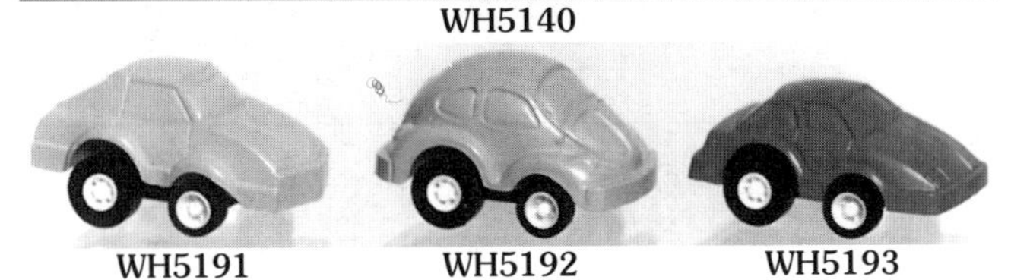

WH5191 WH5192 WH5193

WH5131 Wilfred	5 - 8
WH5140 Crown	6 - 10

CRAYON CARS, 1989

Each 1½" vehicle had a crayon as the body with plastic wheels.

WH5191 Fastback, pink	4 - 5
WH5192 Sportsbug, purple	4 - 5
WH5193 Z-Racer, blue	4 - 5

WH5271 WH5272 WH5273 WH5274

CUPS AND BOWLS, 1989

Two 4½" diameter bowls and two 5-oz cups were issued for this time period. Different winter and summer scenes were on the four pieces.

WH5271 Bowl w/winter scene w/Castle Friends	3 - 4
WH5272 Bowl w/summer lake scene w/Castle Friends	3 - 4
WH5273 Cup w/snow scene w/Castle Friends skiing	3 - 4
WH5274 Cup w/summer scene w/Castle Friends on skateboard	3 - 4

WH5301 WH5302 WH5303 WH5304 WH5305 WH5301

DUDLEY'S EASTER PALS, 1989

Dudley the rabbit and his friends were 6" tall bendie figures.

WH5301 Dudley Rabbit, w/carrot	3 - 6
WH5302 Florence, w/flowers	3 - 6
WH5303 Betty, w/basket	3 - 6
WH5304 Peter Painter, w/egg & brush	3 - 6
WH5305 Tommy, w/top hat	3 - 6
Point of Purchase	
WH5307 Translite	15 - 25

FABULOUS FUNSHADES, 1988

Children's sunglasses with break-resistant dark green plastic lenses had a 1" piece of plastic with a decal that showed the promotion name, White Castle logo, and in the center, a White Castle character "on the beach." Each pair of glasses came on a blister card with a "free FunCord!"

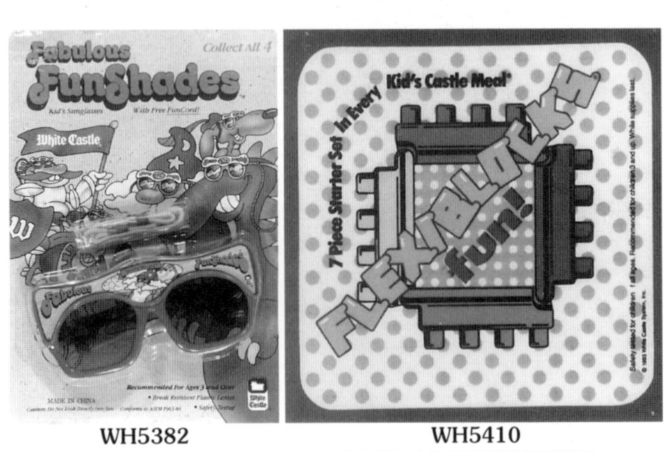

WH5382 WH5410

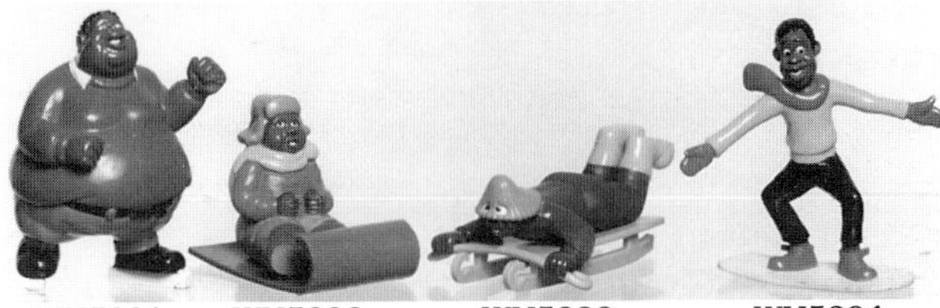

WH5391 WH5392 WH5393 WH5394

WH5381 Woofles, yellow frames w/blue cord	3 - 4
WH5382 Woozy Wizard, blue frames w/yellow cord	3 - 4
WH5383 Wincelot & Wilfred, red frames w/green cord	3 - 4
WH5384 Willis, lime green frames w/orange cord	3 - 4

FAT ALBERT & THE COSBY KIDS, 1990

Based on the popular TV cartoon characters, 4"-5" PVC figures were issued for this promotion.

WH5391 Fat Albert	6 - 8
WH5392 Russell	6 - 8
WH5393 Dumb Donald	6 - 8
WH5394 Weird Harold	6 - 8

WH5400 WH5401

FLEXIBLOKS, 1993

Two different packages were given. One had red and blue blocks, the other yellow and green. The idea was to collect multiple sets to build larger projects.

WH5400 Red and blue blocks	2 - 3
WH5401 Yellow and green blocks	2 - 3
WH5410 Translite	10 - 15

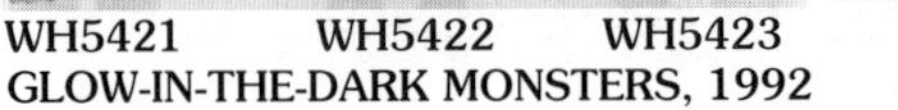

WH5421 WH5422 WH5423 WH5428

GLOW-IN-THE-DARK MONSTERS, 1992

This premium run featured 4½" rubber glow-in-the-dark figures. The monsters were of 2-piece construction and could be separated at the waist. The bag was customized for different markets.

WH5441 WH5443 WH5442 WH5444

WH5421 Wolfman, pinkish color 3 - 5
WH5422 Frankenstein, greenish color 3 - 5
WH5423 Mummy, pale yellow color 3 - 5

Sack

WH5428 Special Price/Locations Plastic Bag 1 - 2

Point of Purchase

WH5430 Display sign 10 - 20

GODZILLA, 1990

Super series featuring this classic monster is one of the most sought-after White Castle premium sets. The theme was "Godzilla Devours Castle Meals."

WH5441 Inflatable 5 - 8
WH5442 Squirter 5 - 8
WH5443 Suction Spinner 6 - 9
WH5444 "Godzilla Devours Castle Meal" Flyer 5 - 8

WH5474 WH5471 WH5472 WH5473

GROWIN' UP FUN HATS, 12/30/90-1/26/91

Thin plastic hats were both the prize and the meal container.

WH5471 Hard Hat, yellow construction style 3 - 5
WH5472 Slugger, blue baseball batting helmet style 3 - 5
WH5473 Fire Chief, red fire helmet style 3 - 5
WH5474 Ballerina, gold tiara wrap-around 3 - 5

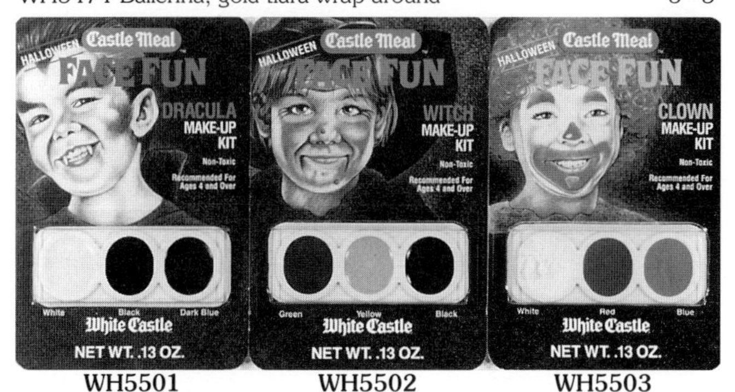

WH5501 WH5502 WH5503

HALLOWEEN FACE FUN, 1988

Make-up kits with three paint bits on a blister pack.

WH5501 Dracula w/white, black, dark blue 3 - 5
WH5502 Witch w/green, yellow, black 3 - 5
WH5503 Clown w/white, red, blue 3 - 5

Sack

WH5510 Sack 2 - 4

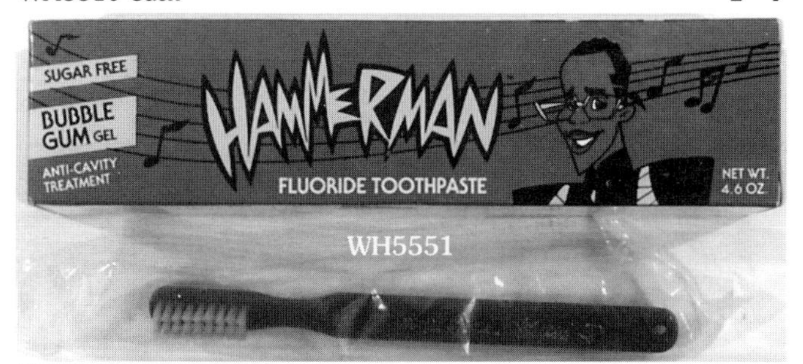

WH5551

HAMMERMAN, 1994

M.C. Hammer hygiene items.

WH5552

WH5553 WH5554

WH5591 WH5592 WH5593 WH5594

WH5551 Bubble Gum Toothpaste w/blue brush 2 - 4
WH5552 Grape Toothpaste w/black brush 2 - 4
WH5553 Bath Sponge 2 - 4
WH5554 Soap 2 - 4

HOLIDAY HUGGABLES, 1990

Soft stuffed-cloth animals with gift tags

WH5591 Teddy Bells, red cloth printed w/yellow bells 4 - 6
WH5592 Kitty Lights, green cloth printed w/colored tree lights 4 - 6
WH5593 Holly Hog, pink cloth printed with holly 4 - 6
WH5594 Candy Canine, white cloth printed with candy canes 4 - 6
WH5595 Winter Castle Scene Box 3 - 9

Smarty Paints WH5701 · Smarty Paints WH5702 · Smarty Paints WH5704 · Smarty Paints WH5703

MAGIC PICTURES (Smarty Paints), 1989

A set of four magic picture booklets.

WH5701 Woofles/Forest Feast 4 - 6
WH5702 Willis/Castle Cookout 4 - 6
WH5703 Wobbles & Woody/Wobbles puts on a show 4 - 6
WH5704 Wilhelmina/Wilhelmina shares her Castle Meal 4 - 6

MARVEL PAILS, 1989

Sand buckets with Marvel characters. Each came with a shovel.

WH5721 Spider Man, blue handle & shovel 4 - 6
WH5722 She-Hulk, yellow handle & shovel 4 - 6
WH5723 Captain America, red handle & shovel 4 - 6
WH5724 Silver Surfer, green handle & shovel 4 - 6

NESTLE QUIK BUNNY, 1990

The Nestlé Quik bunny mascot was featured on four different unique premiums.

WH5801 Straw Holder 4 - 6
WH5802 Color Change Spoon 4 - 6
WH5803 Color Change Cup 4 - 6
WH5804 Mini Plush 4 - 6

PEZ MONSTERS, 1990

Stock Pez dispensers were used without White Castle identification.

WH5801 WH5802 WH5803 WH5804

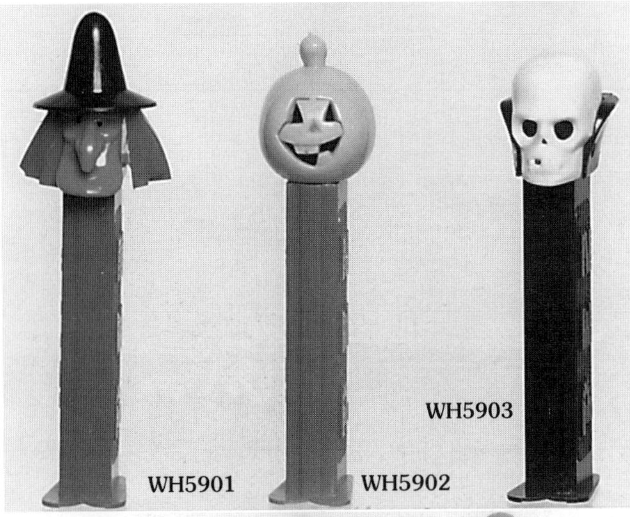

WH5901 WH5902 WH5903

WH5971 WH5972 WH5973

WH5901 Witch, orange base w/green face, orange hair, black hat 5 - 10
WH5902 Pumpkin, green base w/yellow-orange pumpkin head 5 - 10
WH6903 Skeleton, purple base w/white skull, black collar 5 - 10

PUSH 'N GO GO GO!, 1991

Plastic TOMY vehicles. When the driver was pushed down, the vehicle moved forward.

WH5971 Plane 3 - 4
WH5972 Boat 3 - 4
WH5973 Bull Dozer 3 - 4

WH6051 WH6052

REAL GHOSTBUSTERS VISIT CASTLELAND, 2/10/91-3/23/91

Grooming accessories with The Real Ghostbusters theme became premiums. All were made for this promotion and were for the most part consumed.

WH6051 Mint Flavored Toothpaste/Green Toothbrush 3 - 6
WH6052 Hairbrush 3 - 6
WH6053 Soap Dish & Soap 3 - 6
WH6054 Bubblegum Flavored Toothpaste/Pink Toothbrush 3 - 6
Sack
WH6055 The Real Ghostbusters Save Castleland 1 - 3

WH6053 WH6054

WH6060

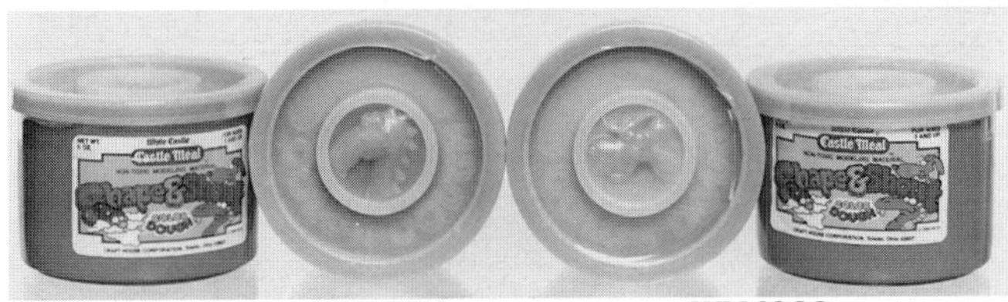

Point of Purchase WH6321 WH6322

WH6060 Sign showing all premiums 10 - 20

SHAPE & SHOUT COLOR DOUGH, 1989

Three characters on top of five different colors of play dough.

WH6301 Green 3 - 6
WH6302 Pink 3 - 6
WH6303 Yellow 3 - 6
WH6304 Blue 3 - 6
WH6305 Orange 3 - 6

SHAPE & SHOUT COLOR DOUGH, 1991

This was simply a repeat of the 1989 promotion without changes.

WH6321 Willis 3 - 6
WH6322 Woofles 3 - 6
WH6323 Woozy Wizard 3 - 6

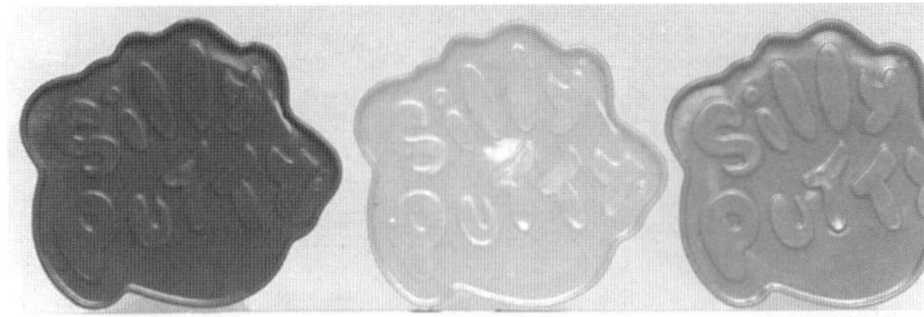

WH6491 WH6493 WH6492

SILLY PUTTY PLASTIC MOLDS, 1993

Solid fluorescent plastic containers of Silly Putty had snap-on lids which served as stamps to imprint "Silly Putty" into the material.

WH6491 Green 1 - 3
WH6492 Orange 1 - 3
WH6493 Yellow 1 - 3

STICKERS, 1988

Each 5¼" square sheet featured one of five Castle Land characters positioned in different poses with several accessories. The stickers could be used over and over again on any surface via static cling.

WH6651 Woozy Wizard 3 - 4
WH6652 Willis the Dragon 3 - 4
WH6653 Friar Wack 3 - 4
WH6654 Wendell & Wally 3 - 4
WH6655 Wilhelmia 3 - 4

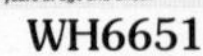

WH6651 WH6653

WH6654 WH6652

WH6655

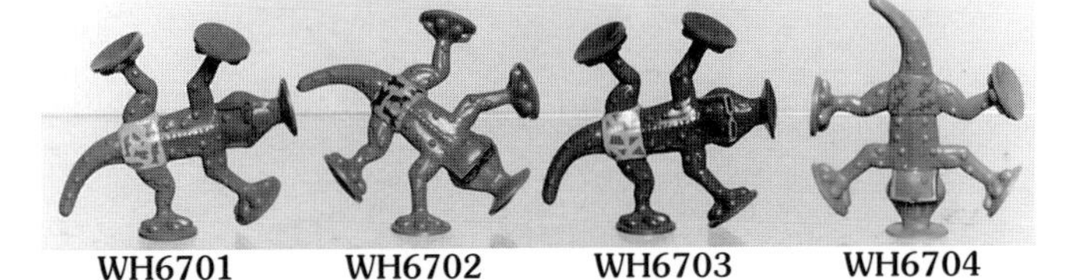

WH6701 WH6702 WH6703 WH6704

STUNT GRIP GECKOS, 1/12/92-2/8/92

Rubber gator figures with painted swim trucks and sunglasses were also used by many other chains. Only some colors and the White Castle ID made them distinctive.

WH6701 Aqua	3 - 4
WH6702 Green	3 - 4
WH6703 Purple	3 - 4
WH6704 Blue	3 - 4

TOOTSIE ROLL EXPRESS, 8/2/92-8/29/92 **WH6806**

Each plastic train unit was mounted on a black plastic base which had four black round-rolling wheels as well as two yellow slanted-oval non-moving wheels.The cars could be coupled in various different ways. A "Tootsie Roll EXPRESS" logo sticker was on one side of each car body; a White Castle logo sticker was on the other. Each car came with a bite-size Tootsie Roll.

WH6801 Hopper car	3 - 6
WH6802 Caboose	3 - 6
WH6803 Coal car	3 - 6
WH6804 Engine	3 - 6
Point of Purchase	
WH6805 Sign	15 - 25

WH6851 WH6854 WH6853

TOTALLY U BACK TO SCHOOL, 1990

Various school-related items were offered. The pencil bag was marked only with "Made in Korea." All other premiums had the promotion name, White Castle logo, etc. printed on them. The lunch boxes were plastic and came in 3 colors.

WH6851 Pencil Case, green	2 - 4
WH6852 Lunch Box, green, yellow or blue	2 - 4
WH6853 Wrist Wallet	2 - 4
WH6854 Name Tag	2 - 4

WH6652 WH6651

WH6653 WH6654

WH6872 WH6871 WH6873 WH6874

TRIASSIC TAKE-APARTS, 1994

Four 2- or 3-piece rubber figures with the White Castle logo stamped on a foot in white. Also used by Denny's, Carl's Jr. and Dairy Queen.

WH6871 Spine-Asaur - Green	3 - 6
WH6872 Sora-Asaur - Blue	3 - 6
WH6873 Mega-Asaur - Red	3 - 6
WH6874 Cool-Asaur - Purple	3 - 6

WH6901 WH6902 WH6903

VACU-FORM BOATS, 1989

Vacu-formed boats with Castle Land characters reclining on top.

WH6901 Willis the dragon, green	8 - 12
WH6902 Woozy Wizard, blue	8 - 12
WH6903 Woofles the dog, yellow	8 - 12

WH6972 WH6973 WH6971 WH6974

WATER BALLS, 1993

Liquid-filled clear-plastic balls encased a colored ball with one of the Castleburger Dudes on it. This inner ball was weighted so the ball always rolled to show the character on top.

WH6971 Castle Cheeseburger Dude, yellow	2 - 4
WH6972 Castle Fry Dudette, pink	2 - 4
WH6973 Castle Drink Dude, orange	2 - 4
WH6974 Castleburger Dude, purple	2 - 4

WH7201 WH7202 WH7203 WH7204

WIND-UP CASTLEBURGER DUDES, 1992

Castleburger Dudes, food items humanized with hands and feet, became plastic wind-up characters.

WH7201 Castle Drink Dude	3 - 4
WH7202 Castleburger Dude	3 - 4
WH7203 Castle Cheeseburger Dude	3 - 4
WH7204 Castle Fry Dudette	3 - 4

WOOLERS, 1987

Four different "magic changing" cards each came with a different activities pamphlet. On the front of each "magic changer" was a 3-D scene whose action changed when the card was tilted at a different angle. Across the top of each card was a 4" ruler.

WH7301 WH7302 WH7303 WH7304

WH7301 Sir Wincelot, Wilfred, Willis Card w/green frame book	5 - 8
WH7302 Wendell, Wally, Wobbles & Woody Card w/pink frame book	5 - 8
WH7303 Wilhelmina, King Woolly, Queen Winnevere Card w/yellow frame book	5 - 8
WH7304 Wizard, Woofles, Friar Wack w/orange frame book	5 - 8

WOOZY MAGIC MANIA MEAL, 6/19/88-7/9/88

Magic watersaurus in four shapes and four colors - soak in water and shapes change.

WH7351 Stegosaurus	5 - 8
WH7352 Brontosaurus	5 - 8
WH7353 Woolly Mammoth	5 - 8
WH7354 Triceratops	5 - 8
WH7355 Willis	5 - 8
WH7356 Woofles	5 - 8
WH7357 Woozy Wizard	5 - 8
WH7358 Wilfred & Sir Wincelot	5 - 8
Box	
WH7360 Woozy Magic Mania Meal	1 - 3

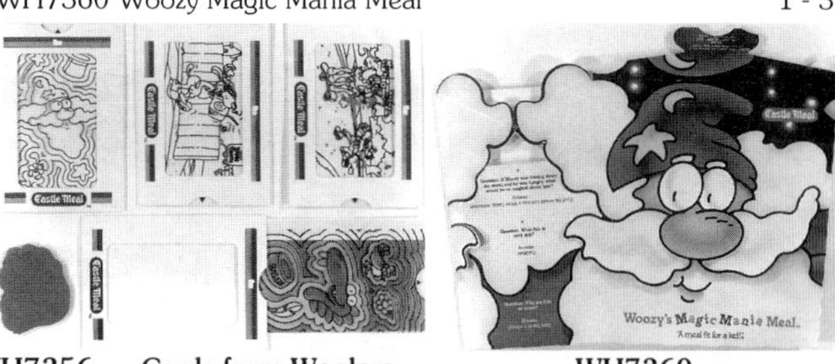

WH7356 Cards from Woolers WH7360

About the Authors

Ken Clee is a Human Resource Consultant in Total Quality Management, and has taught college courses on the subject. Ken is also active in other hobbies as a collector of cartoon/character glasses, California raisin-related collectibles and glass coffee creamers with the dairy names on them. He has been a collector and dealer in records, and is the author of the four-volume reference, The Directory of American 45 R.P.M. Records. In his spare time he enjoys talking to others with common collecting interests, answering mail, and travelling far and wide to flea markets and shows. He enjoys hearing from others curious about the hobby, advanced collectors, and people who want to sell, trade or buy. You can reach Ken at P.O. Box 11412, Philadelphia, PA 19111, phone (215) 722-1979.

Suzan Hufferd is a 24-year employee at the Indiana University Medical Center at Indianapolis in the position as supervisor of a large Endocrinology Research Service Laboratory. She finds it very relaxing to change hats and chase fast-food toys. She is the single mother of five grown children and eight wonderful grandchildren, all of whom enjoy her hobby. About ten years ago, after her children were grown, she was looking for a hobby or something to occupy her time. At a flea market she found herself drawn to toys. One thing led to another, but in the end she became a collector of articulated character figures made by R. Dakin. She began to collect a wider variety of advertising collectibles which led to her interest in fast-food and Kid's Meal premiums. She has since networked with people all over the world pursuing this interest.